The Engineering
and History of *Rocket*

a survey report

The Engineering and History of *Rocket*

a survey report

Michael R Bailey and John P Glithero

National Railway Museum

About the authors

With a DPhil from the Institute of Railway Studies, **Michael Bailey** is a Past-President of the Newcomen Society, an Associate and former Trustee of Manchester's Museum of Science & Industry and President of the Museum Friends. **John Glithero** is a Chartered Engineer with an MSc from Manchester University, researching for his PhD at UMIST. He is a member of the Newcomen Society and the Association for Industrial Archaeology. Both Michael Bailey and John Glithero are consultants in early railway technology. They have undertaken investigation, restoration and conservation work of early locomotives in Britain and Canada, and headed the project team which built the replica *Planet* locomotive.

Published 2000
Reprinted 2001, with corrections

British Library Cataloguing-in-Publication Data

A catalogue record for this publication is available from the British Library

Designed by Jerry Fowler

Printed in Belgium by Snoeck, Ducaju & Zoon

ISBN 1 900747 18 9

Science Museum, Exhibition Road, London SW7 2DD
National Railway Museum, Leeman Road, York YO2 4XJ
http://www.nmsi.ac.uk

Contents

Acknowledgements

The authors are pleased to acknowledge, with gratitude, the contributions of several people who have assisted to a greater or lesser extent with the research and survey for this study, namely:

The several members of staff of the National Railway Museum who have helped in many ways with both the survey the research into *Rocket*'s history. Particular acknowledgement is given to Mr Richard Gibbon for his management of the study at York and for his guidance and other assistance throughout the survey.

The members of staff of the Science Museum. Particular acknowledgement is given to Mr John Liffen whose interest, advice and practical assistance throughout the research programme has been of great assistance in building up a comprehensive understanding of the locomotive's history since 1862.

The 'Tuesday' Group of the Friends of the National Railway Museum for their assistance in cleaning and weighing the components removed from *Rocket* during the survey.

Mr Kenneth Reedie, Curator of Museums and Galleries for Canterbury City Council and the staff of the Canterbury Heritage Museum for their assistance with a brief survey of *Invicta*.

Mr Peter Davidson of Mobberley, Cheshire, for his considerable assistance with the survey and for his interest and advice in interpreting its results.

Mr Alan Stoyel of Faringdon, Oxfordshire, for his assistance in connection with the study.

The members of the Thompson family, particularly Mr Grant Thompson of Canberra, Australia, who have assisted in building up an understanding of the family's role in *Rocket*'s history.

Dr Ray Smith and other members of the Newcomen Society, who have assisted with particular queries in relation to *Rocket*, its drawings and models.

Mr Denis Perriam of Carlisle, for his advice on *Rocket*'s time on the Naworth collieries railway.

The several librarians and archivists responsible for record offices, professional libraries, archive offices and public libraries who have assisted with the research in connection with this study.

1 Introduction

The world's museums of transport, science and industry contain a wealth of machinery and associated artefacts representing much technological progress, particularly over the last 200 years. The collection and display of these artefacts has been a primary objective of the museums for the education of later generations, in order to provide them with a wider appreciation and perspective of technology in their own time. The museums, however, have not always had the resources or the initiative to study their artefacts in the sort of detail that would provide a more comprehensive understanding of design, material and manufacturing progress. There have therefore been calls to pursue a better understanding of the development of engineering and technology through detailed surveys of artefacts amongst the world's extensive museum collections.

During the 1990s a number of comprehensive surveys were undertaken into some of the earliest surviving steam locomotives. These culminated in 1999 with a detailed physical and associated historical survey of George and Robert Stephenson's *Rocket* locomotive of 1829. Temporarily displaced from its 140-year home at the Science Museum in London as a result of gallery redevelopment, *Rocket* spent that year at the National Railway Museum (NRM), York, before returning to the Science Museum as a central exhibit in the *Making the Modern World* gallery.

Rocket is arguably the world's best-known locomotive, although its precise history and its historical context within the origins of the main-line railway system are not always understood. The authors were therefore privileged to be asked to undertake the project to determine a much wider knowledge of the history and engineering of the locomotive and its components. The opportunity to undertake this comprehensive survey of the locomotive had the enthusiastic backing and support of the National Railway Museum and the Science Museum, and the project was undertaken under the supervision of Mr Richard Gibbon, the Head of Engineering Collections at the NRM.

In the 1920s, prompted by *Rocket*'s centenary, the technological developments that led to its design and manufacture were considered in some detail by three respected locomotive consultants, E A Forward, J G H Warren and C F Dendy Marshall. Based on their findings and recommendations, four 'as-built' replicas were made in the 1930s, the design for which was largely adopted for M G Satow's 1979 version, which operates from time to time at the NRM. This present study has sought to build on their work, and on the researches of later historians, to develop a more comprehensive understanding of the technological context in which *Rocket* was built and later modified, together with its design and manufacturing features, and its operating and maintenance history. This has been achieved through the combination of three disciplines:

• industrial archaeology: a comprehensive survey, and systematic paper and photographic recording, of the form, dimension and material of surviving components

• engineering: determining the reasoning behind the locomotive's design, and the manufacturing method of each component

• history: comprehensive archival research to ascertain the events and decisions taken during *Rocket*'s career, and the context in which they occurred.

The survey was carried out in four phases – component removal, systematic recording, historical assessment and reassembly. From this survey, component and arrangement drawings have been prepared using a computer-aided design system. The drawings include all fittings, redundant holes and marks, as well as dimensions. The likely history of each component has been sought using the drawings and the photographic record, in conjunction with the findings of the historical research.

The survey entailed the dismantling of many parts to establish the dimensions, material, condition, features and fittings of every component. In some cases, the evidence also allowed a better understanding of some of the missing components. The way in which the project was planned and executed, and its many findings, both

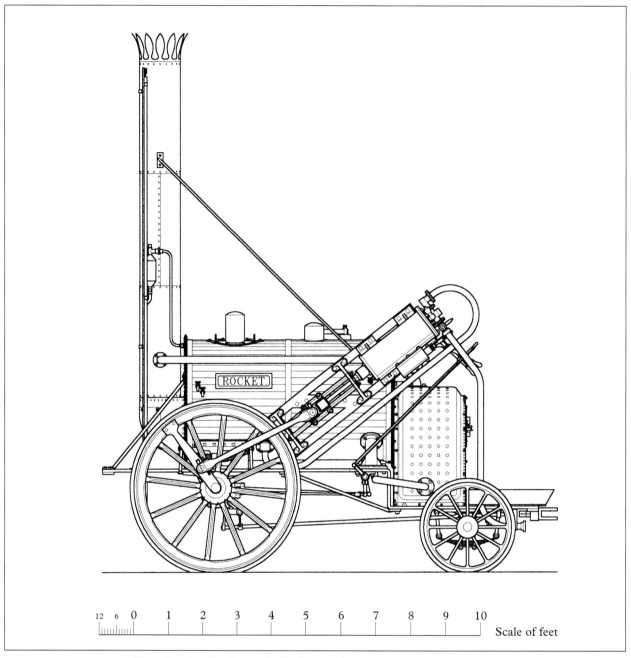

12 6 0   1   2   3   4   5   6   7   8   9   10

Scale of feet

Drawing 1.1 *Rocket* **as built, September 1829**
Scale: 1:32

of major and more general significance, were contained in a report to the National Railway Museum and the Science Museum in November 1999. This report is now being published for the benefit of a wide and discerning readership. It sets down the findings of the survey and of all the accompanying historical research. It has built on the work of the previous locomotive historians and developed some of their findings with new evidence, whilst in other areas further evidence has resulted in new conclusions being drawn. The textual and photographic content of the authors' report has been reproduced in full, as has the full set of component and arrangement drawings.

It was apparent during the course of the project that *Rocket*, as an artefact, was the subject of considerable interest by both a knowledgeable and a general audience. In addition, however, the very notion of learning through the combination of historical and engineering disciplines with those of industrial archaeology was itself a theme that stimulated much comment. Indeed, the many discussions with museum visitors and the various sessions with representatives of television, radio, the national and railway press all served to extend the duration of the study.

What, then, is the reason for this extraordinary level of interest in *Rocket*, which had, since 1990, already earned it the privilege of being represented on the Bank of England five-pound note? There is perhaps a widespread understanding that the technological progress that led to *Rocket* was an integral part of the wider evolution that brought the main-line railway system into being. The railways not only stimulated commerce and industry: they also unlocked an extraordinary latent demand for personal travel. *Rocket* is therefore rightly perceived as the progenitor of this transport revolution.

Although *Rocket* is one of the world's best-known locomotives, its interpretation has been limited to its success at the 1829 Rainhill Trials and to its being the first locomotive fitted with a multi-tubular boiler. However, *Rocket*'s importance as an artefact is much wider, as the locomotive was:

- an important example of a prototype locomotive manufactured during the time of rapid design evolution and component development between 1828 and 1830

- designed and manufactured during the period of transition between the millwright-based manufacturing practice of the early locomotive builders and the factory-based practice that developed from the late 1820s

- the first example of a machine able to convey people at a sustained speed in excess of that which was possible by animal power

- the earliest surviving example of a locomotive which was maintained and modified by railway and contractor teams charged with keeping a fleet of main-line locomotives in service

- employed as a test-bed for dynamic and thermodynamic experiments, at a time of high expectation that further traction improvements, beyond reciprocating engines, were possible.

The main-line railway era began in September 1830 with the opening of the Liverpool & Manchester Railway. It was conceptually different from the earlier, largely uni-directional mineral-carrying public railways in providing bi-directional, timetabled passenger and general goods services. George Stephenson, the line's Engineer-in-Chief, anticipated the requirement for a fleet of locomotives, whose capabilities for speed, load-haulage and economy would need to improve as traffic levels developed. His bold recommendations to the railway's Directors that they should employ locomotives, which he had made before the necessary development work on them had been undertaken, were born of a tenacious advocacy for locomotive-worked railways, for which he is rightly remembered.

Against a background of claims that rope-haulage of trains, using stationary winding engines, would be a more reliable and economic form of motive power, it was to be an extraordinary task to develop locomotive technology from its crude and relatively unreliable 'travelling engine' form, used in the north-east coalfields, to the requisite main-line standard. Between 1828 and 1830, Robert Stephenson, with the close interest and encouragement of his father, undertook a development programme to improve component design and reliability, with an urgency dictated by the imminent opening of the Liverpool & Manchester Railway.

George Stephenson's recommendations to the railway were, however, greeted with scepticism by some Directors. Their response was accentuated by his claim that the Newcastle-on-Tyne factory of Robert Stephenson & Co., with which he was so closely associated, would be the best to manufacture the locomotives for the line. The Directors' continuing doubts led to the competitive locomotive trials held at Rainhill near Liverpool in October 1829. The trials were as much to allow the Stephensons to confirm their bold claims of superior locomotive design against competition from other manufacturers, as they were to dispel any further thoughts about rope haulage.

Only two other manufacturers were sufficiently far advanced in their locomotive work to run candidates at the trials, Timothy Hackworth with *Sans Pareil* and John Braithwaite and John Ericsson with *Novelty*. The trials came at a time when the Stephensons were part-way through their locomotive development programme, the improvements from which had been developed on several prototypes. *Rocket*'s design not only adopted these improvements, but it also incorporated the important innovation of the multi-tubular boiler and separate firebox.

The Rainhill Trials, which were held over several days, received an extraordinary amount of publicity and consequent public attention. The simple expedient of comparing the three locomotive contenders by offering a massive £500 prize, and making it possible for the public to witness the event, led to an immediate comprehension and expectation of the benefits of main-line rail transport, and ultimately of the profitability of the Liverpool & Manchester Railway. *Rocket*, as the victor, has since been seen as the progenitor of the main-line locomotive, even though the Stephensons' development programme still had some way to go.

The development of locomotive technology between the Rainhill Trials and the completion of the prototype *Planet*, delivered in the same month as the opening of the line eleven months later, was rapid and profound. *Rocket* was outmoded before it had turned a revenue-earning wheel. As opportunity arose, therefore, it was rebuilt to incorporate some of the later innovations, but after 1833 it was no longer economic to continue. *Rocket*'s career was then limited to occasional use and, ultimately, sale on the second-hand market.

Rocket's survival is therefore remarkable not only because of the locomotive's public 'persona', but because it is an engineering 'time-capsule'. Its components are a combination of the changing design, material and manufacturing characteristics of locomotive technology at the dawn of main-line railways. The knowledge gained from this project demonstrates the benefits of such a detailed survey combined with intensive archival research. Such an approach could readily be applied to other industrial artefacts to the greater knowledge of us all.

2 *Rocket's* place in locomotive history

Rocket's importance as an artefact is much wider than the preservation of the well-known locomotive that won the 1829 Rainhill Trials, and which is perceived to be the progenitor of the main-line railway locomotive. This chapter therefore records *Rocket's* specific place in locomotive development and the origins of main-line railway operation, both as a background against which the findings of the survey may be assessed and as a guide to its future display and interpretation.

2.1 *Locomotive development 1828–30*

Rocket was manufactured during an intense period of locomotive development, which was necessary to advance its capability from the slow-speed and relatively unreliable 'colliery' type used in the coalfields of north-east England, to a machine capable of meeting the much greater speed, load-haul and reliability requirements of main-line operation. In the 33-month period between January 1828 and September 1830, locomotive technology advanced from Timothy Hackworth's *Royal George* and George Stephenson's *Experiment* to the prototype *Planet*, which became the first design to be manufactured as a class for main-line operation.

The stimulus to this development programme was the strong advocacy for the use of locomotives by George Stephenson (1781–1848), Chief Engineer of the Liverpool & Manchester Railway (L&MR).[1] Reporting directly to its Board of Directors, Stephenson was responsible for recommending the best form of motive power to encourage traffic and maximise return on shareholder investment. By the beginning of 1828, lacking evidence that locomotives could be developed for main-line operation, his advocacy implied a direction of orders to Robert Stephenson & Co.'s factory in Newcastle-upon-Tyne, by then the most experienced in locomotive manufacture. His reputation and career were at risk due to the doubts of the several railway Board members who were critical of him.

As the building of the railway required Stephenson's almost full-time presence in Liverpool and along the line of the railway, he had only limited time to pursue locomotive design improvements. By the return of Robert Stephenson (1803–59) to England from South America at the end of 1827, there was an urgent move towards the development of locomotives for the railway, which was expected to commence operation at the beginning of 1830. At the Newcastle factory, Robert Stephenson began a programme to accelerate locomotive development towards the requisite main-line standards. It was conducted in close consultation, through correspondence, with his father, who stimulated debate about the requisite improvements amongst interested people on Merseyside.

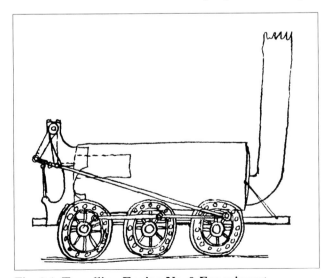

Fig. 2.1 Travelling Engine No. 8 *Experiment*
(as rebuilt on 3 axles – dispatched November 1827)[2]

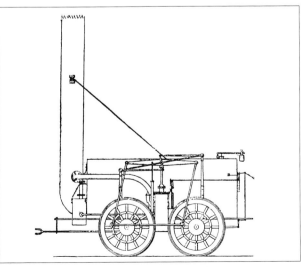

Fig. 2.2 Travelling Engines Nos 9 and 10
(dispatched to Marc Seguin, France, March and April 1828)[3]

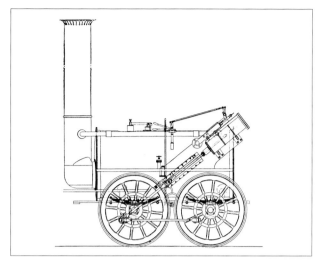

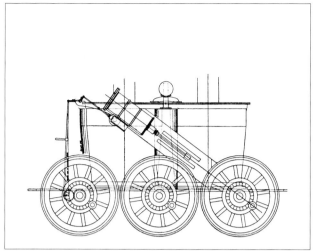

Fig. 2.3 Travelling Engines Nos 11 and 12
Lancashire Witch **and** ***Pride of Newcastle***
(dispatched July and October 1828)[4]

Fig. 2.4 Travelling Engine No. 13 ***Twin Sisters***
also similar No. 14 'Forman's Engine' (dispatched July
1829)[5]

The programme, carried through with the assistance of a draughtsman, George Phipps (1807–88), and the Head Foreman (Works Manager), William Hutchinson (1792–1853), was a systematic appraisal of component improvement rather than the incremental and empirical approach hitherto taken (Section 2.2). This significant change to the method of technological progress saw Robert Stephenson pursue improvements to the following components:

- the boiler: to generate steam at a higher rate, in order to fulfil the load and speed requirements of main-line operations

- the steam pipe: to improve the thermal efficiency of the locomotive through reduced heat losses between boiler and cylinder

- the transmission: to simplify the conversion of the reciprocating piston action into vehicular movement, reducing dynamic forces and improving reliability

- the suspension: to reduce the dynamic forces between locomotive and track, towards increased reliability for them both.

Improvements to the materials used in locomotive manufacture were important in order to fulfil the increasing dynamic and thermodynamic requirements of the developing locomotive. So rapid was design progress, however, that the evolution of suitable materials fell behind, and reliability of main-line locomotives was poor until 1834, by which year the worst of the problems were overcome.

From the commencement of the programme in January 1828 to the completion of the prototype *Planet* locomotive in September 1830, the Stephensons manufactured twenty experimental and pre-production locomotives for customers in Britain, France and the United States, each of which incorporated innovations (Figs 2.1–2.12).

Rocket was thus an important example of this programme, which was designed and manufactured to meet the weight, performance and other specifications determined for the Rainhill Trials (Appendix 1). It was the first to be fitted with a multi-tubular boiler and separate firebox. It also incorporated the most successful components developed by the programme, namely the steel leaf-spring and direct drive between piston and wheel-crank using a cross-head, slide bars and connecting rod. The latter had been introduced in July 1828 on *Lancashire Witch* (Fig. 2.3), which was fitted with a twin-flue boiler. Had the experiments with the tubular boiler and firebox been unsuccessful during 1829, it is likely that *Rocket* would have been fitted with a twin-flue boiler for the Rainhill Trials.

Robert Stephenson generously attributed the responsibility for the construction of *Rocket* to his father and to Henry Booth (1789–1869), the Secretary of the L&MR. In a communication to Samuel Smiles he later wrote 'It was in conjunction with

Mr. Booth that my father constructed the '*Rocket*' engine...'.[8] However, it is clear from his correspondence with both men (Section 3.3) that much of the initiative for component improvement, and the coordination of design and manufacture, lay with him.

Rocket demonstrated endurance, reliability and increased speed at the Rainhill Trials, which were then quickly improved upon with the subsequent development programme. An important consideration that accelerated this programme in the eleven months between the Rainhill Trials and the opening of the L&MR was the increasing availability of the line itself for use as a test track.[15] The Stephensons, with the aid of their assistants Joseph Locke (1805–60), John Dixon (1796–1865) and William Allcard (1809–61), took full advantage of this availability to undertake further trials using *Rocket* and the growing locomotive fleet (Section 3.6).

The *Planet* class, the prototype of which was delivered to Liverpool shortly after the opening of the line, incorporated significant improvements over the earlier locomotives, including *Rocket*. It became the first class of main-line locomotives, with over 40 examples being used on the earliest railways in Britain, continental Europe and North America. The post-Rainhill improvements included:

- improved steam generation by the adoption of a greater number of tubes of smaller diameter providing a larger heating surface, the provision of a smokebox, improved blastpipe and firebox integrated within the boiler barrel

- increased thermal efficiency by the incorporation of a dome and internal steam pipe and the use of inside cylinders

- improved dynamics through the provision of horizontal inside cylinders, substantial outside frame and the use of a leading-carrying axle

- improved adhesion by the use of driving wheels at the rear of the locomotive, adjacent to the firebox.

Rocket was retrospectively fitted with some of these improvements when opportunity arose but, after 1833, it was no longer considered economic to make further modifications (Section 3.8). *Rocket* (and *Invicta*)[16] are thus important artefacts which reflect the design and material achievements from this era of rapid technological progress.

2.2 Transition of design practice up to the 1830s

Rocket is also important in representing one of the earliest achievements of mechanical design engineering, by providing a design 'envelope' within which the innovations could be incorporated, whilst meeting a stipulated weight limitation and using different materials according to component specification. This contrasts with the earliest steam locomotives, which were developed and assembled in accordance with the long-established machinery- and engine-fitting practices of millwrights and

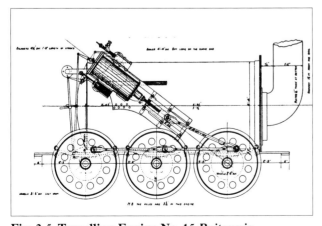

Fig. 2.5 Travelling Engine No. 15 *Britannia*
(dispatched July 1829)[6]

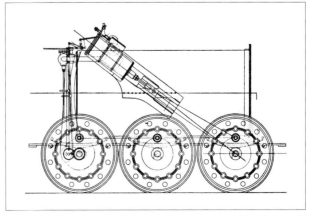

Fig. 2.6 Travelling Engines Nos 16 and 17 *Rocket* **and** '**Whistler's Engine**' (dispatched September 1829)[7]

Fig. 2.7 Travelling Engine No. 19 *Rocket*
(dispatched September 1829)[9]

Fig. 2.8 *Rocket*-**type locomotives**
(dispatched January and February 1830)[10]

engine-wrights, and of other tradesmen working to their overall schemes. For these locomotives, schematic pre-production drawings only were produced and neither general arrangement nor component drawings were prepared.[17]

At the beginning of the development programme, Robert Stephenson recognised the need to introduce a design discipline which was separate from the manufacturing function, and which would seek to provide a much improved size and weight envelope within which components would be manufactured and fitted.[18] George Phipps was recruited for this purpose from Alexander Galloway's employment in London. He began producing general arrangement drawings from May 1828, commencing with those for *Lancashire Witch* and *Pride of Newcastle*, the first new locomotives to incorporate steel springs and direct drive.

Further improvements on the later locomotives, including *Rocket*, were made possible by the increasing detail incorporated into the arrangement drawings – the motivation for which was largely weight reduction – together with a significant improvement in power/weight ratio. By the summer of 1830, Phipps' arrangement drawings of *Planet*-class locomotives made possible the introduction of significant dynamic and thermo-dynamic improvements within the strict axle-load limitations imposed by the 35-lb-per-yard rails of the L&MR.

It is apparent that Phipps would have prepared an arrangement drawing for *Rocket*, but there is no knowledge of the whereabouts of this drawing, if it has survived. Fig. 2.8 shows the arrangement drawing for the subsequent group of four *Rocket*-type locomotives for the L&MR.

Rocket (and *Invicta*, albeit modified) are thus important survivors from this early period, demonstrating the significant progress that was being achieved from the late 1820s to accommodate innovation whilst improving power/weight ratio, particularly in comparison with earlier surviving locomotives, such as *Locomotion*.[19]

2.3 Increase in speed

Operating speed on locomotive-hauled railways prior to the Rainhill Trials was typically 5–8 miles per hour. The main emphasis of the trials was on the loads that could be hauled on different gradients as well as the economy of their fuel and water consumption.[20] While some loaded trials had been undertaken on the level at 10 miles per hour, the fastest recorded speed by the new *Lancashire Witch*, in January 1829, was 8.8 miles per hour up an incline of 1:432, hauling thirteen loaded chaldron waggons.[21] This was only half of the speed that could be achieved on a rope-worked incline, such as the Brunton & Shields Railway.[22]

To meet the 'Stipulations and Conditions' for the Rainhill Trials (Appendix 1), *Rocket*'s design and manufacture incorporated significant dynamic improvements as well as the ability to generate more steam. It was 'made expressly for 12 miles an hour' when hauling a load of three times its own weight.[23] It achieved this speed on its initial trial outing at Killingworth (Section 3.4).

Rocket went on to exceed the expectations for main-line steam locomotive operation by its performance at the Rainhill Trials. It easily exceeded the initial load trial requirement of 10 miles per hour (Appendix 1). With the incentive of the 'Ordeal' requirements (Appendix 3), requiring the participants to achieve an average rate of not less than 10 miles per hour, its speed potential could be fully demonstrated. With the assigned load, *Rocket* achieved runs of between 14 and 24 miles per hour.[24]

At the conclusion of the Trials, with *Rocket*'s supremacy assured, George Stephenson took advantage of the presence of the assembled crowd along the Trial route:[25]

> ... to show that it had been working quite within its powers, Mr. Stephenson ordered it to be brought on the ground and detached from all incumbrance, and in making two trips it moved at the astonishing rate of 35 miles an hour.

Fig. 2.9 *Invicta* (dispatched April 1830)[11]

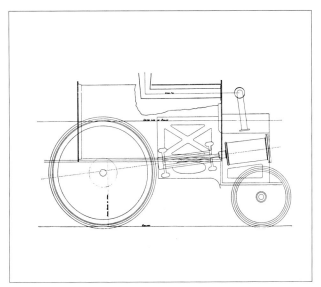

Fig. 2.10 *Phoenix* and *North Star* (dispatched June and August 1830)[12]

These demonstration runs, which probably took place on Wednesday 14 October 1829, were more than victory runs. With the experience of just a few runs since its completion six weeks earlier, *Rocket* had quadrupled the previous recorded maximum speed for a locomotive and obtained a world record for a passenger-carrying vehicle. For the first time, a speed had been achieved which was in excess of that which could be achieved on horseback and sent the symbolic message that mankind was approaching an era in which it would no longer be dependent on horses for travel.

2.4 Locomotive maintenance and modification

Rocket was the first locomotive to be adopted for main-line railway service, although its public-service career on the L&MR was very short (Section 3.7).[26] Its preservation therefore provides an excellent opportunity, through survey, to understand early main-line maintenance practices, particularly for the boiler and wheels, and repair practices arising out of its occasional accidents.

The higher main-line operating speeds, for which the locomotives proved capable, subjected them to dynamic forces well beyond previous experience on the slow-speed colliery lines in the north-east of England and elsewhere. This was compounded by material unreliability (Section 2.3) and the inadequacy of some initial fitting practices. In addition, the intensity of service on the railway was much greater than had been anticipated, requiring the locomotives to spend much less time out of service for maintenance than had previously been the case.[27]

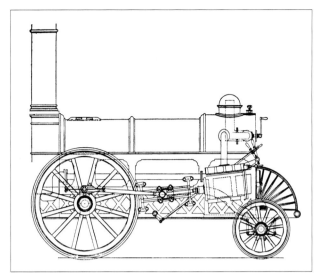

Fig. 2.11 *Northumbrian* and *Majestic* (dispatched July and November 1830)[13]

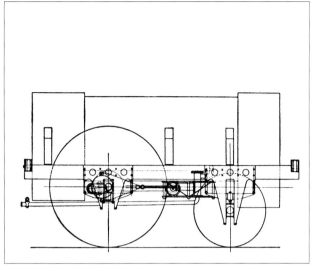

Fig. 2.12 *Planet* (dispatched September 1830)[14]

The problems of maintaining an adequate locomotive fleet led the railway to develop, from 1832, a much higher capability for maintenance in its locomotive running sheds (in Edge Hill, Liverpool and Ordsall Lane, Salford), with correspondingly less dependence on outside firms (Section 3.7). As experience grew and the sheds became better equipped with machine tools, their small workshops became the progenitors of the latter-day large railway workshops.

The *Rocket* survey has thus sought to identify examples of replacements, modifications and repair work of the railway's early maintenance teams, with which to provide wider evidence relating to their developing role.

2.5 *Dynamic and thermodynamic experiments*

Rocket was demonstrably better than its competitors at the Rainhill Trials, and the Stephensons' development programme for the reciprocating locomotive went on to produce significant improvements in both performance and efficiency with the *Planet* design.[28] However, in the early 1830s there was a general expectation that a variety of inventions, and even other forms of transport, would produce better operating economies.

Such was the anticipation that 'further improvements' could be made, that the L&MR considered offering a second 'premium' as early as December 1829.[29] It received several approaches suggesting improvements from potential entrepreneurs, ranging from established manufacturers to amateur inventors.[30] The railway sympathetically received a small number of the more promising ideas and agreed to make the railway, as well as some of its locomotives and rolling stock, available for testing purposes.

Following various trials, none of the schemes was taken up because they compared unfavourably with the performance and efficiency of the developing 'Stephenson' locomotive, the superiority of which these 'improvements' only served to reinforce. Following its withdrawal from regular services in 1833 (Section 3.8), *Rocket* was employed as a test vehicle for at least two of these schemes. As an artefact, therefore, *Rocket* takes on a further significance in that it provides the opportunity, through survey, to obtain a better understanding of these alternative technologies.

1 Michael R Bailey, 'George Stephenson – Locomotive Advocate: The Background to the Rainhill Trials', *Transactions of the Newcomen Society*, 52 (1980–81) pp171–9.

2 Notebook of John Rastrick, University of London, Goldsmith's Library, Department of Palaeontology, MS 155, volume IV, entry for 21 January 1829.

3 Drawing reproduced in F Achard, 'The First British Locomotives of the St. Etienne–Lyon railway', *Transactions of the Newcomen Society*, VII (1926–27) pp68–80.

4 R Stephenson & Co. drawing collection, Science Museum, inv. 1924-159, drawing no. 2A.

5 *Ibid.*, drawing no. 5.

6 *Ibid.*, drawing no. 4.

7 *Ibid.*, drawing no. 3.

8 Samuel Smiles, *The Life of George Stephenson, Railway Engineer* (London, 1857) p282, and later editions.

9 *Mechanics' Magazine*, XII, (324), p145, 24 October 1829.

10 R Stephenson & Co. drawing collection, *op. cit.* (4), no. 9.

11 *Ibid.*, no. 8.

12 *Ibid.*, no. 11.

13 *Ibid.*, no. 12b.

14 *Ibid.*, no. 15.

15 Michael R Bailey, 'Robert Stephenson & Co. 1823–29', *Transactions of the Newcomen Society*, 50 (1979–80) pp123–7.

16 Preserved by the Transport Trust and displayed at the Canterbury Heritage Museum.

17 The earliest known surviving pre-production locomotive drawings are those showing alternative parallel motion schemes for the first locomotives made by R Stephenson & Co., n.d. but *c.* 1824 and annotated in George Stephenson's hand, Tyne and Wear Museums, ref. TWCMS: C6181.

18 Bailey, *op. cit.* (15).

19 Preserved as part of the national collection and displayed at the Darlington North Road Museum.

20 For example, Nicholas Wood, *A Practical Treatise on Rail-Roads, &c.*, second edition (London, 1831) pp305–424 and appendix note F, pp478–96.

21 James Walker, *Report to the Directors on the Comparative Merits of Loco-motive & Fixed Engines*, second edition (London, 1829) p20.

22 John U Rastrick, *Report to the Directors on the Comparative Merits of Locomotive & Fixed Engines*, second edition (Birmingham, 1829) p14, states that he and Walker travelled at 15 mph on the line, and at 18 mph for a short distance.

23 Robert Stephenson and Joseph Locke, *Observations on the Comparative Merits of Locomotive & Fixed Engines as Applied to Railways &c.* (Liverpool, n.d. but *c.* 1830) p27.

24 *Ibid.*, p79.

25 *Ibid.*

26 The L&MR had earlier acquired *Twin Sisters*, but this was only ever used for building and repairing the line and was not taken into 'capital stock' or given a running number.

27 Report of the Board of Directors, L&MR, Fifth Annual Meeting, Liverpool, 28 March 1831.

28 Michael R Bailey, 'Learning Through Replication: The *Planet* Locomotive Project', *Transactions of the Newcomen Society*, 68 (1996–7) pp109–36.

29 Minutes of the Board of Directors of the L&MR 1823–30, PRO, Rail 371/1, p252, entry for 12 December 1829.

30 *Ibid.*, also Board Minutes 1830–3, PRO, Rail 371/2, and the Railway's Sub-Committee of Management, 1831–33, PRO, Rail 371/8, *passim*.

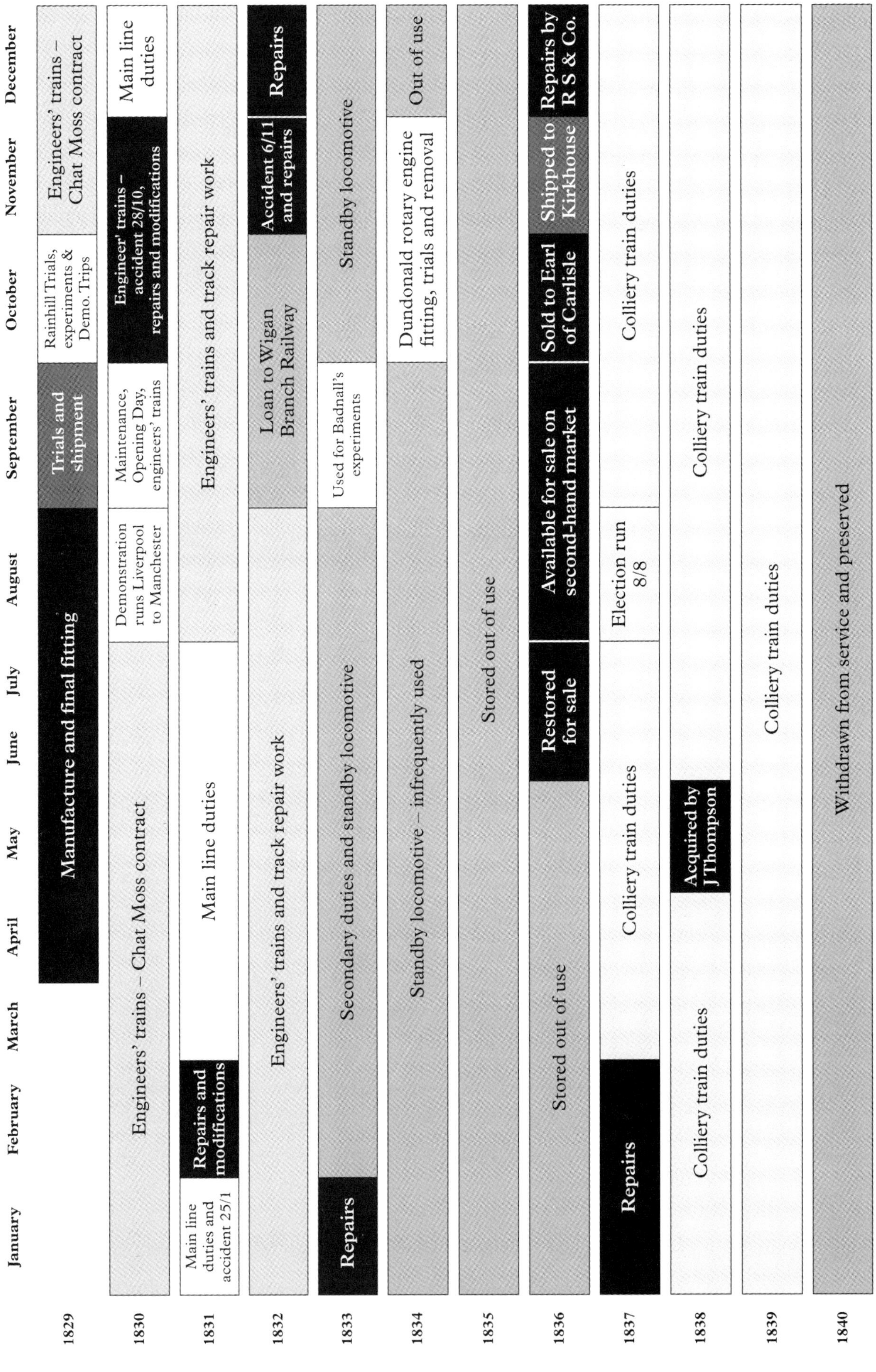
January
February
March
April
May
June
July
August
September
October
November
December
1829
Manufacture and final fitting
Trials and shipment
Rainhill Trials, experiments & Demo. Trips
Engineers' trains – Chat Moss contract
1830
Engineers' trains – Chat Moss contract
Demonstration runs Liverpool to Manchester
Maintenance, Opening Day, engineers' trains
Engineer' trains – accident 28/10, repairs and modifications
Main line duties
1831
Main line duties and accident 25/1
Repairs and modifications
Main line duties
Engineers' trains and track repair work
1832
Engineers' trains and track repair work
Loan to Wigan Branch Railway
Accident 6/11 and repairs
Repairs
1833
Repairs
Secondary duties and standby locomotive
Used for Badnall's experiments
Standby locomotive
1834
Standby locomotive – infrequently used
Dundonald rotary engine fitting, trials and removal
Out of use
1835
Stored out of use
1836
Stored out of use
Restored for sale
Available for sale on second-hand market
Sold to Earl of Carlisle
Shipped to Kirkhouse
Repairs by R S & Co.
1837
Repairs
Colliery train duties
Election run 8/8
Colliery train duties
1838
Colliery train duties
Acquired by J Thompson
Colliery train duties
1839
Colliery train duties
1840
Withdrawn from service and preserved

Fig. 3.1 Timeline of *Rocket*'s operating career

3 *Rocket*'s history

3.1 *Introduction*

Rocket was an operational locomotive for about 11 years, from its manufacture in 1829 until it was withdrawn from service in *c*.1840. During this time it was rebuilt and modified on three occasions both to improve its operating characteristics and following accident damage. A timeline of its operating career is shown as Fig. 3.1. On its withdrawal from service it was stored, dismantled partially and with varying degrees of care, for 22 years before undergoing a major restoration prior to display as a museum artefact. From 1862 it has been displayed by the Science Museum and its predecessors at South Kensington – whose curators have made occasional alterations following critical reconsideration of the 1862 restoration.

Rocket has been the subject of several previous papers and has been referred to many times in books dealing with the history of locomotives and early railways. The following is a list of the most learned writing about the locomotive:

J G H Warren, *A Century of Locomotive Building By Robert Stephenson & Co. 1823–1923* (Newcastle-upon-Tyne, 1923) in particular pp175–227.

C F Dendy Marshall, 'The Rainhill Locomotive Trials of 1829', *Transactions of the Newcomen Society*, vol. IX (1928–9) pp78–93.

R Stephenson & Co. Ltd, *Memorandum on the Replica of the* 'Rocket' (limited circulation, 1929).

Robert E Carlson, *The Liverpool & Manchester Railway Project 1821–31* (Newton Abbot, 1969) pp219–234.

Brian Reed, *The* Rocket, *Loco Profile No. 7* (Windsor, n.d. but 1971).

Brian Webb and David A Gordon, *Lord Carlisle's Railways* (The Railway Correspondence and Travel Society, 1978) pp99–101.

R H G Thomas, *The Liverpool & Manchester Railway* (London, 1980) in particular pp63–75 and pp173–4.

Michael R Bailey, *Robert Stephenson & Co. 1823–36*, unpublished MA thesis, (University of Newcastle-upon-Tyne, 1984) pp115–19.

Each author has contributed to a developing knowledge about *Rocket*'s origin, design, manufacture and operation. With due acknowledgement to each of the above authors, the following chapter has built on their work, whilst addressing each aspect of *Rocket*'s history with a new interpretation developed in association with the survey. The chapter includes new evidence, drawn from primary sources, which is put forward to assist in the interpretation, and to minimise the risk of carry-over of errors and misinterpretation of evidence from previous authors.

The programme of archival research has been undertaken in the following archives and libraries: National Railway Museum archives, Science Museum Library, Science Museum technical and correspondence files, Public Record Office, Scottish Record Office, Lancashire County Record Office, Cumbria County Record Office, Liverpool Record Office, Durham University Library, Manchester Local Studies Library, Salford Local Studies Library, St Helens Local Studies Library, Carlisle Local Studies Library, Newcastle-upon-Tyne Local Studies Library.

3.2 *Specification and development*

Rocket was designed and built in response to an open invitation for engineers to submit prototype locomotives for comparative trials at Rainhill in October 1829. The decision to proceed with the trials was made by the L&MR Board on 20 April 1829. It was minuted:[1]

> That a Premium of £500 be advertised for a Locomotive Engine which shall be a decided improvement on those now in use, as respects the consumption of smoke, increased speed, adequate power, & moderate weight…

The Board's 'Preparation Committee', composed of five Directors, Messrs Cropper, Sandars, Rotheram, Benson and Moss, drew up the 'Stipulations and Conditions' for the trials, which were dated 25 April (Appendix 1). It is most likely that George Stephenson, as the Company's Chief Engineer, was consulted in the drafting to ensure the correct interpretation of engineering requirements, and he thus had the opportunity to influence the design constraints. The Committee's draft was adopted by the full Board on 27 April[2] and submitted for advertisement in Liverpool and national newspapers.[3]

In order to meet the trial 'Stipulations and Conditions', the Stephensons sought an arrangement for the 'Premium Locomotive Engine' (as *Rocket* was known before naming)[4] that would provide speed potential while maintaining sufficient adhesion to draw a gross weight of between 15 and 20 tons. With the initial emphasis on a speed target of 10 miles an hour, rather than a heavy haul capability, the option to provide a six-wheel locomotive was discarded, probably as offering a poorer power/weight ratio than could have been achieved by a four-wheeled locomotive, the determining factor being the size, weight and steam-raising capability of the boiler. *Rocket*'s arrangement was thus largely developed from that of the *Lancashire Witch* and *Pride of Newcastle* locomotives (Appendix 10). *Lancashire Witch* was demonstrably the best light locomotive that had yet been made (Section 2.1), and was seen by John Rastrick (1780–1856) and James Walker (1781–1862) during their fact-finding tour of England prior to their reports to the L&MR Board in March 1829. Rastrick estimated in his report that the locomotive had attained nearly 22 'effective' horsepower.[5]

The French engineers, Léon Coste and Auguste Perdonnet, having seen *Lancashire Witch* in 1829, wrote [translation]:[6]

> This is the very best that has been erected… It is from the workshops of Mr. Robert Stephenson at Newcastle, and seems destined to be used as the model for all those which will be used on the Liverpool to Manchester line.

Whilst the frame, boiler and cylinder arrangement remained largely unchanged, the 0-4-0 wheel arrangement with 4-ft driving wheels was altered to an 0-2-2 arrangement with 4 ft 8½-in. driving wheels. In addition to a weight reduction, this overcame the difficulties of the additional friction of a four-coupled locomotive not manufactured to tight enough tolerances. Unequal tyre wear added to the resistance, as Robert Stephenson wrote in August 1829:[7]

> The failure of the hoops [tyres] on travelling Engines I am inclined to attribute to the horizontal connecting rods confining the wheels when partially and unequally worn to revolve in the same time whilst the circumferences are unequal. This indeed, appears the only distinction between the two applications. In the small Engine [*Rocket*] the objection will not exist, and I am further persuaded a considerable loss of power is to be ascribed to this defect.

Innovation on the locomotive was limited to the boiler and the valve gear, either of which could have been abandoned in favour of that used on *Lancashire Witch* if development work could not be completed in time for the trials. There is no evidence to suggest that any development work on the variable cut-off valve, introduced on the latter,[8] was ever considered for *Rocket*.

Henry Booth originated the notion of a multi-tubular boiler with which to increase steam generation. Booth used the notion as a means to ally himself to George Stephenson and become a partner with him in the Trials venture:[9]

> I mentioned my scheme to Mr. Stephenson, and asked him if he would join me in building a locomotive to compete for the prize of £500 offered by the Directors, subject of course to the conditions prescribed. Mr. Stephenson took a day or two to look into the merits of the plan I proposed, and then told me he thought it would do, and would join me in the venture.

The proposal for a multi-tubular boiler was however only a notion, the requirement to design and build a workable and reliable boiler with a separate firebox being left to

George and Robert Stephenson to implement. Only after the successful conclusion of the development work undertaken during the summer of 1829 could reliance be placed on its use for the 'Premium Engine'. By the end of September, Robert Stephenson felt that his primary role in developing the locomotive with the new boiler warranted an involvement in the partnership. Booth later wrote:[10]

> The important day of the competition was the 8th October 1829, but some time previous to that date Mr. Stephenson told me that his son Robert [who was building the engine at Newcastle] was very desirous to become a partner with his father and me in the venture for the prize. I had no wish to dilute my interest in the little speculation I had entered upon, but as father and son seemed bent on it, made no objection, and it was settled that we should share the profit or loss in the speculation proportionately, that is in thirds.

The decision to include Robert Stephenson in the partnership was probably taken in the few days preceding the Rainhill Trials as the 'Premium Locomotive Engine' was debited only to 'H Booth and G Stephenson' in the Robert Stephenson & Co. accounts on 1 October.[11] When the prize money was awarded on 20 October, following the Rainhill Trials, the £500 premium was awarded to 'Mr. Henry Booth, Mr. Stephenson and Mr. Robt. Stephenson.'[12] By the time the L&MR resolved to purchase *Rocket* from the partnership on the 6 November, £550 was 'ordered to be paid...[to] Robert Stephenson & others.'[13]

Although the Stephensons had undertaken all the development work on the boiler and firebox, Henry Booth's claim to precedence with the notion of a multi-tubular boiler was frequently publicised after the Rainhill Trials,[14] and was publicly accepted by the Stephensons. They no doubt considered it expedient to maintain a close relationship with Booth who himself limited his claim by later referring to *Rocket* as having: '...a boiler of a new construction, suggested by the writer of this account...'[15]

3.3 *Manufacture, fitting and erection*

The design and development work for *Rocket* was undertaken at Robert Stephenson & Co.'s factory in South Street, Newcastle-upon-Tyne. The layout, weight and adhesion estimates were determined by Robert Stephenson in close consultation with George Phipps and William Hutchinson (Sections 2.1 and 2.2). The broad design envelope would have been agreed during May, leading to preparatory manufacture of boiler barrel, pattern-making for cylinders, wheel-hubs and other castings. Stephenson had the confidence to leave the manufacturing work in Hutchinson's care during mid-June. He was married in London on 17 June and had a four-day honeymoon travelling through Wales to Liverpool, before resuming consideration of *Rocket* and other matters.[16]

The development work to turn Henry Booth's notion for a multi-tubular boiler into a well-engineered vessel with a separate firebox was first considered by George Stephenson. Henry Booth later wrote that:[17]

> This new plan of boiler comprised the introduction of numerous small tubes two or three inches in diameter, and less than an eighth of an inch thick, through which to carry the fire...by which plan we not only obtain a very much larger heating surface, but the heating surface is much more effective, as there intervenes between the fire and the water only a thin sheet of copper or brass, not one-eighth of an inch thick... Mr. Stephenson approved the plan, and agreed to my proposal. He settled the mode in which the fire-box and tubes were to be mutually arranged and connected...

It is likely that the two Stephensons discussed the best way to fit the boiler tubes and achieve a separate firebox when Robert Stephenson met his father in Liverpool on 21 June. Robert Stephenson's contribution to the development debate was crucial, as later recalled by Phipps:[18]

> It must not be supposed, however, that when Mr. Robert Stephenson decided upon the construction of the *Rocket* there were no difficulties to be overcome in the application of Mr. Booth's invention, for many a time good inventions fail of success through the absence of

sufficient care and mechanical skill. Having made the original drawings under Mr. Robert Stephenson, I can bear witness to the care and judgment bestowed by him upon every detail. The arrangement of the tubes with the method of securing their extremities, the detached firebox, and many other matters of detail, all requiring much consideration. Mr. Stephenson was well aided in all the mechanical details by the late Mr. William Hutchinson.

Phipps subsequently added a further recollection concerning the firebox:[19]

> The arranging, i.e. the spacing of these [firebox stays], their size etc., was much thought about by Mr. Stephenson and remains unaltered to the present time.

Stephenson himself was more modest in his later claims regarding the multi-tubular boiler, stating that: '...the perfect establishment of the success of the multi-tubular boiler is more immediately due to the suggestion of Mr. Henry Booth, and to my father's practical knowledge in carrying it out.'[20]

The copper firebox 'saddle' (crown and sides – Section 4.6.2) was manufactured in Liverpool by James Leishman and John Welsh, a firm of coppersmiths, brass founders and pewterers, their instructions perhaps arising out of an approach by both the Stephensons on or after that date, although evidence is lacking on this detail.[21] The cost of this firebox saddle was £58. 2s. 0d.[22]

The boilerplate for *Rocket*'s boiler was supplied by Joseph and William Bennitt of Dudley.[23] All the Stephenson company's plate was supplied from the Staffordshire firm at this time in the absence of satisfactory plate from the Bedlington Iron Company, the thickness of which varied beyond acceptable tolerance.[24] Other rolled-iron sections used in the locomotive's manufacture were supplied from Bedlington, whilst other iron used for components forged by the smiths was supplied by a Newcastle agent, Francis Sanderson.[25] Non-ferrous components, other than the firebox, were supplied by three Newcastle brass founders and plumbers, John Abbott, Henry Marshall and Thomas Donnison.[26] Although there is no specific evidence regarding the copper for *Rocket*'s tubes, John Abbott was subsequently listed as supplying copper tubes to the Stephenson company for later locomotives.[27] The springs were supplied by French & Donnison, a firm of coach makers, whilst the timber for the driving wheels and possibly the boiler lagging was supplied by a timber merchant, Cuthbert Burnup.[28]

To assist Hutchinson and the several craftsmen engaged on *Rocket*'s manufacture, Phipps prepared a chalk drawing of its layout. He later wrote: '...a drawing of the *Rocket*, full size was made by me on the floor of our office while under construction.'[29] The chalk drawing was later interpreted in his obituary as having been made on the floor of the drawing office,[30] but it would have been of more assistance to the craftsmen to have used the erecting-shop floor. The 'marking out' of machines and components using a chalk drawing was a common practice, which continues to be used in some manufacturing establishments.

Apart from his supervision of *Rocket*'s development, Robert Stephenson shared his time across several projects during the summer of 1829, including the building of the Canterbury & Whitstable Railway. He was absent from Newcastle for several days but, by 3 August, the majority of the components had been completed under Hutchinson's supervision. Stephenson was then able to take stock of progress and consider the likely all-up weight and the best location for the axles for optimum adhesion. He reported to Henry Booth:[31]

> Since my arrival arrangements have been made which I expect will enable us to have the premium Eng working in the Factory say this day 3 weeks – this will give us time to make experiments or any alterations that may suggest themselves. The tubes are nearly all made, the whole number will be completed by to-morrow night, they are an excellent job – the only point I consider at all doubtful is the clinking of the ends of the tubes.

> The body of the boiler is finished and is a good piece of workmanship. The cylinder and other parts of the Engine are in a forward state. After weighing such parts as are in progress the following is an Estimate of the weight:-

	c.	q.	lbs.
Boiler, without the tubes	9	3	7
25 Copper tubes	4	2	22
Frame carriages and bolts	4	3	3
1 pair of 4ft 8½in wheels and axle	13	1	0
1 pair of waggon wheels and axle	5	0	0
4 Springs and Bolts	2	0	20
Copper fire place including bars, etc.	6	0	0
Chimney and soot	2	0	0
4 Supports for Boiler on Frame	1	2	4
2 Engines complete each 8 cwt.	16	0	0
Water in Main Boiler	11	3	0
Water in Copper fire box	3	0	0
	cwt 80	0	0

This weight I believe will cover everything. The wheels I am arranging so as to throw 2½ Tuns upon the large wheels in order to get friction upon the rail. Will there be any fatal objection to this? You had better get the tender made in Liverpool, the coach makers that made the last tender will make one neater than our men. The barrel might be covered with something like the body of a coach. It may be lighter than the last.

We are daily expecting the arrival of the fire box. I hope you will despatch it as quickly as possible, as we shall require it in 4 or 5 days...

If the two large wheels having 2½ Tuns upon them is an objection, please inform me, some reduction may perhaps be made, but it must be very little or the friction upon the rail will be inadequate to the load assigned.

On 21 August, after a further period of absence from Newcastle, Stephenson reported further progress to Henry Booth, and addressed the Rainhill Trial stipulation no. 5, which anticipated the pressure-testing of the boiler up to 150 lb per square inch (Appendix 1):[32]

Having been a good deal from home since I wrote you last, I have not had an opportunity of writing you particulars of our progress so promptly as I promised. The tubes are all clunk into the Boiler which is placed on the frame:- wheels, springs, and axle carriages are all finished. The clinking of the tubes is tight with boiling water. I am arranging the hydraulic pump to prove the boiler up to 160 lbs. before proceeding any further. The cylinders and working gear is very nearly finished. I expect the mode for changing the gear will please you it is now as simple as I can make it and I believe effectual. The fire box is put into its place, but it is not quite square built which gives rise to a little apparent neglect in the workmanship, I have endeavoured to hide it as much as possible. To-morrow week I expect we shall be ready for trial in the evening.

I should like much to see you at NCastle on the following Monday to make further trial, so that we might consult respecting any alteration that may suggest themselves during trial...

Stephenson remained in Newcastle to supervise the final fitting, erection and testing work. He reported on progress to Booth on 26 August:[33]

On Wednesday I had the boiler filled with water and put up to the pressure of 70 lb. per sq. inch when I found that the yielding of the boiler end injured the clinking of the tubes. I therefore thought it prudent to stop the experiment until we got some stays put into the boiler longitudinally. The boiler end at 70 lb. per sq. inch came out full 3/16 of an inch. This you may easily conceive put a serious strain on the clinking at the tube ends.

To-day I had the pressure up to little above 70 the tubes were nearly every one tight, but the deflexion of the end still was more than it was prudent to pass over. I am therefore putting in 5 more stays which I believe will be effectual. A circumstance which has occurred within a few days induces me to regard severe pressures upon boilers as injudicious – we put up two hydraulic presses in a paper mill, which are to bear 6½ Tuns per square inch – the pipes which lead to the presses from the pumps were proved up to the pressure previous to leaving the factory and continued to act well for a week, when they burst with 5 tuns per square inch – A new set of pipes were made which withstood the proof pressure but afterwards burst with a much less pressure – Query therefore is it judicious to prove the boilers to 150 lbs. per sq. inch I should say not. – A pressure of lbs. 100 per sq. inch would not I think be objectionable. If the Engines were not so limited in weight then I would say prove them to 150 lbs. or more.

The Chimney is made 14 inches diameter, being a little less than the area of the horizontal tubes. I think it should be less, the air being cooler and consequently occupies less space in the Chimney than in the tubes. I am still sanguine as regards the weight, 4½ Tuns I believe will cover all. Of course I am calculating that if the Engine is reduced in weight below 4 the load dragged will be reduced in the same proportion…

The putting in of the stays will delay the trial of the Engine until Tuesday [1 September]. If anything unexpected start up I will let you know…

The wheels are made 4 ft 8½ ins. – the small pair 2 ft 6 ins.

The deflection of the boiler delayed the completion of the locomotive for a few days whilst further stays were inserted, and Stephenson reported again to Booth on 31 August:[34]

After the stays were put in, we tried the boiler up to 120 lbs. per sq. inch, when I found it necessary to put in two more stays in order to make the ends withstand 150 – this would be totally unnecessary if the fixed pressure for trial were 120. We can however make it stand the required pressure altho I scarcely think it prudent from what I stated in my last.

The putting in of these stays has put off the trial of the Engine off until Wednesday [2 September]. The Mercurial guage [sic], is nearly finished, it will look well – The pipes being of wrought Iron has taken more time than I expected. The Wheels of the Engine are painted in the same manner as coach wheels and look extremely well. The same character of painting I intend keeping up, throughout the Engine it will look light which is one object we ought to aim at…

An entry relating 'Painting Trav. Eng. Wheels' was entered into the Company's accounts for £1. 0s. 8d.[35]

Stephenson's later suggestion that it was his father's 'practical knowledge' that led to the successful completion of the multi-tubular boiler may thus be seen as a fond attribution rather than an accurate indication of events. The evidence indicates that, even allowing for George Stephenson's strong interest in the boiler, it was very much the work of Robert Stephenson and his Newcastle team that brought about its successful implementation.

3.4 Testing and shipment

The locomotive was completed to Robert Stephenson's satisfaction on 2 September 1829. In the absence of any test track at the Newcastle factory, it was then transported to Killingworth Colliery where arrangements had been made to steam the locomotive and carry out load-haul tests along the colliery's railway line. The tests would have been undertaken through the agreement and cooperation of George Stephenson's long-standing colleague, Nicholas Wood (1795–1865), the colliery's Viewer, who had also been appointed as one of the three judges for the Rainhill Trials.[36] The Killingworth tests were undertaken between 3 and 5 September. The Stephenson Company's stable account is credited with 5/- for the movement from Newcastle to Killingworth Colliery, but only one day at the Colliery 'with Premium Engine', for which 10/- was recorded.[37] On the completion of the tests, Stephenson reported to Booth on 5 September:[38]

I daresay you are getting anxious but I have delayed writing you until I tried the engine on Killingworth Railway. It appeared prudent to make an actual trial and make any alterations that might present themselves during an experiment of that kind. The fire burns admirably and abundance of steam is raised when the fire is carefully attended to. This is an essential point because a coke fire when let down is bad to get up again; this rather prevented our experiment being so successful as it would have been throughout – We also found that from the construction of the working gear that the Engine did not work so well in one direction as in the other, this will be remedied. The mercurial guage was not on, not from any defect but from my wish to get the Engine tried. We started from Killingworth Pit, with five waggons weighing four Tuns.

Add to this the tender and 40 Men we proceeded up an ascent 11 or 12 feet per Mile at 8 Miles per hour after we had fairly gained our speed.

We went three Miles on this Railway the rate of ascents and descents my father knows – on a level part laid with Malleable Iron Rail, we attained a speed of 12 Miles per hour and without thinking that I deceived myself (I tried to avoid this), I believe the steam did not sink on this part. On the whole the Engine is capable of doing as much if not more than set forth in the stipulations. – After a great deal of trouble and anxiety we have got the tubes perfectly tight. As requested by you in Mr. Locke's letter, I have not tried the boiler above 120 lbs. the Mercurial Guage and some other nick nacks are yet to be put on. On Friday next [11 September] the Engine will leave by way of Carlisle and will arrive in L'pool on Wednesday week [16 September]...

	T.	C.	Qr.
The weight of the Engine complete	3	10	1
Water say		15	0
Tuns	4	5	1

When *Rocket* was returned to Newcastle, Stephenson undertook a series of tests of different-size blast pipes to test their vacuum effect in its lower chimney area. It is likely that the tests were prompted by the Killingworth test runs. Following a lengthy and largely uninformed correspondence in *The Engineer* during 1857, which misguidedly became known as the 'blast pipe controversy',[39] Stephenson chose to write his recollections of the testing of the blast pipe, in the form of a narrative to Samuel Smiles for inclusion in his forthcoming *Lives of the Engineers*. He wrote:[40]

...During the construction of the '*Rocket*' a series of experiments was made with blast-pipes of different diameters, and their efficiency was tested by the amount of vacuum that was formed in the smoke-box. The degree of rarefaction was determined by a glass tube fixed to the bottom of the smoke-box and descending into a bucket of water, – the tube being open at both ends. As the rarefaction took place the water would of course rise in the tube, and the height to which it rose above the surface of the water in the bucket was made the measure of the amount of rarefaction.

These experiments certainly showed that a considerable increase of draught was obtained by contracting the orifice, and accordingly the two blast-pipes in the '*Rocket*' were contracted slightly below the area of the steam ports, – and before she left the factory the water rose in the glass tube three inches above the water in the bucket... The '*Rocket*' worked perfectly well with the double blast-pipe, and to the best of my recollection, the prize was won without any alteration having been made in that part of the engine.

These tests and the locomotive's subsequent movement and delivery to Liverpool were described over 28 years later, in 1858, in a memorandum written by the newly appointed Chief Draughtsman of Robert Stephenson & Co., J D Wardale. Wardale wrote the memorandum to coincide with two drawings of *Rocket* that he prepared in 1858, purporting to be a representation of it when it left the Newcastle factory in 1829 (Section 3.10). In writing it, he was reliant upon the memories of those employees who had been with the firm 29 years earlier, and such other notes as had survived in the factory. The accuracy of the recollections is thus uncertain. Wardale wrote that *Rocket* was:[41]

...then brought back to the Works and such alterations made as the experiments at Killingworth showed were necessary.

These alterations being completed it was then taken to pieces and sent by cars and waggon to Carlisle. The boiler, which was the last thing sent from the Factory, left at 4 o'clock on Saturday afternoon, the 12th day of September 1829, arriving at Carlisle on the Monday afternoon following at 2 o'clock. Arrived at Carlisle it was then transferred to a lighter, lying in the Canal basin, and conveyed to Boness, and there put on board the 'Cumberland' steamer, which took it to Liverpool, where it arrived on Friday the 18th. It was then transferred from the steamer to carts and waggons and taken to the railway workshops at Crown Street and there put together and the Engine tried.

The Stephenson Company's ledger records an 'allowance' of £1. 16s. 0d for the carriage of 'No.19 Tr. Eng. (Premium)', which provides some further evidence that *Rocket* was probably hauled across to Carlisle for shipment.[42] Jeaffreson reported that *Rocket* was shipped from the Tyne and 'arrived at Liverpool so long after her time that she had been given up for lost, and the sum for which the locomotive had been insured had been actually paid to Robert Stephenson & Co. when the ship and her cargo entered Liverpool water safe and sound.'[43] This was a misunderstanding on the author's part, referring instead to Stephenson's Travelling Engine No. 17 (Fig. 2.6), which had been built at the same time as *Rocket*, and was actually lost at sea on its delivery voyage to Liverpool (en route to the Baltimore & Ohio Railroad in the USA).[44]

The L&MR had arranged for the 'specimen engines' to be carted to the Millfield Yard, adjacent to its Crown Street Station in Liverpool, to be erected 'by the Company's men under the directions of the Proprietors of the Engines, or their Superintendents'.[45] On 28 September, Henry Booth reported to the railway's Board that 'two locomotives (Specimen Engines) had arrived at the Yard. The one belongs to Mr. Burstall and the other to himself and Messrs Robt. Stephenson.'[46] *Rocket*'s arrival provided the opportunity for a schematic drawing to be prepared which was first published in the *Mechanics' Magazine* for 24 October 1829 (Fig. 3.2).[47] One of the Stephenson company's fitters, Ralph Hutchinson, accompanied *Rocket* to Liverpool, and spent a total of 22 days there, both supervising re-erection and being in attendance ready to undertake any repairs or alterations that were called for.[48] He was probably called on to replace the locomotive's carrying wheel-set, although there is no contemporary evidence to indicate why the original set, used for the Killingworth test, was replaced. It could have been damaged in transit, but it is also possible that a wooden wheel-set was contemplated to save weight. Later evidence of the change was provided by a close observer of *Rocket* at the time, Robert Stannard (d. 1891), the son of the contractor for the Chat Moss–Salford stretch of the railway, who later recalled that:[49]

Fig. 3.2 The earliest illustration of *Rocket*
Source: *The Mechanics' Magazine*, 24 October 1829

> ...the pair of trailing wheels under the firebox – which were similar in character to the driving wheels, but smaller in size – only arrived on the day before [the Rainhill Trials]. When these wheels were placed under the frame it was found, to the great annoyance of the erectors, that the journals were too large to fit the bearings. It was impossible to get them altered in time for the trial; but the difficulty was overcome by substituting a pair of cast iron wheels, with a square-ended axle..., taken from a tip wagon at the last moment; and on these she ran at the Rainhill trials.

Further evidence that a change of wheels had been made was provided by John Rastrick who examined *Rocket* on 5 October. He noted that the locomotive was fitted with: '2 small wheels 2' 8½" Dr. Cast Iron case hardened' fitted to 'Axis for small Wheels 3 In Dr.'[50] These wheels were thus 2½ inches larger in diameter than those originally fitted to *Rocket*. According to Stannard, *Rocket*'s 'own' wheels, presumably of 2 ft 6 in. diameter, were fitted 'when the trials were over'.[51]

As Stephenson had indicated in his letter of 3 August, *Rocket*'s tender appears to have been made in Liverpool, this being the understanding reached by J D Wardale in his 1858 memorandum.[52] It is likely that the tender was made by Thomas Clarke Worsdell (1788–1862), assisted by his son, Nathaniel (1809–86). The Quaker family of coach-makers, originally from London, had established their workshop in Crown Street, Liverpool in 1827.[53] In consultation with George Stephenson they had made the earliest first-class carriages for the L&MR. Nathaniel Worsdell later indicated that the yellow livery for the carriages was decided by Stephenson in 1828, when discussing their design with his father. Worsdell wrote in 1880:[54]

> He might say that the finest carriage was really of a canary colour – for George Stephenson after producing and modifying the sketch said 'We shall paint it yellow' – and they did paint it yellow – and he was so much pleased with the colour of it that all the first class carriages they built for the Manchester and Liverpool Railway were painted yellow.

The yellow (and black) livery of the coaches appears to have copied that generally adopted by the fastest road coaches and would appear to have been chosen to indicate speed and reliability to the railway's potential passengers. The choice of yellow and black for *Rocket*'s livery therefore appears to have pursued the same theme. The white chimney was no doubt chosen to emphasise cleanliness and freedom from smoke.

In his 1858 memorandum, Wardale suggested that *Rocket* was painted after erection in Liverpool. Although Robert Stephenson had written that the painting had been undertaken in Newcastle (Section 3.3), it is likely that a final coat was applied in Liverpool or, at least, paintwork damaged in transit would have been touched up. Robert Stannard later recalled that, as a boy, he had had a ride on *Rocket*'s tender the evening after the first day's trial run and that, 'As the [water] butt had been newly painted only the day before, I stuck on very literally while we ran some four miles out and back.'[55]

The name, *Rocket*, appears to have been applied to the locomotive just prior to the Rainhill Trials. The earliest reference to the use of the name is on 5 October 1829, on which day John Rastrick noted it in his notebook,[56] although it was still referred to as a 'Specimen Engine' in the L&MR Board minutes of that day.[57] Thomas has suggested that the name was chosen by George Stephenson from a reference to Congreave's military rockets in an article about the railway in the *Quarterly Review* for March 1825.[58] However, no contemporary evidence has been found to confirm this.

3.5 *The Rainhill Trials and following performance trials*

Rocket was no doubt tried out on the L&MR in the first few days of October 1829, both to ensure that it was working satisfactorily and to demonstrate it to Henry Booth and George Stephenson. Its first recorded run was when the Directors of the Railway visited Rainhill on Monday morning, 5 October. They travelled:[59]

> from Huyton in cars drawn by Mr. Stephenson's locomotive, which moved up the inclined plane from thence with great velocity. They were accompanied by many scientific gentlemen, whose presence was hailed with numerous cheers.

The party included the three Rainhill judges, John Rastrick, Nicholas Wood and John Kennedy (1769–1855), who made a 'formal inspection' of the participants on arrival. Their first action was to draw up a short list of requirements for the trials, due to begin the following day (Appendix 2). The Rainhill Trials were due to start on Tuesday 6 October, but the first day was limited to demonstration runs and the following day the weather was too wet to proceed. The wording of the trial requirements required clarification to avoid misunderstandings, and a more explicit set was issued before the commencement of the trials proper on Thursday 8 October (Appendix 3). The trials ran intermittently between then and Wednesday 14 October, with *Rocket* undertaking its formal trials before the judges on 8 October.[60] The judges first ascertained the precise weight in working order of each locomotive. *Rocket*'s was determined to be 2 tons 12 cwt 1 qr on the driving wheels and 1 ton 12 cwt 3 qr on the carrying wheels, a total of 4 tons 5 cwt. The tender, with coke and water, weighed 3 tons 4 cwt 0 qr 2 lb.[61]

Rocket's first trial on the morning of 8 October was composed of ten timed round trips along the 1 mile length of track on the Rainhill level, which represented 5 miles of acceleration and deceleration and 30 miles at an operating speed, chosen to represent a journey between Liverpool and Manchester (Appendix 10.2). Hauling two carriages loaded with stones to a gross weight, including its tender, of 12 tons 15 cwt, calculated to be three times that of *Rocket* itself, the trial took 3 hours 11 minutes and 48 seconds to complete. During this time, the crew became more adept at driving and firing, as trip speeds gradually rose from 12.47 to 14.54 mph, with the last trip being undertaken at 19.15 mph (Appendix 10.2).

The second trial followed after an interval of just 15 minutes, being long enough to take on water and coke. It was similarly undertaken, with average trip speeds rising from 13.06 to 15.06 mph and again ending with a flourish, on the last west–east run, of 24.11 mph. A comprehensive evaluation of *Rocket*'s performance at the Trials was published by Nicholas Wood in the second and third editions of his Treatise.[62] It should be noted, however, that he miscalculated that *Rocket* had achieved '29 ⅑' mph on the last run, an overstatement that has been repeated in some histories.[63] *Rocket* had, nevertheless, demonstrated its reliability for continuous operation under load by travelling 70 miles with only one brief stop.

On several occasions, when *Rocket* was not required for the formal trials, the Stephensons and Booth used it to give demonstration runs. Attached to a carriage holding 20 to 30 passengers, *Rocket* ascended the 1:96 Whiston inclined plane at between 15 and 18 mph. This was part of the campaign to reinforce a wider perception of reliability and capability for locomotive haulage, being demonstrably the motive power for future main-line railway operation. Henry Booth afterwards wrote:[64]

> …the ease and regularity with which this was effected produced a general and confident impression, that even up the inclined planes, the Locomotive Engine would be the power employed.

This perception was reinforced when, probably on 14 October, *Rocket* highlighted the considerable improvement potential of the locomotive by achieving a speed in excess of the 30 mph which Braithwaite and Ericsson's *Novelty* had achieved during the demonstration runs a few days earlier:[65]

> …and to show that it had been working quite within its powers, Mr Stephenson ordered it to be brought on the ground and detached from all incumbrance, and in making two trips it moved at the astonishing rate of 35 miles an hour.

Responding to *Novelty*'s achievement, *Rocket*'s run was not only a new speed record, but demonstrated in front of the assembled crowd the capability of locomotives to convey people at sustained speeds greater than could be achieved on horseback (Section 2.3).

The Rainhill judges' report was completed and signed in Manchester on 16 October. It stated:[66]

In conclusion we consider Mr. Stephenson's Engine has completed in every respect with the Stipulations and Conditions issued by the Directors and dated 25 April 1829.

1st The Engine makes no smoke and consequently complies with the provisions of the Railway Act 7. Geo. IV.

2nd The Engine has drawn after it on a level plane more than three times its own weight including the Tender and Water Tank at more than 10 miles pr hour with a pressure of Steam not exceeding 50 lbs per square inch.

3rd There are two safety valves one of which is completely out of the control of the Engine man, and neither were fastened down during the working of the Engine.

4th The Engine and Boiler are supported on Springs, & the height of the chimney from the ground to the top does not exceed 15 feet.

5th The Engine with its complement of water in the Boiler being under 4½ tons, has been placed on four wheels. The Boiler, Fire Tube Cylinders &c having not been subject to a pressure of 150 lbs per Sq inch but we have no doubt they would be sufficiently strong to resist that proof if put to it.

6th There is a mercurial guage affixed to the Engine showing the pressure of the Steam in the Boiler...

On 20 October, at the first meeting of the L&MR Board after receipt of the judges' report, the Directors:[67]

Resolved unanimously that the Premium of £500 offered by the Directors for the most improved Loco motive Engine, subject to certain Stipulations and Conditions, be awarded to the Proprietors of the 'Rocket' Steam Engine, viz:

Mr. Henry Booth, Mr. Stephenson and Mr. Robt. Stephenson.

Further reward for the Stephensons was immediate, as four locomotives 'on the principle of the 'ROCKET' were ordered from Robert Stephenson & Co. on 26 October.[68]

A further programme of performance trials was undertaken with *Rocket* at the conclusion of the formal Rainhill event. The completed sections of the railway were used as a test-track to allow a better understanding of the locomotive's handling, speed and load-haul capabilities than had been possible at Killingworth or in Liverpool prior to the competition. A modification was made to the two exhaust pipe exits in the base of the chimney, by combining them into a single blast pipe. Although Robert Stephenson later stated in his response to the 'blast pipe controversy', that 'The '*Rocket*' worked perfectly well with the double blast-pipe' at Rainhill (Section 3.4), he went on to state:[69]

The experiments already mentioned proved that the double blast-pipe in the '*Rocket*' was capable of producing a considerable rarefaction in the chimney, and the alteration from two blast-pipes to one was made by myself rather with a view of lessening the space occupied by them in the chimney.

Stephenson appears to have understated the significance of the modification, however, as the provision of the single blast pipe with a narrow exit resulted in a significant increase in steam generation, which allowed for improvements in its sustained performance capability. Nicholas Wood summarised the modification in 1831:[70]

After these [Rainhill] experiments were concluded... Mr. Stephenson had also improved the working of the '*Rocket*' engine, and by applying the steam more powerfully in the chimney, to increase the draught, was enabled to raise a much greater quantity of steam than before.

The results of the extensive performance trials were recorded by Wood, Robert Stephenson and Joseph Locke.[71] Driving and firing techniques improved and, together with the blast-pipe modification, *Rocket*'s performance far exceeded that achieved at the Rainhill event. The opportunity was taken by members of the L&MR Board to capitalise on these improvements by publicising them to overcome any lingering doubts amongst fellow Board members regarding the use of locomotives.

Fig. 3.3 Sketch of *Rocket* in *c*.1830
Source: drawn by A B Clayton, lithographed by the First Artists, probably published by
Engelmann, Graf and Coinder: reproduced in C F Dendy Marshall, *Centenary History of the
Liverpool and Mancehster Railway*, London, 1930, Plate XIII, opp. p32

A Liverpool newspaper recorded that on 29 October, following a fortnight of trials after Rainhill:[72]

> ...we understand that it *[Rocket]* has drawn the still more astonishing load of 42 tons, or ten times its own weight, at the rate of 14 miles an hour, which is by far the greatest task that has ever been performed by a locomotive carriage... Another class of experiments was afterwards tried in order to ascertain with what load, and at what rate it would ascend the inclined plane at Huyton, when it was found that with 14 tons it travelled the mile and a half in five minutes and 35 seconds, or 16 miles an hour, and with 16 tons in seven minutes and 10 seconds, or 12½ miles an hour. These performances far exceed the warmest anticipations of the friends of locomotive carriages, and afford additional and incontestable evidence of their superiority to all modes of conveyance which at present exist.

Although the performance trials had been an important diversion for George Stephenson, his primary responsibility remained the completion of the railway, which still had several months of work remaining. *Rocket* was to be an important aid to speed up spoil and ballast movement and, on 19 October, the Board of Directors agreed to Stephenson's recommendation that it should be transferred to the Manchester end of the line for this work.[73] In his report to the Board on 25 October, Stephenson confirmed that:[74]

> The '*Rocket*' locomotive engine...is about to be put on Chat Moss, to drag the gravel for finishing the permanent way...

However, *Rocket*'s movement to the Manchester end of the line was delayed by at least a month, the policy change being influenced by the extraordinary public interest and enthusiasm aroused by the Rainhill Trials and the subsequent performance trials. Reflecting the mood of enthusiasm, John Dixon, the resident engineer for the Manchester end of the railway (Section 2.1), wrote that 'The *Rocket* is by far the best Engine I have ever seen for Blood and Bone united.'[75]

The events of October and November were covered at length in newspapers and other journals, both during and after the trials.[76] This widespread attention, together with that for the Edge Hill tunnel, was encouraged by the railway's Directors, who responded enthusiastically to a clamour of applications to see the tunnel and take rides behind *Rocket* and the other locomotives:[77]

> The public...continue to take advantage of the opportunity afforded them by the directors, of visiting and inspecting the tunnel on Fridays. The charges for admission to this stupendous undertaking, and a ride on the locomotive engines, are extremely moderate.

Fig. 3.3 appears to reflect the excited atmosphere of a journey behind *Rocket* at this time. On 6 November the Directors even went so far as to advertise *Rocket*'s movements in the newspapers to attract further interest:[78]

ANOTHER EXHIBITION OF
MR STEPHENSON'S STEAM CARRIAGE
THE ROCKET
Will take place at RAINHILL, THIS AFTERNOON,
at ONE O'CLOCK when, as we presume, some further
EXPERIMENTS will be made on the RAILROAD
The fact of the Exhibition may be implicitly relied on.

The excursions were undertaken largely by 'high-born' persons, anxious to partake in the novelty of rail travel and to inform their associates of their impressions. It was reported that during November:[79]

> ...the following distinguished individuals visited the Railway at Rainhill: Lord and Lady Grosvenor, Lord and Lady Grey, Lord and Lady Henry Cholmondeley, Lord and the Ladies Molyneux, Hon. Mr. and Miss De Roos, Lady Wilton, Hon. E G and Mrs Stanley, the Hon. Miss Stanley...and Mr [Thomas] Creevey [MP]. The superior powers of the locomotive carriage, the *Rocket*, were again exhibited, the carriage frequently going at the rate of 28 miles an hour, and averaging, during the excursion, including the inclined plane at Huyton, 22½ miles an hour.

Fig. 3.4 Revised illustration of *Rocket*
Source: *Mechanics' Magazine*, 28 November 1829

Fig. 3.5 Sketch of *Rocket* published in 1830
Source: Henry Booth, *An Account of the Liverpool and Manchester Railway* (Liverpool, 1830)
opp. p74

Thomas Creevey later wrote of his excursion behind *Rocket* on 14 November:[80]

> I had the satisfaction, for I can't call it <u>pleasure</u>, of taking a trip of five miles in it, which we did in just a quarter of an hour – that is, 20 miles an hour. As accuracy upon this subject was my great object, I held my watch in my hand at starting, and all the time; and as it has a second hand, I knew I could not be deceived... But observe, during these five miles, the machine was occasionally made to put itself out or <u>go it</u>; and then we went at the rate of 23 miles an hour, and just with the same ease as to motion or absence of friction as the other reduced pace. But the quickest motion is to me <u>frightful</u>: it is really flying, and it is impossible to divest yourself of the notion of instant death to all upon the least accident happening.'

The Board of Directors may have had another agenda in delaying *Rocket*'s move to Chat Moss and stimulating wide interest in the railway by these public relations initiatives. By the end of November, demand for the railway's shares had jumped significantly:[81]

> The shares in the Manchester and Liverpool Railway, which a few months ago were selling at £118 a share, are now selling for £175, being at a premium of £75. They have risen with great rapidity since the experiments at Rainhill, and such is the estimation in which they are now held, that it is very difficult to procure them on any terms. The demand is very considerable, and there are scarcely any in the market.

The directors issued a statement that Friday 27 November would be the last day to view Edge Hill tunnel, and to ride behind *Rocket*.[82] The following day, a revised drawing of *Rocket* appeared in the *Mechanics' Magazine* (Fig. 3.4), together with drawings of its Rainhill competitors.[83]

3.6 Works locomotive and opening of the railway

Rocket was transferred to the Manchester end of the railway at the end of November 1829 where it was used to convey fill and ballast from Salford for the Chat Moss contract, under the directions of the contractor, Robert Stannard (Senior). No alterations were made to *Rocket* during this time, Robert Stannard (Junior) later recording that it was sent '...to my father's cutting, where she worked regularly without any alteration being made until the following spring.'[84] It was probably used for an inspection special, however, which was laid on for the railway's directors on 2 or 3 December 1829, when 8 or 10 miles of the line were yet to be completed.[85]

The initial track-bed across Chat Moss was made ready for a single line of track shortly afterwards, and although far from complete and still requiring much consolidation, *Rocket* drew the first train across the Moss on 28 December.[86] The train conveyed the railway's directors and associates, and with

> a load of several carriages and about forty passengers, *Rocket* crossed Chat Moss in 17 minutes at an average speed of 16 mph, and on the return trip attained a speed of 30 mph.

As the consolidation work progressed, further confidence was gained in the Chat Moss track-bed. On 14 April, *Rocket* was used to carry out a load trial with a train of between 40 and 45 tons, which it achieved at just over 15 miles per hour.[87] Much work remained on the Chat Moss contract, however, and *Rocket* continued on these duties for several weeks after the opening of the railway in September 1830, until the track-bed had consolidated. Although then out of the public eye, *Rocket*'s Rainhill success continued to be reported, including a description by Henry Booth in his book describing the new railway.[88] This included a third sketch of the locomotive (Fig. 3.5), with an exaggerated slope to the firebox crown, which has later contributed to confusion over its actual form (Section 4.6).

From mid-January 1830, *Rocket* was no longer the centre of attention as the new batch of locomotives, ordered in October (Section 3.5), began to arrive from the Stephenson works in Newcastle. Incorporating improvements determined by *Rocket*'s performance trials, the *Meteor*, *Comet*, *Dart* and *Arrow* locomotives (Fig. 2.8) were used for trial and demonstration purposes. *Meteor* made its first run on 18 January.

The improvements were described:[89]

> The cylinders are larger, and placed almost horizontally, and the diameter of the wheels is four inches greater than in the *Rocket*. These alterations are expected to give the new engine greater speed, and to make its motion more regular and steady. There has also been an improvement made in the means of stopping it, by which it may be brought to a stand still almost instantly, even when proceeding at the most rapid speed. The carriage went yesterday at the rate of thirty miles an hour.

Although the report may be exaggerated, the emphasis given to the braking capability suggests an improvement from that adopted on *Rocket*, either to the handbrakes on the tender, or through a change in the valve motion and the use of counter-pressure braking (Section 4.10). Following a line inspection to Manchester in June, the railway's directors held a brief board meeting there, followed by a 'cold collation'. The return train, hauled by *Arrow*, was required to make an urgent stop:[90]

> ... after crossing Chat Moss, the carriage, when going at the rate of twenty miles an hour, was stopped in the space of about seventy yards for the purpose of permitting one of the party to alight, which was accomplished, and in one minute from the stoppage the carriage was again on its way.

The four *Rocket*-types were in turn superseded: in June by *Phoenix*, in August by *Northumbrian* and in September by *Planet*.[91] Such was the speed of improvement (Section 2.1) that, by the opening of the L&MR in September, *Rocket* was outmoded in terms of speed, load-haul and economy. The unsteadiness of the *Rocket*-type locomotives at speed gave rise to the introduction of the inside-cylinder *Planet*-type. For the outside cylinder locomotives, it was noted that:[92]

> ...each stroke had a tendency to move that side of the carriage to which it was applied at a quicker rate than the opposite side; and the alternate advancing of the two fore-wheels caused considerable unsteadiness of motion, which entirely disappeared when the steam was shut off, and the carriage allowed to proceed by its acquired velocity. The effect of this unsteady motion is not only to impair the durability of the machine, but to diminish its power very considerably, by causing the flanches of the wheels to rub against the sides of the rails.

On Saturday 21 August 1830, the railway operated three well-publicised special trains between Liverpool and Manchester and return, hauled by *Phoenix*, *Arrow* and *Rocket*. It was 'the rehearsal of what is to be encountered on the 15th September, when this great national work is to be opened to the Public.'[93] The three trains were full with:[94]

> 270 ladies and gentlemen in the carriages, and perhaps about thirty servants and other individuals on the engines... For a considerable distance from Manchester both sides of the [rail] road, as well as all the bridges which cross it, were crowded with people congregated to behold this novel exhibition, and to admire the triumph of mechanical science in the construction of the beautiful machines which thousands then saw for the first time in their lives.

In addition to these rehearsals, the Directors were anxious that no mishap should occur on the railway's opening day, and ordered that all its locomotives:[95]

> with the exception of the '*[Twin] Sisters*', shod. be taken off the way on the 1st Septr. next, for the purpose of undergoing complete repairs, & for all requisite experiments prior to the opening day

It is likely that each locomotive was also repainted for the occasion. *Rocket* may have been repainted from its yellow livery at this time, if it had not previously been altered. Isaac Boulton later recalled that on the railway's opening day 'she had most certainly a wooden tender, with a wooden cask on it painted green, to hold the water.'[96]

The events surrounding the opening of the railway on 15 September 1830 were well recorded in newspapers and journals during the following few days.[97] *Rocket*, drawing three carriages, was driven by driver White,[98] under the direction of Joseph Locke. The event that occurred at the Parkside water stop was the first recorded mishap to befall the locomotive, although there is no suggestion that *Rocket* itself sustained any damage. As it passed (at a reported speed of 8–10 miles per hour) the stationary train in which sat the Prime Minister, the Duke of Wellington, it struck and wrenched off an open door of the Duke's carriage. This had been grabbed by the Liverpool MP and former President of the Board of Trade, William Huskisson, throwing him under *Rocket*'s wheels. Huskisson's death gave rise to much comment and, although the accident happened very quickly and with little time for the driver to respond, questions were posed regarding the ability of steam locomotives to stop in emergencies.[99] Perhaps influcnced by previous articles suggesting that braking could be instantaneous,[100] response time was little considered in the debate. *Mechanics' Magazine* reported:[101]

> The gear of an engine can be reversed almost instantaneously, and the momentum of any weight attached to it can be checked by what is technically called a break; and if there had been a due use of these expedients in the present instance, no accident would have occurred... Whether it was owing to any defectiveness in the arrangements for reversing the gear of the *Rocket*, and applying the break, or to want of attention in the engineer and breaksman, that the engine was not stopped, we are not prepared to say... We are inclined to think that it must have been the reversing gear, and not the engineer, which was in fault...

However, following the coroner's inquest, held on 23 September, it was reported that:[102]

> The jury gave no deodand; and this finding would set the question at rest, had there been any doubt that the fatal injury had been purely accidental, and that not the slightest imputation of blame rests on the machines, the railway, or any individual.

No further action against *Rocket* or its driver was reported after the inquest.

3.7 *Operation, accidents and modifications*

The start-up of services on the L&MR had required detailed planning for the adequate provision of water, fuel and lubricants for the locomotive fleet.

The Directors had asked George Stephenson to pay particular attention to the quality of the water to be used for the locomotives. At the Manchester end of the line, for example, the quality of the water offered by the 'Manchester and Salford Water Works Company' was approved before a contract was signed for the supply of 10,000 gallons a day, which was to be pumped into a large tank above the tracks between the Irwell bridge and Water Street, for an annual charge of £70.[103] It is likely that the water was then, as now, soft and relatively free from impurity, which would no doubt have contributed to the good condition of *Rocket*'s surviving boiler and firebox back (Sections 4.4.1 and 4.6.3).

The railway company entered into a contract for the supply of locomotive coke from the Duke of Bridgewater's coke plant at Worsley. The coke was delivered into the company's Crown Street yard in Liverpool for 20/2d per ton. The company closely monitored the coke consumption of the locomotives and sought an alternative supply in 1831, but declined a higher tender. It even considered building its own coke ovens as a means of reducing the cost, but the initiative did not proceed. Not until 1833 did it succeed in reducing the price of the Worsley coke by 3/6d per ton, with delivery being taken in Manchester.[104]

There is a long-held tradition within the Filtrate Lubricants Company of Leeds that its founding company, W & E Joy, which started up in business in 1807 as seed crushers and oil refiners, first supplied lubricating oil for use on *Rocket*. The oil, which was apparently known as 'Joy' oil, was said to have been crushed and refined at Thwaite Mills, Stourton, Leeds. It has not been possible to verify this claim, but mechanical lubricants at this time contained rape and linseed oils, as well as palm and sperm oils, and it could well be that the company's rape-oil-based lubricants were used.[105] Main axle bearings were usually lubricated with tallow, but in 1835, Henry Booth patented a substance that was said to have a more durable viscosity. His formula consisted of mixtures of tallow and palm oil emulsified by being heated with washing soda to just under boiling point with vigorous stirring to produce a butter-like grease.[106]

After the opening of the railway, *Rocket* returned to its ballast-leading duties at the Manchester end of the line. Isaac Boulton later recorded that it was 'at work night and day, taking rock, &c., from Eccles to Chat Moss.'[107] A slightly improved representation of the locomotive at that time, based on those previously shown in the *Mechanics' Magazine* (Figs. 3.2 and 3.4), was published in Nicholas Wood's *Treatise* in 1831 (Fig. 3.6).

The extraordinary interest in the new form of transport saw several people ask the locomotive drivers for footplate rides. Robert Stannard Jnr 'frequently rode on her',[108] and many years later, Isaac Boulton also owned up to one such ride:[109]

> One day I was on the Rocket's foot-plate, and a part of the old Rocket became detached. It almost instantly got into my hands, and has remained in my possession ever since.

The Directors issued a notice banning unauthorised persons from riding on footplates, but the problem persisted and a fatality resulted.[110] On Thursday evening, 28 October 1830, Henry Hunter, a 31-year-old man, rode on the back of *Rocket*'s tender from Salford to Chat Moss with a works train, after the last passenger service had passed. After material had been deposited at Chat Moss, *Rocket* was propelling its empty train back to Salford when, about 11 pm, one of the tender axles broke, the jerk projecting Hunter under the wheels of the tender and locomotive. He was afterwards 'found to be quite dead'. *Rocket* was derailed and its driver, possibly White, was seriously injured, but the fireman sustained only a few bruises; neither was named.[111]

The use of locomotives to propel as well as draw trains was a further innovation of main-line railway operation. The question had been addressed the previous April,

Fig. 3.6 Illustration of *Rocket*
Source: Nicholas Wood, *A Practical Treatise on Rail-Roads* &c., London, 1831, opp. p382

when George Stephenson was asked by the railway's directors to report 'on the advantages & disadvantages of <u>propelling</u> as compared with <u>drawing</u>, with reference to convenience, power, & safety'.[112] Stephenson reported the following week, and his views entered in the Company's Report Book, which, however, has not survived.[113]

The extent of *Rocket*'s damage was not recorded, but Stannard later wrote that, following the accident, it had been sent to the workshops for repair and modification.[114] In the absence of any main-line operating experience, however, the railway's earliest maintenance facilities were limited to two running sheds, at Edge Hill, Liverpool, and Ordsall Lane, Salford, equipped with basic machine tools and general maintenance teams, which George Stephenson had been instructed to provide in June 1830.[115] Major modifications were therefore undertaken by contractors, of whom the Liverpool engineering and ironfounding firm of Foster & Griffin were awarded the majority of the work. They had two separate premises at 3–4 Beckwith Street, close to Salthouse Dock and Duke's Dock, and at 4 Queen Anne Street, to the north-east of the city centre.[116] By 1832, the company had expanded into a third site in 4 Dublin Street, adjacent to the new Clarence Dock.

From the evidence of the locomotive's surviving components, it seems most likely that after its accident *Rocket* underwent several modifications during November 1830. These were probably carried out by Foster & Griffin, either at their workshops or by their men at the railway's Edge Hill workshops. The work included the fitting of a steam dome and internal steam pipe, the refitting of the spring safety-valve, the installation of the water-jacketed firebox back and attendant water feedpipes, the raising of the fire grate, the fitting of an extended smokebox, ash-box and shorter chimney, and the resiting of the boiler's blow-down valve and wash-out holes. *Rocket*'s 'Mercurial guage' may also have been removed and put to one side at this time, as it was later refurbished and used in the Edge Hill workshops.[117] The work would have been conducted under the supervision of William Allcard (Section 2.1), who had then been appointed as the engineer responsible for the Liverpool end of the railway.

Figures 3.7 and 3.8 appear to show *Rocket* in its modified form as recorded by T T Bury just a few weeks later. Although detail of the smokebox is difficult to determine, it appears to show the front-end modification, including an ash-box and door, and shorter chimney (Section 4.8). Although the tender was the cause of the accident, the Bury illustrations suggest that *Rocket* retained a barrel tender after the modifications. Stannard later recalled that 'it was eventually replaced by a wrought iron box tank carried on the same tender.'[118]

The expense of such major modifications was almost certainly justified by the urgent need for the railway to provide sufficient locomotives for its passenger traffic, which had built up quickly after the opening of the railway. When *Rocket* was released back into traffic, it was drafted into passenger and passenger-related services. From 11 October, these duties had included the requirement for a pilot engine 'with a good Coal Lamp affixed to the Tender' to precede the 4.30 pm Liverpool to Manchester train to ensure the line was free from obstructions.[119]

Rocket was employed as pilot on 8 December, when the train collided with an obstruction at Elton-Head. The obstruction, which had been placed on the line after *Rocket* had passed, over a mile ahead of the train, derailed the train engine, *Meteor*. *Rocket*'s driver, Mark Wakefield, was ordered to keep closer to the trains in future.[120]

Drivers White (above) and Wakefield are the only two recorded names for *Rocket*'s drivers, and the duration of their association with the locomotive is unknown. Three claims have been made for individuals thought to have been *Rocket*'s fireman at one time or another, but none can be substantiated.[121]

On Tuesday 25 January 1831, *Rocket* was involved in its third serious accident in three months, when it was derailed and turned over onto its side in Olive Mount cutting whilst hauling the 2 pm 'second class' Liverpool to Manchester train. It was stated at the time that the accident was '…in consequence of the breaking of one of her wheels, which, owing to the negligence of a workman, got jammed fast at a *sideing*',[122] but the railway's Board Minutes make no reference to confirm the cause.

Figs. 3.7 and 3.8 Two illustrations of *Rocket* in *c*. December 1830
Source: drawn by T T Bury, published 1 February 1831, by R Ackermann, London

Rocket was taken back to the Edge Hill workshops for repairs, although again the full extent of the damage was not recorded. One of the cylinders and/or its mounting bracket may have been damaged, as it seems that the opportunity was taken to alter the cylinder arrangement to that which had been successfully adopted on *Meteor*, *Comet*, *Dart* and *Arrow*. *Rocket*'s cylinder angle was lowered from 38 degrees to 8 degrees to permit more stable running at higher speeds and the cylinders were inverted, placing the valve chests on the top. To achieve this cylinder relocation, the original light mounting plates were cut off and large new plates fitted to the sides, braced across the rear of the firebox. A number of other components required consequential refitting. The work was, again, probably carried out by Foster & Griffin under William Allcard's supervision. Isaac Shaw visited 'the workshop of the railway', apparently in February 1831, where he saw '...the old conquering hero, the *Rocket*, undergoing repairs, and having its cylinder and piston dropt.'[123]

Rocket probably returned to passenger service and, in common with the rest of the locomotive fleet, it would have had to meet additional safety requirements that were being developed from main-line operating experience, namely:

• from 18 October 1830: 'no person [should] be allowed to ride on the Engine-Tender, except the Engine-man & Fireman, Mr. Stephenson, Mr. Dixon, Mr. Allcard, Mr. Gooch, Mr. Melling, Mr. Harding and the Directors and Treasurer'[124]

• from the same date it was ordered: 'That the maximum speed of the Engine do not in any part of the Road exceed Twenty Miles per hour; and that, as heretofore, the speed be slower in those parts of the way, which are under repair, at the crossings of the public roads, and over the high Embankments'

• from 15 June 1831, it became the duty of firemen to blow horns when approaching the gates across public roads,[125] and

• from 17 August 1831, locomotives travelling towards Manchester were required to show red lights, and those travelling towards Liverpool 'the ordinary yellow lights'.[126]

The locomotive shortage eased during the year as further *Planet* and *Samson*-class locomotives were delivered to the railway and, by the autumn of 1831, *Rocket* had returned to duties as a works locomotive. On 3 October consideration was given by the railway's Board to a request to buy the locomotive from Thomas Legh MP, the proprietor of the adjacent Haydock Collieries. It was minuted: 'That while the Company have not moving Power sufficient for the necessary Repairs of the Road, it would not be expedient to part with any of their present Engines.'[127]

It is likely that *Rocket* remained as a works locomotive until the following summer, by which time the Liverpool & Manchester locomotive fleet numbered twenty-seven. The Wigan Branch Railway, which had been built to connect with the L&MR at Parkside, was to be worked by the latter for an initial period of three months when it opened on 3 September 1832.[128] *Rocket* was made available to operate the new services, probably from their commencement. It was on the Wigan branch that *Rocket* became involved in its fourth serious accident on 6 November. At 8.30 am it was returning to Wigan 'with the usual Coach Train' when it met a coal train, hauled by a locomotive of the Warrington & Newton Railway, coming in the opposite direction, 'the two Engines running against [each] other'. Nobody was hurt, 'but the Engine and Tender were much damaged.'[129]

The L&MR engaged its solicitors, Pritt, Clay & Co. to collect evidence about the accident and Henry Roscoe was engaged as legal counsel to represent the railway. The evidence indicated that it was the fault of the Warrington & Newton Railway's driver, and Roscoe was required to seek damages and, if necessary, to sue that railway. *Rocket*'s damage cost £74. 14s. 7d to repair, to which was added the legal bills of £18. 15s. 10d, both being submitted as a claim against the Warrington company.[130] A lengthy litigation took place, during which the latter paid just £50, leaving the Liverpool & Manchester Directors to argue about the recovery of the outstanding sum.[131]

Rocket was once more taken back to the Edge Hill workshop for repairs, which were carried out between November 1832 and January 1833, although the extent of the repairs required is not recorded. By this time, the Edge Hill workshop had been enlarged and was, itself, capable of undertaking the work. In April 1832, the Board of Directors had agreed with William Allcard that as 'A good deal of Boiler mending being now required' the railway should employ 'three Boiler makers, instead of employing Foster & Griffin for that kind of work.'[132]

The growth of the maintenance facilities had previously been piecemeal, and spread between the Edge Hill and the small Crown St workshops in Liverpool, and that at Ordsall Lane, Salford. In August 1832, it was agreed to concentrate the repair and heavy overhaul work at Edge Hill, and maintain the Salford shed as a light-repair facility.[133] Following this move, decisions were taken to invest in about £1000-worth of machine tools, including a hydraulic press for fitting wheels to axles.[134]

Rocket's repair work was carried out under the direction of John Melling (1781–1856), who had been appointed as superintendent of the workshops. In addition to the repairs, the opportunity was taken to give *Rocket* a major refurbishment. The work included the fitting of a new set of copper boiler tubes, although this may not have been the first such re-tubing to have been carried out (Section 4.7.12).[135] The cost came into question and William Allcard 'was instructed to ascertain whether Copper Tubes 3 inches diameter could not be obtained at a lower rate pr. lb. than tubes 1⅝ inch diameter.'[136] The re-tubing work was partly carried out by Thomas Hunt, who later wrote that he had been a pupil at Edge Hill under Melling early in 1833, his first job being to assist with the removal of *Rocket*'s tubes.[137]

Although the copper tubes had lasted typically between 25,000 and 30,000 miles, the Directors reported that over the whole fleet they 'were almost continually bursting' and that 'a considerable saving is expected to take place by the recent application of brass tubes to the engines.'[138] The railway adopted brass tubes for all locomotives in April 1833, three months after *Rocket*'s return to service, and there is no record of whether it was later fitted with them.[139] It is likely that *Rocket*'s cylinders were re-bored during January as new pistons, reportedly of 8¼ inches diameter (an increase of a ¼ inch), were supplied by Robert Daglish & Co. of the St Helens Foundry. They were fitted with brass rings and steel springs (Sections 4.9.3 and 4.9.4).[140]

Melling appeared to take advantage of the damage claim against the Warrington railway to embellish the locomotive with additional brass-work. William Allcard reported to the Sub-Committee of Management 'that there was a great deal of unnecessary ornamental Brass Work put on the *Rocket* engine without authority.' Melling was reprimanded and told that 'in future it could not be permitted – good & substantial workmanship was what was required for the Loco-Motive Engines with as little unnecessary expence as possible.'[141]

3.8 Standby duties and trials use

Rocket's repair and refurbishment could have been a significant factor in its later survival. By the end of 1832, the L&MR had sufficient motive power to meet its anticipated requirements, and it began to dispose of its older locomotives, which were obsolescent and expensive to run compared to the *Planet*-types.[142] *Comet* was sold to a contractor in December 1832, and, but for the refurbishment, *Rocket* might also have been sold at this time.[143]

The ongoing problem of fire hazard prompted the L&MR's decision, on 24 January 1833, to fit ash-boxes under the fire grates of the locomotives.[144] It is not recorded whether *Rocket* was so fitted, and in spite of the railway reiterating its intention that all locomotives should be fitted with 'closer ash boxes' in 1835, there is no evidence on the locomotive to suggest that this was done (Section 4.6.4).[145] In February 1833, the railway's management agreed to their engineers' recommendation to adopt the use of 'black varnish instead of the bright polish, for the hand gear and working parts of the Loco-motive Engines.'[146]

A further general adoption for all locomotives was made by the railway's management in April 1833, on Melling's recommendation.[147] This was:

> …that the Excentric Drivers should be tapped fast into the Axle Shaft, so that when once set right, they might not be liable to get wrong, as they frequently did, either from accident or design…

Although attention would have been given to the passenger and goods locomotives first, *Rocket*'s drivers [dog-rings] may have been altered accordingly during that summer (Section 4.9.5).

During 1833, after its refurbishment, *Rocket* seems to have been used only for standby duties and occasional works trains. Edward Woods (1814–1903), who joined the railway as Assistant Engineer in January 1834 and became its Chief Engineer in 1836, later wrote that during his time with the railway, *Rocket* 'was not frequently used, and rarely, if ever, in the service of the ordinary traffic of the line'.[148]

The early 1830s was a period of intense interest in steam engine development, and a number of inventors sought to promote their ideas with the railway's Directors, and to try them out on its locomotives. *Rocket*'s availability meant that it was considered as a test-bed for some of these trials.

The first major proposal was received from the American engineer, Jacob Perkins (1766–1849), who promoted his patent water 'circulator' which was designed to improve the thermal efficiency of boilers and reduce coke consumption.[149] Following his initial approach to the railway in July 1832, arrangements were made to fit five locomotives with 'circulating' plates, between December 1832 and February 1833, for the purpose of demonstration and trial.[150] As *Rocket* was in the Edge Hill workshop at the time, it is possible that it was used as one of the trial locomotives, but the Board minutes do not confirm this, mentioning only the *Planet* locomotives, *Venus* and *Vesta* by name. Furthermore, there is no evidence on *Rocket*'s surviving components that can be attributed to the Perkins experiments. By the end of 1833, it was clear that the experiments offered no fuel saving and the Board refused to sanction any further expenditure.[151]

Rocket was used on 22 and 23 September 1833 as a vehicle to undertake dynamic experiments on behalf of the freelance engineer, Richard Badnall, who was associated with Robert Stephenson Snr (1788–1837), and with whom he entered a partnership the following month.[152] Badnall promoted the idea of improving railway alignments by grading them to take advantage of gravity for acceleration and retardation in accordance with prevailing loads and stopping places, using a form of pendulum motion. His 'undulating railways' would continue to use steam locomotives, but he argued that their economy would be significantly enhanced by favourable gradients. The L&MR agreed to make locomotives available on the 1:96 Sutton incline in order that Badnall could test the momentum characteristics under differing lengths of gradient, speed and load.[153]

Part way through the trials on 23 September, '*Rocket* was not sufficiently in order to make further trials alone', and a short time later it was withdrawn from the trials as it was 'so much out of order'. The remainder of the trials, conducted with other locomotives, gave rise to lengthy correspondence in the *Mechanics' Magazine* regarding the dynamic principles that Badnall was seeking to demonstrate.[154] After their initial enthusiasm for the trials, it became apparent to the railway's Directors that the predicted cost savings were not going to be fulfilled, and they withdrew their cooperation with Badnall.

Rocket was either returned to standby duties at this time, or set aside, probably at the Edge Hill workshops. When De Pambour conducted his experiments on the railway during July and August 1834, he noted that '...the first engines used by the company at the opening of the railway... have nearly ceased to be used on the railway; they scarcely ever undergo any repairs, and none of them will figure in our experiments.'[155] *Rocket* was not allowed to deteriorate, however, as, when David Stevenson visited the railway in the latter half of 1834, he noted that it 'has been little used, and is still in good repair.'[156]

Rocket was next employed as a test bed for Lord Dundonald's 'Rotary Engine' in October 1834, for which purpose the locomotive was rebuilt. Rear Admiral Lord Thomas Cochrane, the tenth Earl of Dundonald (1775–1860), had resigned his naval commission in 1825 after an active career and, in his father's footsteps (1748–1831), took to amateur invention.[157] He became a strong advocate, with several other 'inventors', of the rotary engine, this being a positive-displacement engine, rather than a turbine (Fig. 3.9):

Dundonald anticipated that his engine, originally developed as a form of marine propulsion, could also be adapted to locomotive propulsion.[158] He took out a patent on it in 1833.

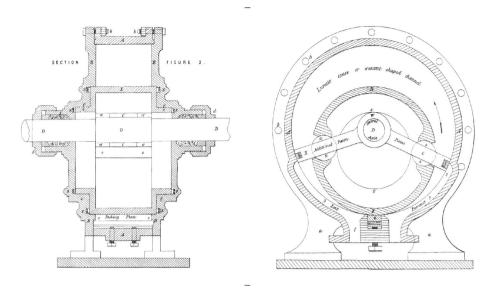

Fig. 3.9 Views of Lord Dundonald's rotary engine

He argued that his rotary engine, together with a novel form of railway, would provide the following advantages:[159]

Simplicity, Strength and durability of the Machinery
Increased velocity
Uniformity of impulse
Diminution of oscillation
Durability of the Rails

Security from accidents by the abasement of the centre of gravity – By the instantaneous cessation of the propelling power, and simultaneous action of the retarding force of friction arising from the whole weight of the matter in motion – especially if, per chance, any deviation should take place from the line of rails.

In December 1833, Dundonald approached Sharp Roberts & Co. of Manchester to take up and promote the manufacture of his engine. This was brought to the attention of the L&MR, which wrote to Dundonald for further details.[160] After further correspondence in 1834, a pair of rotary engines was made for application to a locomotive, probably by John Seaward & Co., marine engineers of the Canal Iron Works, Limehouse, on the River Thames, which had been manufacturing Dundonald's rotary marine engines.[161]

Dundonald visited Liverpool in October 1834 to consider a trial of these engines on a locomotive. The Liverpool & Manchester Directors received a note from him stating that:[162]

having observed the construction of the Company's Loco Motive Carriages, he was of opinion that a trial of his revolving Engine might be made on the *Rocket* in a manner that would sufficiently prove the power of his Engine; and so convinced was his Lordship that the expense would not exceed £30. that he was willing himself to pay any additional cost.

The choice of *Rocket* was no doubt made both because of its availability and favourable condition, and because the rotary engines could be fitted to its driving axle which was 'straight', unlike the cranked axles of the Planet-class. By 20 October, *Rocket*'s rebuilding was not complete, but costs were mounting alarmingly:[163]

The Treasurer stated that the cost of fitting up and fixing Lord Dundonald's Rotary Machine to the *Rocket* Engine, already amounted to near £80, and the arrangements were not yet sufficiently completed to allow of any satisfactory and conducive trial.

There is no known illustration of the rotary engine as fitted to *Rocket*, but a schematic illustration of a driving wheel-set fitted with a pair of rotary engines had been included in a pamphlet produced by Dundonald eleven months earlier (Fig. 3.10).[164]

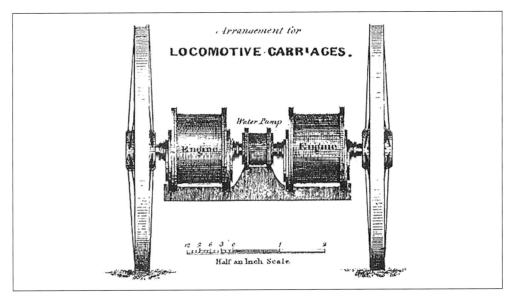

Fig. 3.10 Lord Dundonald's rotary engine adapted to locomotive propulsion

The rotary engine and water pump fitted to *Rocket*'s driving axle would have required torque arms and drag-links to take the reaction of the engines, and would have increased the unsprung weight, with consequent risk to the track. Other modifications would have included the fitting of a steam pipe, perhaps leading from the dome and routed through the front tube-plate, smokebox and the rear of the ash-box to reach the engines. The exhaust pipes would also have been routed through the ash-box. The valve-gear, pistons and connecting rods would have been disconnected. The surviving smokebox was probably fitted in 1836 (Section 4.8), and thus evidence of the steam-feed and exhaust arrangements is no longer available. However, a blanked-off hole in the top of the front tube-plate may well have been that used for the steam pipe during the trial (Section 4.7.11).

The arrangement would not have allowed for vertical movement between the wheel-set and the frame without some form of flexible steam-tight joints for the steam pipe. There is no evidence to suggest that this was considered and the trial, on or about 22 October was a failure, probably largely for this reason. The engines themselves, however, did not fulfil Dundonald's expectations, it being later recorded that *Rocket* 'could not be made to draw a train of empty carriages.'[165] He promptly withdrew from any further trials and asked for a statement of expenditure with which to settle the costs. This was provided by Henry Booth on the railway's behalf, who commented in his reply:[166]

> A gentleman of mechanical knowledge has suggested to [John] Melling a mode of Connecting the Rotary Engine with the driving wheels of the Loco-motive, by three Cog Wheels – one of them fixed on the axis of the Rotary, one on the nave of the Driving Wheel and one intermediate, hung on a Connecting link, to allow a yielding to the motion of Springs, on which the Rotary is supposed to be placed...

On 27 October, the railway's Board of Directors:

> Read a Letter from Lord Dundonald upon his leaving Liverpool thanking the Directors for the facilities they had afforded him of making trial of his Rotary Engine on the Rail Way & expressing his unabated confidence in the efficiency of his Engine provided some unobjectionable plan were discovered of applying its powers to a Loco-Motive Carriage.

Dundonald pursued his quest to equip a locomotive with his rotary engines through a lengthy dialogue with the London & Greenwich Railway.[167] In spite of their interest in the engines as expressed in this correspondence, the railway contacted the Liverpool & Manchester Directors to say that:[168]

> ...it was not the intention of that Company to take any steps in reference to Lord Dundonald's Rotary Engine – which was ordered, in consequence, to be taken from off the *Rocket* to which it had been attached and be laid up, to wait Lord Dundonald's orders.

A month later Dundonald, whilst promising to pay for the outstanding sum due on *Rocket*'s conversion 'before the end of the year', requested 'that the Engine might be sent pr. Canal to London, which was ordered accordingly.'[169] Dundonald's later relations with the London & Greenwich Railway regarding the use of the rotary engine turned sour when the railway withdrew its interest and he resorted to litigation over promises he alleged had been made.[170]

There continued to be wide and long-lasting interest in rotary engines, and over 50 patents had been taken out for them by the date of George Stephenson's critical 1848 paper, although applications to locomotives were experimental and none entered regular service.[171]

Rocket may not have been reassembled after the removal of the rotary engines, and may have remained at the Edge Hill workshops from that time, as there is no further reference of its employment on the L&MR. In June 1836, Henry Booth reported to the railway's Board that he had received an application from an unnamed applicant to purchase the locomotive second-hand. The Directors agreed to the application, subject to price, in anticipation of which they ordered:[172]

> that a good Drawing should be made of her to exhibit the form and construction of the first Engine employed on the Rail Way.

This order is probably the first example of an appreciation of the historical significance of a locomotive engine, and may also reflect the first example of a sentimental attachment. It is most likely that the completed drawing was that which has been known for many years as the 'Crewe' drawing (Fig. 3.11, p107).[173] The drawing appears to show *Rocket* in its mid-1836 form as made ready for sale on the second-hand market. In preparing it for sale, which did not go ahead straight away, the Edge Hill workshops refitted it as a reciprocating locomotive. It is also very likely that the replacement smokebox, with its oversize ash-box (Section 4.8), was fitted at this time, as depicted in the drawing.

3.9 Second-hand employment on the Naworth collieries railway

Rocket was purchased on behalf of the Earl of Carlisle in October 1836. The Earl's standard-gauge railway system, serving his colliery network in the Naworth coalfield of Cumberland, was opened on 15 July 1836, from Halton-Lea-Gate near Midgeholme on the Alston–Carlisle turnpike road (NY654585) across Tindale Fell to Brampton Staithes (NY538612), with attendant branches to the several collieries. It had been converted and extended from the earlier Tindale Fell Waggonway, and linked with the Newcastle & Carlisle Railway, the western end of which was opened four days later at Brampton Junction (Milton – NY552601).[174] The line, which was originally worked by horses, had been converted and extended by Lord Carlisle's innovative colliery agent, James Thompson (1794–1851). He first considered locomotive power, to reduce the cost of coal, coke and lime haulage between Midgeholme and Hallbankgate (NY578598), in October 1836. At Hallbankgate traffic descended a 1:28/18 self-acting inclined plane to Kirkhouse, where Thompson established the railway's workshops, and from where traffic was collected by the Newcastle & Carlisle Railway. James Loch, Lord Carlisle's London agent, wrote to the latter on 2 October:[175]

> Thompson thinks that there could be considerable saving made, if the coals were to be brought down by a Locomotive to the top of the inclined plane. I am doubtful of this, but have desired him to make his calculations...To enable him to make these I have sent [John] Ramshay down by way of Liverpool & Bolton with letters to Booth & Sinclair the Managers of the Liverpool and Manchester & Bolton & Leigh Railway companies [to see] if they have any of their light Locomotives for sale & what they will cost...

The importance of acquiring a locomotive with a light axle-load was due to the light rails employed on the railway, which ranged from 28 lb to 36 lb per yard.[176] John Ramshay, Lord Carlisle's steward, was delayed in getting to Lancashire until the second week of October.[177] His negotiations were sufficiently encouraging for James

Thompson to travel to Liverpool a few days later, accompanied by his brother, Mark (1808–1850), to complete the purchase arrangements on behalf of the Earl of Carlisle.[178] On 24 October, Henry Booth reported to the Liverpool & Manchester Board 'that he had sold the old *Rocket* & Tender to Mr. James Thompson of Carlisle for £300.'[179] Although Booth had understandably rounded the figure, the actual purchase price was £295. 19s. 5d.[180] This figure suggests that a number of spare parts ('duplicates') were included which, being non-standard, the railway would have wished to sell on, and Thompson would have wished to acquire to assist with *Rocket*'s maintenance. This probably included a spare driving wheel-set (Section 4.3.1). The purchase may therefore have been £250 for the locomotive and tender and the balance for the spares. This sale price would still have been high for *Rocket*, which was both of outdated design and older than other locomotives sold by the L&MR a year earlier for the same or lower prices.[181] This suggests that the price reflected the value of the repairs, probably undertaken in June, to make *Rocket* suitable for sale.

In November 1836, *Rocket* was shipped from Liverpool to Port Carlisle, where it would have been transshipped, and conveyed along the Carlisle Ship Canal, probably on the Carlisle Canal Company's 'swift iron boat "the Arrow".'[182] It was carted from the Canal basin to the Newcastle & Carlisle Railway's station,[183] and conveyed by the railway to Kirkhouse on or before 30 November, at a cost of 19s. 2d.[184]

It would seem, however, that the locomotive was either not immediately available for service, or required repairs shortly after its arrival, but evidence is lacking as to the nature of the problem. In addition, buffing timbers and bracing was bolted onto the front bufferbeam and frame to suit the lower height of the colliery system's chaldron waggons (Section 4.2.2 and 4.2.3). Robert Stephenson & Co. undertook the work during December, presumably at Kirkhouse.[185]

A further indication of a problem occurred in January 1837, when an 'Engine axle' was carted to Hexham, the western extremity of the rail route from the Tyne at that time, perhaps to be conveyed to the Stephenson factory for repair or replacement.[186] The delay in making *Rocket* available for service has caused some confusion for the Thompson family, who later believed that James Thompson had acquired it in March 1837.[187] It is more likely that *Rocket* began service hauling coal trains between Midgeholme and Hallbankgate in March, following the repairs and modifications.

In August 1837, *Rocket* was used as one mode of transport in a contrived speed trial to take the voting returns, after the national election of 7–8 August, from Alston to Carlisle. A time of 62 minutes was achieved for the 30 miles, but *Rocket*'s contribution for the stretch between Halton-Lea-Gate and Kirkhouse has been grossly exaggerated in subsequent articles. The source of the exaggeration was a report in the *Carlisle Journal* for 15 September 1848, following an obituary for George Stephenson.[188] The high-speed run is discussed further in Appendix 8.

James Thompson used a vignette of *Rocket* and coal train on the Earl of Carlisle's stationery, albeit depicted 'as built' rather than its contemporary appearance (Fig. 3.12).[189] With the encouragement of James Thompson's long working relationship with the Earl of Carlisle, it was agreed by the Earl and his advisers that all the colliery operations should be leased to Thompson, to whom ownership of the capital assets would also pass.[190] The 21-year lease commenced on 12 May 1838, following valuation of all assets the previous day by five independent people.[191] *Rocket* passed into Thompson's ownership at a valuation of £150, half that of the purchase price just 18 months earlier. It was described in the valuation as '1 locomotive Engine at Mack Dolls Hole & Tender', although this precise location has not been identified. A further valuation was held on 8 August 1838, because of a previous lack of distinction between 'live' and 'dead' stock in the transfer value. *Rocket* was again valued at £150, as part of the 'dead' stock.[192]

Rocket would no doubt have been provided with a supply of coke from Thompson's coke ovens at Midgeholme. Confirmation of this is suggested by a single entry in a statement of traffic for the year ending 11 May 1839. Under the category 'Coke', an entry for the 'Midgeholme Ovens in Tons & Cwt' reads 'Loc. Engine 38 [tons] 0 [cwt]'.[193] This is, however, only a small quantity in relation to a year's work. The equivalent statement for the following 12 months contains no such entry.

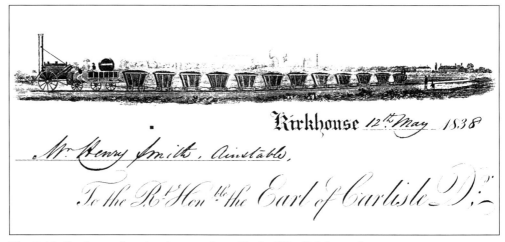

Fig. 3.12 *Rocket* **and train vignette from Earl of Carlisle's stationery**

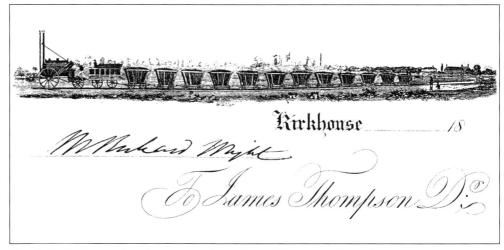

Fig. 3.13 *Rocket* **and train vignette from James Thompson's stationery**

In the absence of any further evidence, it is likely that *Rocket* was withdrawn from service in 1839 or 1840, possibly because it was too expensive in its consumption of coke and because of increasing maintenance costs. Thompson refurbished and erected two of the older 'colliery' type of coal-burning locomotives at Kirkhouse in 1839–40 for subsequent use on his coal trains.[194] It is clear, however, that Thompson retained a sentimental attachment to *Rocket*, which probably resulted in its continued existence. He continued to use the vignette on his stationery up to the time of his death in 1851, although a subtle change had been made to 'modernise' the tender (Fig. 3.13, p107).[195]

Thompson retained *Rocket*, rather than scrap it outright. It was 'laid up in ordinary' inside a small shed at Kirkhouse. Thompson's reasoning for keeping the locomotive is best described by the author of a newspaper article in 1848: '...it now stands no less a monument of the genius of the inventor than as a mark of esteem in which his memory is held by Mr Thompson, who has to boast of an unvarying and unbroken friendship with Mr Stephenson of nearly 25 years standing.'[196]

Two or more well-executed drawings of *Rocket*, which were prepared at about the date of its withdrawal, provide important evidence of the form that it apparently took at the end of its career in *c.*1840. The first drawing (Fig. 3.14, p107), which was acquired by the National Railway Museum in 1992, had apparently remained in the possession of Robert Stephenson & Co. Ltd. and its successor, Robert Stephenson & Hawthorns Ltd., for many years until the closure of its Darlington factory. This 'Stephenson' drawing bears no watermark to indicate the date when it was prepared.

The second, privately owned, drawing (Fig. 3.15, p107) is an important piece of evidence which came to light during the research for this 1999 project. It is very similar, but not identical, to the 'Stephenson' drawing, and appears to be contemporary with it. It bears an 1839 watermark, suggesting that the drawing was prepared in that year or soon after, probably 1840. The drawing, which has been professionally restored, remains in an early frame, which is endorsed with a note to indicate that it had hung on the wall of James Thompson at Kirkhouse. Research into the Thompson family history by a member of the family,[197] has indicated that this 'Thompson' drawing was probably bequeathed through three or four generations, concluding with a Mr Dixon-Brown, who apparently owned it until the late 1960s or early 1970s. It was acquired at auction in 1972.

The variations between the 'Stephenson' and 'Thompson' drawings indicate that they were drawn by a different hand, but both appear to have been copied from a master drawing, suggesting that both are perhaps apprentice drawings.

3.10 Preservation and display

Rocket remained at Kirkhouse, out of use, from *c.*1840 to 1851. Although Thompson had retained it out of sentiment and historical association, some components were removed, either as spare parts adapted for use on other machines, or for their scrap value. The copper firebox was probably removed for scrap at this time. When, in 1862, *Rocket* was being prepared for exhibition at South Kensington (p44), the Patent Office Museum representative, Samuel Ford, visited Kirkhouse and discussed the missing components with one or both of Thompson's sons, George and Thomas. He wrote to his superior:[198]

> I beg leave to inform you that I have seen Mr. Thompson who was at a great deal of trouble to see if anything could be found belonging to the 'Rocket' but nothing turned up.

In 1851, it was arranged for *Rocket* to be displayed at the Great Exhibition in London. This was probably on the initiative of Robert Stephenson, who was a Commissioner for the Exhibition. He wrote from Egypt at the beginning of 1851 to his London agent, Edward Starbuck, to say that he had promised Col. Reid, one of the administrators of the Exhibition, that, should there be a slow take-up of exhibition space:[199]

> I had in my mind the notion of sending the old Engine with what the Stockton & Darlington was opened [*Locomotion* – together with] – the *Rocket* and one of our last improvements [i.e. a new locomotive from Robert Stephenson & Co.] ...being a commissioner I did not after some reflection think it right to force any thing upon the commission of substance – but you can do as you may think proper after consulting Col. Reid.

James Thompson's son, Thomas, later wrote that *Rocket* was dispatched from Kirkhouse on 3 February 1851, the short timescale suggesting that Thompson was responding to Stephenson's initiative.[200] The locomotive, without its tender, was forwarded to the Stephenson works in Newcastle to be restored to a standard suitable for the Great Exhibition. Thomas Thompson wrote that:[201]

> We expected it would have a prominent place in the Exhibition of 1851 and sent it to New-Castle to be fit up for that purpose but by some misfortune it was neglected until too late.

It is not known if any work was carried out on *Rocket* at the Stephenson works, but after a few days it was decided that it would not be forwarded to the Great Exhibition. There is no evidence to confirm the reason for it being withheld, but the considerable (albeit late) interest and take-up of space for 'modern' exhibits may have influenced Robert Stephenson or Edward Starbuck to reverse their earlier idea.

Rocket remained at the Stephensons' Newcastle factory from 1851 to 1862. It may have been the intention to return it to Kirkhouse, but James Thompson, who had been in poor health since 1847, died on 14 July 1851, and the administration of his estate became a protracted affair.[202] Although *Rocket* would have had low priority in this context, its presence at Newcastle was a legal liability, and the cost of the work carried out on it for Thompson appears to have remained outstanding.

The solicitors acting on behalf of the estate, Messrs Mounsey, Bowman & Sutcliffe of Carlisle, recorded in March 1852 that debts on the estate to Robert Stephenson &

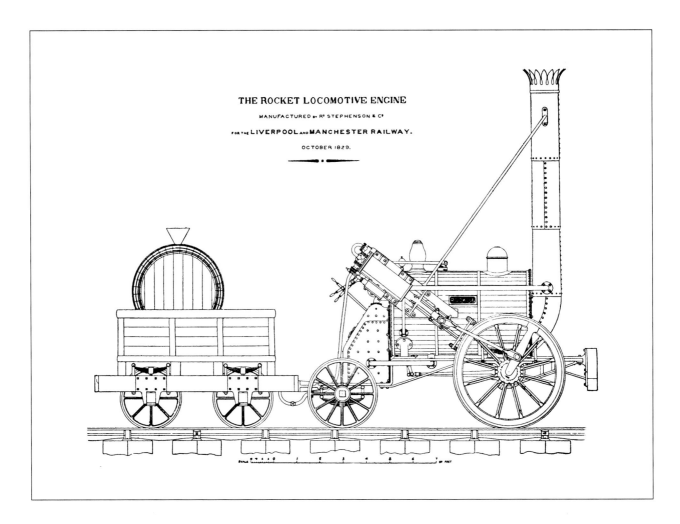

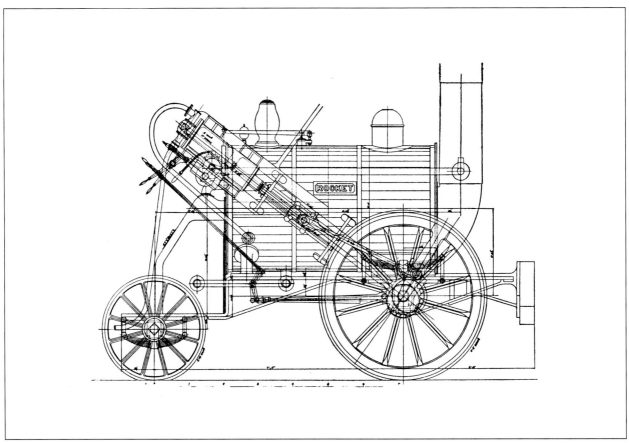

Figs 3.16 and 3.17 Drawings prepared under the direction of J D Wardale 1858–9

Co. of £206. 6. 3, for 'Engine Materials &c', being 'Debts on Simple Contract due at Mr. Thompson's death', had by then been paid.[203] However, it seems that some debts arising from work on *Rocket* remained unpaid, and a protracted dispute with Thompson's estate may have resulted. When the South Kensington Museum sought to acquire it *c.*1860 (below), the Stephenson Company responded by saying 'that nothing at present could be done about its disposal, until the money still due upon it was paid.'[204]

Thompson's lease on the Naworth colliery operations was acquired by his widow, Maria, and two of their sons, George and Thomas (M Thompson & Sons), effective from 2 September 1852.[205] *Rocket* had thus passed into their ownership, but with the family's full attention on the running of the extensive colliery operations, it remained at Newcastle *pro tem.* At some stage, some thought was given to making it available to the British Museum, 'but nothing came of it.'[206]

Rocket was apparently left in a dismantled state, the Stephenson Company perhaps not being willing to commit further funding to it. A visit was made to the Stephenson Works by members of the Institution of Mechanical Engineers in 1858:[207]

> ...and, on enquiry being made for the *Rocket*, it was stated that so many parts were wanting that to make a complete engine of it a large portion would have to be made anew. The boiler, or a portion of it, together with some of the gearing, was stowed away in one of the yards, but if our information be correct, there was nothing like a perfect machine.

One of the Stephenson Company's employees later recalled that:[208]

> It was at Stephenson's when I was there, and for five or six years was kept in a shed specially built for it. No one appeared to care for it, and it was allowed to rust...

In 1857, the Patent Office Museum opened, largely through the energies of Bennet Woodcroft FRS (1803–1879), who went on to encourage the collection of artefacts of national and international importance in the history of technology.[209] Woodcroft approached Robert Stephenson for the loan of *Rocket* for the new museum in 1857, but the response is not recorded. Stephenson may have postponed responding to Woodcroft's request until J D Wardale, the newly appointed Head Draughtsman at the Newcastle factory, had been able to prepare some drawings of *Rocket*. These were to be prepared from whatever evidence he could find at the factory, including the memories of some of the longer-serving employees, in addition to taking measurements from the locomotive itself. Wardale took his measurements from *Rocket* as it was then 'standing in a Lumber Yard at South Street',[210] suggesting it may have been left in the open rather than under cover. Wardale also prepared four pages of notes regarding *Rocket*'s history, apparently drawn from surviving works records and memories (Section 3.4).

Wardale's drawings (Figs 3.16 and 3.17) were an attempt to recreate the appearance of the locomotive in its 'as-built' condition, an objective which, in many respects, was not fulfilled. The drawings are misleading on several counts, most notably the portrayal of a firebox with a sloping back, and a dome. A number of later features, such as the buffer beam and supplementary frames, should have been omitted.

Bennet Woodcroft again sought to acquire *Rocket c.*1860, when he was assisted by one of the Patent Office Museum's early curators, Francis (later Sir Francis) Pettit Smith, whose communication, through a mutual contact, with Robert Stephenson & Co. resulted in the news that debts on the locomotive were still owing.[211] There is no evidence to indicate how the outstanding debt was eventually dealt with, but George and Thomas Thompson (on behalf of M Thompson & Sons) donated *Rocket* to the Commissioners of Patents (the Patent Office Museum) by letter dated 14 July 1862. F P Smith's one-time association with George Stephenson may have been an important persuasion in this consideration. Thomas Thompson wrote:[212]

> ...we have very great pleasure indeed in presenting the old engine to the Kensington Museum and only regret it is not more perfect in its parts... now that it is going under your protection, we feel sure it will occupy a place worthy of so interesting a relic of the Railway Locomotive, as well as a memorial of the genius and consummate skill of your old and esteemed friend the late George Stephenson.'

Figs 3.18 and 3.19 *Rocket* **photographed outside the South Kensington Museum**
Photographed by Colonel A Stuart Wortley, probably in March 1876
Source: Science Museum copy negative no. 454/56 and copy transparency RLO/C000170

Robert Stephenson & Co. was immediately informed, in order that it should assist in preparing *Rocket* for display, by Charles Manby, the Company's London Manager, and Honorary Secretary of the Institution of Civil Engineers.[213] Samuel Ford, who reported to F P Smith, was dispatched to Newcastle to supervise *Rocket*'s preparation on behalf of the Museum. He reported on arrival:[214]

> I found the old <u>Eng.</u> in a very imperfect state…the firebox is taken out and the connecting rod, part of the valve motion, chimney & Dome are missing…The Eng. is now being removed to a more convenient part of the shop…

Ford noted a varied level of interest in the restoration, which took the form of a crude replication of the main missing components. J D Wardale 'was very kind to me', but the manager, William Weallens 'was not very encouraging at first but he soon came round and promised to restore some of the missing parts.'[215] He later wrote that:[216]

> I get on much better with the Foreman than with Mr. Weallens. I have arranged with the Foreman to have an Iron Firebox in the place of wood as proposed by Mr. Weallens – I have pushed the job on as much as possible, but of course we cannot expect them to neglect their own work. Mr. Wardale assists me all he can.

The Foreman was George (Geordie) Crow, who allocated four or five men to the restoration, working to drawings prepared in the drawing office.[217] The cosmetic restoration took about five weeks to undertake from mid-July to the end of August 1862, but Ford provided no detail as to the nature of the work that was being carried out. He reported that 'Mr. Wardale has to make several drawings before the men can commence upon some of the repairs' and suggested he returned to London as he could do nothing 'untill the Boiler Makers have finished.'[218] It is likely that a wagon wheel-set was provided for the carrying wheels as part of the restoration.

Rocket was forwarded to South Kensington on a railway wagon and arrived on 6 September 1862, the London & North Western Railway Company having agreed to convey it without charge over its line.[219] It was placed on display in the Patent Office Museum's 'Brompton Boilers' building, an annexe of the South Kensington Museum's Education Department. Its appearance had been largely determined by the Newcastle restoration, which had not been based on sound historical evidence, and which has since led to misunderstandings, both regarding appearance and the origin of the components.

Rocket was transferred, on loan to the South Kensington Museum's Special Loan Collection of Scientific Apparatus, located in its Southern Galleries, in March 1876.[220] It is most likely that the two earliest known photographs of *Rocket* were taken during this move (Figs 3.18 and 3.19). The photographer was Colonel A Stuart Wortley, the newly appointed Curator of the Patent Office Museum. As interest grew in the history of technology, *Rocket* also featured in a number of periodicals which illustrated it in the form to which it had been restored.[221] It remained on loan until 1878, when it was returned to the Patent Office Museum.[222] In 1884 ownership of the Patent Office exhibits was transferred to the Government's Science and Art Department, which managed the South Kensington Museum. *Rocket* was transferred to the South Kensington Museum in 1886.

In April 1892, the Museum sought to improve *Rocket*'s appearance, by replacing the unsuitable carrying wheels that had probably been provided in 1862. A new cast-iron wheel-set was made by H & S Barker & Co. Ltd of the Don Iron & Wheel Works, Mexbro' near Rotherham.[223] Segmental wooden reinforcing blocks and their securing rim, fitted between the spokes of the left-hand driving-wheel (apparently during the 1862 restoration), were removed at this time (Section 4.3.1). They did not feature in two ink and colourwash drawings prepared in 1892 by Thomas Coates of London, which remain in the Science Museum collection. The side view drawing has been copied as Drawing 3.1.

The first considered curatorial opinion about the accuracy of *Rocket*'s components did not arise until after the foundation of the Science Museum in 1909, and after Ernest A Forward had been appointed as Curator with responsibility for the locomotive. He produced a memorandum about the erroneous and missing components in or

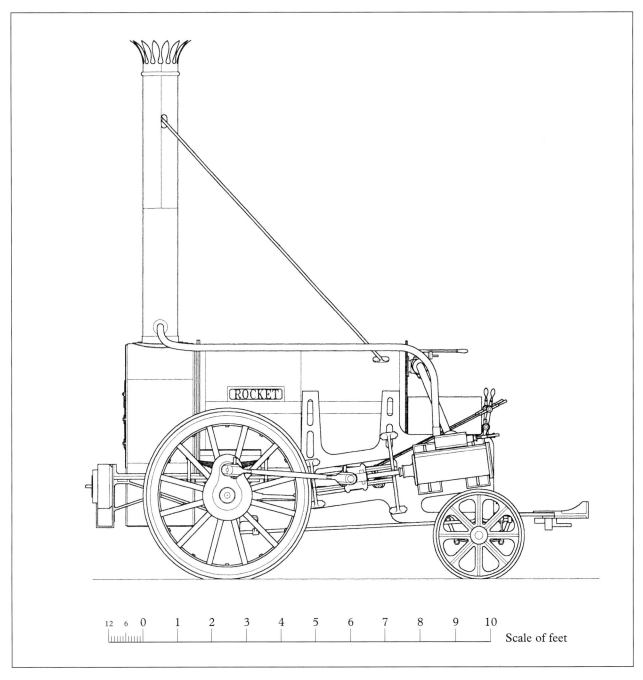

12 6 0   1   2   3   4   5   6   7   8   9   10

Scale of feet

Drawing 3.1 *Rocket* from Coates's 1892 drawing
Scale: 1:32

before 1914, in which he recorded the ambition that 'Any restoration should tend to complete the engine as it was in its last working state...'[224] He noted that the replica firebox, exhaust pipes and chimney were incorrect. He also suggested that replica components should be made and added to the locomotive, namely a half-firebox to show its form, improved connecting rods, relocated exhaust pipes, a chimney of the correct height, a dome casing, safety valves, water gauge, two tubes to illustrate their fitting and a pair of carrying wheel axleboxes. Forward's colleague, H W Dickinson, also expressed interest in the locomotive and published a small review of its components, following a survey he carried out, also in 1914.[225] With the onset of the 'Great War', however, it is likely that any thoughts to alter *Rocket*'s appearance were put aside. In addition to the replica firebox, *Rocket* had been fitted with replica wooden connecting rods in 1862, which Forward observed were in need of repair in 1914. By 1922, both the firebox and the connecting rods had been removed, but there is no file note to explain this action.[226] In 1923, the supplementary Kirkhouse buffers and brace (Section 4.2.2 and 4.2.3) were removed. Although these dated from the locomotive's career on the Naworth collieries railway, there was, again, no file note explaining their removal.[227] The locomotive was moved in 1923 to Gallery 4, in the Science Museum's East Block, where it remained on display until the Second World War. Considerable thought and attention was given to *Rocket* in the months preceding the manufacture of the replica locomotive for the Henry Ford Museum in 1929, and again when the sectioned replica was made for the Science Museum in 1934–5 (Appendix 6).[228]

A further alteration was made to *Rocket* by 1931, again with no explanatory technical file note, but which was perhaps prompted by the 1929 investigations. The erroneous exhaust pipes, dating from 1862, were removed, but no attempt appears to have been made to replace them with replicas of the correct form.[229] The final alteration to be made to *Rocket* was the removal of the 1862 chimney and stays, and the fitting of a replacement chimney with replica skeletal spark-arrestor. There was, again, no technical file-note made to accompany this alteration, which was probably made in 1935 (Section 4.8.2).[230] No further changes have been made to *Rocket* since this time.

Arrangements were made to remove many of the Science Museum exhibits to a safer location during the Second World War. *Rocket* was removed in September 1941 and sent to Brocket Hall, near Welwyn Garden City in Hertfordshire. It was returned in June 1945, but as the Museum was not reopened until February 1946, the opportunity was taken to dismantle the locomotive to allow a series of photographs to be taken (Appendix 4). There is no file note about this dismantling, nor any indication as to whether a survey was carried out at this time. The locomotive was returned to Gallery 4 where it remained on display until 1964. It was then moved to the Museum's new *Land Transport* gallery and displayed there from September 1967 until the gallery's closure in June 1996, apart from a period of loan to the Merseyside County Museums between April and November 1980.

Rocket was loaned to Japan between March and September 1998, where it formed the centrepiece of the 'Treasures of the Science Museum' exhibition at the Festival UK '98 British cultural event, in the cities of Kobe, Kitakyushu and Tokyo. On its return to Britain, *Rocket* was placed on display, throughout 1999, at the National Railway Museum, York, during which period the survey described in Chapter 4 was undertaken.

1 Minutes of the Board of Directors of the L&MR, 1823–1830, Public Record Office (PRO), Rail 371/1, p201, entry for 20 April 1829.

2 *Ibid.*, p202, 27 April 1829.

3 For example, *Liverpool Mercury*, 1 May 1829.

4 For example, R Stephenson & Co. Ledger, 1823–1831, R Stephenson & Co. Collection, National Railway Museum, folio 217.

5 John U Rastrick, *Liverpool and Manchester Railway, Report to the Directors on the Comparative Merits of Loco-Motive and Fixed Engines as a Moving Power*, second edition, corrected (1829). Also Notebook of John Rastrick, University of London, Goldsmith's Library, Department of Palaeontology, MS155, vol. IV, entries for 13–28 January 1829. For a discussion on Rastrick's views about *Lancashire Witch*, see Michael R Bailey, 'George Stephenson – Locomotive Advocate: The Background to the Rainhill Trials', *Transactions of the Newcomen Society*, 52, (1980–1) p177.

6 Coste and Perdonnet, 'Sur les chemins à ornières', *Annales des mines*, second series, vol. VI, (1829) p199. Also, *Mémoire sur les chemins à ornières*, (Paris, 1830).

7 Letter from Robert Stephenson to Henry Booth, Newcastle-upon-Tyne, 3 August 1829. Original letter formerly retained in the archive of the London & North Western Railway, but destroyed by fire when on loan to the Brussels Exhibition of 1910. Photographed copy in PRO RAIL 1008/88/1/2.

8 Coste and Perdonnet, 1829, *op. cit.* (6), p289.

9 Account by Henry Booth, reproduced in *Alfred Booth, Some Memories, Letters and Other Family Records*, written and arranged by his daughter, Harriet Anna Whitting. Printed for private circulation (Liverpool, 1917) pp21–2.

10 *Ibid.*

11 Ledger, *op. cit.* (4), folio 217.

12 Board minutes, *op. cit.* (1), entry for 20 October 1829.

13 Minutes of the Finance Committee of the Liverpool & Manchester Railway, 1824–1831, PRO, Rail 371/9, entry for 6 November 1829.

14 For example, the Directors' Report to the Fifth Annual Meeting of the L&MR on 28 March 1831, states that 'The Company are also under great obligations to their Treasurer, Mr Booth, for the plan of the Boiler, which has given the Locomotive Engine such additional power.'

15 Henry Booth, *An Account of the Liverpool and Manchester Railway* (Liverpool, 1830) p74.

16 Letter from R Stephenson to Thomas Richardson, London, 16 June 1829, reproduced in J C Jeaffreson, *The Life of Robert Stephenson, FRS.*, two vols, (London, 1864) vol. I, p137. Present whereabouts of the letter unknown.

17 Letter from Henry Booth to Samuel Smiles, 6 October 1857, quoted in Robert Smiles, *Memoir of the Late Henry Booth*, (London, 1869) pp40–1.

18 Letter from G Phipps to *The Engineer*, published within the article 'Links in the History of the Locomotive' no. IX, 17 September 1880, p217.

19 Letter from G Phipps to *The Engineer*, 24 September 1880, p230. Phipps added that John Scott Russell's claim to have used a system of firebox stays in 1827, made in the discussion on a paper by J P Flannery on 'Boilers for Very High Pressure' in May 1878, was unknown to Robert Stephenson in 1829.

20 Statement by Robert Stephenson contained in Samuel Smiles, *The Life of George Stephenson, Railway Engineer* (London, 1857) p283.

21 Ledger, *op. cit.* (4), folios 228, 310 and 317, showing Leishman and Welsh (incorrectly spelt Welch) as supplier number 27 to the Stephenson factory. Their premises were at 20 Redcross Street, Liverpool, close to Graving Docks numbers 1, 2 and 3, suggesting the smiths' experience with copper sheeting for ships (*History, Directory & Gazetteer of the County of Lancaster*, Edward Baines (Liverpool, 1824) vol. I, p284).

22 Ledger, *op. cit.* (4), folio 228, debit entry for quarter ending 31 December 1829.

23 *Ibid.*, folios 191 and 210.

24 Letter from George Stephenson to Robert Stephenson, Liverpool, 8 January 1828, Science Museum, MS1149.

25 Ledger, *op. cit.* (4), folios 191, 203, 207, 215 and 220. Sanderson's premises were at 35–36, Foot of Butcher Bank, Newcastle, as shown in Pigot & Co.'s *National Commercial Directory* (London & Manchester, 1834).

26 *Ibid.*, folios 203 and 215. John Abbott had premises in High Street, Gateshead, Henry Marshall in Marshall's Court, Newgate Street, Newcastle, and Thomas Donnison near to the Stephenson factory in Forth Street. See *History, Directory and Gazetteer of the Counties of Durham and Northumberland* (1828) pp658–684.

27 *Ibid.*, folio 277, entry for 30 September 1830.

28 *Ibid.*, folios 197, 203 and 215. French & Donnison had premises in Orchard Street, Newcastle, adjacent to the Stephenson factory, whilst Burnup's premises were at 6 Jesmond Terrace (*Gazetteer, op. cit.* [26]). There is a long tradition in the family of Mr Donald MacCallum of Milton Keynes, that an ancestor, John Summers, made the original springs for *Rocket*. As his occupation was stated to be a 'coach-smith', he could have been an employee of French & Donnison, but this cannot be verified. Correspondence with Michael Bailey, June 1999.

29 Letter from G Phipps, *op. cit.* (18).

30 Obituary, George Henry Phipps, *Proceedings of the Institution of Civil Engineers* (1889) p330.

31 Letter from Robert Stephenson, *op. cit.* (7).

32 Letter from Robert Stephenson to Henry Booth, Newcastle-upon-Tyne, 21 August 1829. Original letter formerly retained in the archive of the London & North Western Railway, but destroyed by fire when on loan to the Brussels Exhibition of 1910. Photographed copy in PRO RAIL 1008/88/1/3.

33 Letter from Robert Stephenson to Henry Booth, Newcastle-upon-Tyne, 26 August 1829. Original letter formerly retained in the archive of the London & North Western Railway, but destroyed by fire when on

loan to the Brussels Exhibition of 1910. Photographed copy in PRO Rail 1008/88/1/4.

34 Letter from Robert Stephenson to Henry Booth, Newcastle-upon-Tyne, 31 August 1829. Original letter formerly retained in the archive of the London & North Western Railway, but destroyed by fire when on loan to the Brussels Exhibition of 1910. Photographed copy in PRO Rail 1008/88/1/5.

35 Ledger, *op. cit.* (4), folio 229, Incidental account for the quarter ending 31 December 1829.

36 Together with John Rastrick and John Kennedy. *Report of the Competition on the Liverpool and Manchester Railroad* (Manchester, 16 October 1829).

37 Ledger, *op. cit.* (4), folio 215.

38 Letter from Robert Stephenson to Henry Booth, Newcastle-upon-Tyne, 5 September 1829. Original letter formerly retained in the archive of the London & North Western Railway, but destroyed by fire when on loan to the Brussels Exhibition of 1910. Photographed copy in PRO Rail 1008/88/1/6.

39 Correspondence to the Editor, *The Engineer*, vol. IV, 17 July – 30 October 1857, pp42–324, *passim*.

40 Robert Stephenson narrative to Samuel Smiles, January 1858, published in *Lives of the Engineers*, vol. III, 'George and Robert Stephenson' (London, 1862), pp501–503, and subsequent editions.

41 Manuscript memorandum by J D Wardale to accompany his two drawings of *Rocket*, dated 25 January 1858. Present whereabouts of original document unknown. Photograph copy of page 1 (of 4) is retained in the Science Museum *Rocket* technical file (negative no. 1401), together with a transcription of pages 1, 2 and 4. A different copy of the transcription of all four pages, which was passed to R Stephenson & Co. by J D Wardale on 16 July 1913, is now retained in a folder in the R Stephenson & Co. Collection, *op. cit.* (4).

42 Ledger, *op. cit.* (4), folio 216.

43 Jeaffreson, *op. cit.* (16), p140.

44 Michael R Bailey, 'Robert Stephenson & Co. 1823–1829', *Transactions of the Newcomen Society*, vol. 50 (1979–80), p127.

45 Board minutes, *op. cit.* (1), entry for 14 September 1829.

46 Board minutes, *op. cit.* (1), entry for 28 September 1829.

47 *Mechanics' Magazine*, XII, (324), 24 October 1829, p145.

48 Ledger, *op. cit.* (4), folio 265, shows debit entries to both George and Robert Stephenson's current accounts, each allocated 5/- per day towards Hutchinson's wages and other costs.

49 Letter from Rob. Stannard to *The Engineer*, 17 October 1884, p303.

50 John Rastrick's 'Rainhill' Notebook, Science Museum, inv.1945-108, p18. The notebook had been acquired in 1929 by C F Dendy Marshall, after whose death in 1945 the notebook was auctioned by Sotheby's. It was acquired by the Science Museum through the generosity of H W Dickinson who paid for it

personally, 'as a memento of the twenty-five years existence of the Newcomen Society. It is a small return for the advantages I enjoyed at the Museum, which afforded me the opportunities to acquire the knowledge that has been such a treasure to me and of use to the Society'. The hammer price was £58. 0s. 0d.

51 Letter, Rob. Stannard, *op. cit.* (49).

52 *op. cit.* (41).

53 W H Chaloner, 'The Worsdells and the Early Railway System', *The Railway Magazine*, vol. LXXXIII (October 1938), p235.

54 Articles, 'Presentation to Councillor Nathaniel Worsdell', *The Crewe Guardian* and *The Crewe and Nantwich Chronicle*, Saturday 16 October 1880.

55 Letter from Robert Stannard, *op. cit.* (49).

56 Rastrick's Notebook, *op. cit.* (50), p18.

57 Board minutes, *op. cit.* (1), entry for 5 October 1829.

58 R H G Thomas, *The Liverpool & Manchester Railway* (London, 1980), p65.

59 *Gore's General Advertiser*, Thursday 8 October 1829.

60 The most comprehensive description of *Rocket*'s performance at the Rainhill Trials is contained in John Rastrick, Nicholas Wood and John Kennedy, *Report of the Competition on the Liverpool and Manchester Railroad* (Manchester, 16 October 1829). Photograph copies in Science Museum, negative nos 201/46 to 210/46. The first contemporary published description of the Rainhill Trials was in *Mechanics' Magazine*, vol. 12, October 10–31 1829, pp114–16, 129–42, 145–52, 161–67. A comprehensive evaluation of *Rocket*'s performance at the Trials was subsequently published by Nicholas Wood, *A Practical Treatise on Rail-Roads*, second edition (London, 1831) pp361–81, repeated in the third edition (London, 1838) pp301–23. See also, J G H Warren, *A Century of Locomotive Building By Robert Stephenson & Co. 1823–1923* (Newcastle-upon-Tyne, 1923) pp188–200.

61 Rastrick Notebook, *op. cit.* (50), p26, entry for 8 October 1829.

62 Wood, *op. cit.* (60), second edition, p371, third edition, p314.

63 For example, Thomas, *op. cit.* (58), p73.

64 Booth, *op. cit.* (15), pp78–9.

65 Robert Stephenson and Joseph Locke, *Observations on the Comparative Merits of Locomotives & Fixed Engines, as Applied to Railways*, being a Reply to the report of Mr James Walker to the Directors of the Liverpool and Manchester Railway, Compiled from the Reports of Mr George Stephenson, with an Account of the Competition of Locomotive Engines at Rainhill in October 1829, and of the Subsequent Experiments, Liverpool, (n.d. but 1830) p79.

66 Rainhill Judges' Report, *op. cit.* (60).

67 Board minutes, *op. cit.* (1), entry for 20 October 1829.

68 *Ibid.*, entry for 26 October 1829.

69 Robert Stephenson narrative, *op. cit.* (40), p503.

70 Wood, *Treatise*, second edition, *op. cit.* (60), p399.

71 *Ibid.*, pp399–413. Also, Stephenson and Locke, *op. cit.* (65), p79. Also reported in *The Mechanics' Magazine*, 12, (326), pp180–1, 7 November 1829.

72 *Liverpool Mercury*, 6 November 1829, p358.

73 Board minutes, *op. cit.* (1), entry for 19 October 1829.

74 Report, George Stephenson to the Board of Directors of the Liverpool & Manchester Railway, published in *The Kaleidoscope*, Tuesday 15 December 1829, pp189–90.

75 Letter from John Dixon to James Dixon, Patricroft, 16 October 1829, formerly in possession of Mr Waynman Dixon, but present whereabouts unknown. See J G H Warren, *A Century of Locomotive Building by Robert Stephenson & Co. 1823–1923* (Newcastle-upon-Tyne, 1923) pp206–7.

76 For example, *The Times*, 8 October 1829, and *The Mechanics' Magazine, op. cit.* (60).

77 *Liverpool Mercury*, 30 October 1829, p350.

78 *Liverpool Mercury, op. cit.* (72), p360.

79 *Liverpool Mercury*, 27 November 1829.

80 Diary of Thomas Creevey, MP, 14 November 1829, quoted in Rt Hon. Sir Herbert Maxwell (ed.), *The Creevey Papers* (London, 1903) pp203–4.

81 *Liverpool Mercury*, 27 November 1829, p381.

82 *Ibid.*

83 *The Mechanics' Magazine*, XII, (329), 28 November 1829.

84 Letter from Robert Stannard, *op. cit.* (49).

85 *Liverpool Mercury*, 11 December 1829, p408.

86 *Manchester Guardian*, 2 January 1830, p3. Other later reports refer to this journey as being on 1 January 1830. For example, see Samuel Smiles, *The Life of George Stephenson, Railway Engineer* (London, 1857) and subsequent editions.

87 *Liverpool Mercury*, 16 April 1830, p126.

88 Booth, *op. cit.* (15), opp. p74.

89 *Glasgow Herald*, Friday 22 January 1830, quoting from 'Liverpool Paper'.

90 *The Kaleidoscope*, X, (522), Liverpool, Tuesday 29 June 1830, p423.

91 Board minutes, *op. cit.* (1), pp292–6, 300. Also minutes of the Board of Directors of the L&MR 1830–1833, PRO Rail 371/2, pp 6, 21 and 41.

92 Article, 'Improvements in Locomotive-Engines', *The Mechanics' Magazine*, XV, (397), 19 March 1831, p35.

93 *Wheelers' Manchester Chronicle*, 28 August 1830, p3.

94 *Manchester Guardian*, Saturday 4 September 1830, p2. A further three trains were operated on the following Saturday, 28 August, but excluding the use of *Rocket*.

95 Board minutes, *op. cit.* (91), p18, 2 August 1830.

96 Letter from I W B. [Isaac Boulton] to *The Engineer*, 26 September 1884, p244.

97 For example, see *Gore's General Advertiser*, no. 3379, Thursday 16 September 1830, p3; *The Times*, 17 Sept 1830, p3; *Liverpool Mercury*, XX, 17 September 1830, pp303–4; and *Manchester Guardian*, 18 September 1830, pp1–6.

98 Joseph Kirwan, *A Descriptive and Historical Account of the Liverpool and Manchester Railway* (Glasgow and London, 1831) p18. No other contemporary reference to the driver has been found, but in 1843 it was claimed that *Rocket*'s driver was Mark Wakefield both during the Rainhill Trials and for the opening of the Liverpool & Manchester Railway, *Veritas Vincit* [pseud.], letter, 'Railway Locomotive Management', *The Railway Times*, VI, (286), Saturday 24 June 1843, p691.

99 Article in the *Morning Herald*, quoted in article, 'The Accident', *The Mechanics' Magazine*, 14, (372), 25 September 1830, pp67–9.

100 *Vide supra* (89).

101 *The Mechanics' Magazine, op. cit.* (99), p69.

102 *Liverpool Journal*, 25 September 1830.

103 Board minutes, *op. cit.* (1), pp324–5, entry for 10 May 1830; also, Board minutes, *op. cit.* (91), p15, entry for 26 July 1830, and p21, entry for 9 August 1830. For illustration of the water tank see T T Bury's lithograph 'Entrance into Manchester across Water Street' (R Ackermann: London, February 1831).

104 Board minutes, *op. cit.* (91), p144, entry for 22 August 1831, pp146–7, entry for 5 September 1831, p194, entry for 16 January 1832. Also minutes of the Sub-Committee of Management of the L&MR, 1833–39, PRO Rail 371/10, p10, entry for 18 April 1833.

105 Correspondence between Thwaite Mills Museum, National Railway Museum and Michael Bailey, October 1996.

106 Patent no. 6814, enrolled on 14 April 1835.

107 Letter from I W B [Isaac Boulton] to *The Engineer*, 21 November 1884, p398.

108 Letter from Rob. Stannard to *The Engineer*, 16 January 1885, p47.

109 Letter from I W B, *op. cit.* (96). The present whereabouts of Boulton's papers and of the *Rocket* component are unknown.

110 *Wheelers' Manchester Chronicle*, Saturday 30 October 1830.

111 *Ibid.*, also *Manchester Guardian*, Saturday 30 October 1830, p3, and Charles Hulbert, *Memoirs of Seventy Years of an Eventful Life* (Manchester, 1852) Letter XIII, 'The Parish of Eccles', pp88–9. Hunter was probably the son of a 'respectable widow', Sarah Hunter, proprietor of the 'Hare and Hounds' tavern in Eccles (Lancashire Directory, 1830).

112 Board minutes, *op. cit.* (1), p318, entry for 19 April 1830.

113 *Ibid.*, p320, entry for 26 April 1830.

114 Letter from Rob. Stannard, *op. cit.* (49).

115 *Ibid.*, p332, entry for 31 May 1830, and p334, entry for 7 June 1830.

116 *Gore's Directory of Liverpool and its Environs*, 1829 and 1832 editions.

117 Sub-Committee minutes, *op. cit.* (104), p20, entry for 16 May 1833.

118 Letter from Rob. Stannard, *op. cit.* (49).

119 Board minutes, *op. cit.* (91), p43, entry for 11 October 1830.

120 *Ibid.*, pp66–7 and 70, entries for 9 and 13 December 1830. Also, article, 8. [Dec.] 'Accident on the Manchester Railway' in the *Chronicle of Annual Register*, p205–6.

121 Thomas Mercer (1804–97) and John Murphy (n.d.)

are both quoted as being firemen by W H Williams, 'Early Railways in South-West Lancashire', *Transactions of the Historic Society of Lancashire and Cheshire*, vol. LXXIV (1922) pp139–40. Also Edward Entwistle (1815–1904), article, 'Edward Entwistle, Oldest Living Engine Driver', *Success*, May 1904.

122 *Manchester Guardian*, Saturday 5 February 1831, p3, also quoting the *Liverpool Albion* of earlier date.

123 I Shaw, *Views of the Most Interesting Scenery on the Line of the Liverpool and Manchester Railway Part I*, (Liverpool, 1831), notes accompanying plate VIII, 'The *Planet* Locomotive Engine'.

124 Board minutes, *op. cit.* (91), p45, entry for 18 October 1830.

125 Minutes of the Sub-Committee of Management of the L&MR 1831–1833, PRO Rail 371/8, p14, 15 June 1831.

126 *Ibid.*, p31, 17 August 1831.

127 Board minutes, *op. cit.* (91), p155, entry for 3 October 1831.

128 Sub-Committee minutes, *op. cit.* (125), p163, entry for 25 July 1832, pp167–8, entry for 1 August 1832, and pp175–6, entry for 23 August 1832.

129 *Ibid.*, p208, entry for 7 November 1832.

130 *Ibid.*, p209, entry for 14 November 1832 and p223, entry for 26 December 1832. Also Board minutes, *op. cit.* (91), p321, entry for 7 January 1833, and minutes of the Board of Directors of the L&MR 1833–1836, PRO Rail 371/3, pp92–3, entry for 11 November 1833.

131 *Ibid.*, Board minutes for 11 November 1833 at which a vote to pursue payment was taken. The resolution of the issue was not recorded in the minutes.

132 Sub-Committee minutes, *op. cit.* (125), p129, entry for 19 April 1832.

133 Board minutes, *op. cit.* (91), p268, entry for 13 August 1832.

134 *Ibid.*, and Sub-Committee minutes, *op. cit.* (125), *passim*.

135 *Journal of Elemental Locomotion*, no. IV (January 1833), p107.

136 Minutes of the Sub-Committee, *op. cit.* (125), p212, 15 November 1832.

137 Letter from Thomas Hunt to *The Engineer*, 24 October 1884, p320.

138 R Cort, *Rail-Road Impositions Detected* (London, 1834), p17.

139 Minutes of the Sub-Committee of Management of the L&MR 1833–1839, PRO Rail 371/10, p7, entry for 10 April 1833, p11, entry for 18 April 1833, and p12, entry for 24 April 1833.

140 Letter from Rob. Daglish & Co. to the Board of Education, South Kensington (the Science Museum), 13 March 1907, ScM. Reference ScM. 60. The Daglish Company went into receivership in 1932 and its papers are believed to have been thrown away at that time (Advice of St Helens Local History Library).

141 Minutes of the Sub-Committee, *op. cit.* (125), p224, entry for 27 December 1832.

142 Sub-Committee minutes, *op. cit.* (125), pp21–2, entry

143 *Ibid.*, pp221–2, 224, entries for 19 and 27 December 1832.

144 *Ibid.*, p233, 24 January 1833.

145 Sub-Committee minutes, *op. cit.* (139), p139, entry for 10 December 1835.

146 Board minutes, *op. cit.* (91), p236, entry for 7 February 1833.

147 Sub-Committee minutes, *op. cit.* (139), pp3–4, entry for 3 April 1833.

148 Letter from Edward Woods to *The Engineer*, p95, 6 February 1885.

149 Patent no. 6128, enrolled 2 January 1832.

150 Board minutes, *op. cit.* (91), p262, entry for 23 July 1832; p264, entry for 30 July 1832; p281, entry for 10 September 1832; p308, entry for 3 December 1832; p313, entry for 10 December 1832, also entry for 18 February 1833.

151 Minutes of the Board of Directors of the L&MR 1833–1836, PRO Rail 371/3, several entries up to and including 6 January 1834, pp1–113 *passim*.

152 *The Mechanics' Magazine* XX, (531), 12 October 1833, pp20–22, and no. 534, 2 November 1833, pp69–72.

153 Board minutes, *op. cit.* (151), p38, entry for 27 May 1833 and p68, entry for 26 August 1833. Also, Sub-Committee minutes, *op. cit.* (125), p51, entry for 19 September 1833.

154 *The Mechanics' Magazine*, articles and correspondence, 9 November 1833 to 10 January 1835, *passim*.

155 Chev. F M G De Pambour, *A Practical Treatise on Locomotive Engines Upon Railways* (London, 1836) translated from the French edition published at the beginning of 1835, pp30–1.

156 David Stevenson, 'Observations on the Liverpool and Manchester Railway', *Transactions of the Royal Scottish Society of Arts*, I, 1832–1840, p46. Read before the Society on 25 February 1835.

157 11th Earl of *Dundonald* and H R Fox Bourne, *Life of Thomas, 10th Earl of Dundonald* (London, 1869). Also Hon. J W Fortescue, *Dundonald* (London, 1895). For a recent account of Lord Dundonald's rotary engine locomotive experiments see Robin Barnes, 'The 10th Earl of Dundonald, His Rotary Engine and His Locomotive', *Backtrack*, 13, (11) (November 1999), pp586–590.

158 Patent no. 6530, 'Steam Engines, Propulsion of Vessels, &c.', enrolled 20 June 1834. A subsequent patent, no. 6923, enrolled on 5 May 1836, 'Propulsion of Carriages, Vessels, &c.' was more particularly designed for 'Purposes of Locomotion'.

159 Memorandum by George Landmann, Civil Engineer, and George Walter, Secretary, of the London & Greenwich Railway, 1 December 1834, Scottish Record Office, GD233/69/22.

160 Board Minutes, *op. cit.* (151), p107, entry for 16 December 1833.

161 Extensive correspondence in the Scottish Record

Office, references GD233/2/31 and 32, but no specific reference to the rotary locomotive engines.

162 Board minutes, *op. cit.* (151), p195, entry for 3 October 1834.

163 *Ibid.*, p199, entry for 20 October 1834.

164 Pamphlet, 'The Steam Engine Simplified' by the Earl of Dundonald, 5 November 1833, Scottish Record Office, GD233/2/34/1.

165 Member, Institution of Mechanical Engineers, discussion following the paper, 'On the Fallacies of the Rotary Engine' by George Stephenson (President), read in Birmingham, 26 July 1848, *Proceedings of the IMechE.*, I, 1847–1849, p4.

166 Letter from Henry Booth to the Earl of Dundonald, Liverpool 23 October 1834, Scottish Record Office, GD233/2/34/20.

167 Correspondence and memoranda in the Scottish Record Office, GD233/69/22.

168 Board minutes, *op. cit.* (120), pp208-224, 24 November 1834.

169 Board minutes, *op. cit.* (151), p216, entry for 22 December 1834.

170 Correspondence *op. cit.* (167). See also, R H G Thomas, *London's First Railway The London & Greenwich* (London, 1972) pp173–176.

171 George Stephenson, 'On the Fallacies of the Rotary Engine', *op. cit.* (165), pp1–2.

172 Minutes of the Board of Directors of the L&MR 1836–1839, PRO Rail 371/4, p32, entry for 27 June 1836.

173 The drawing was probably passed from the L&MR to the Grand Junction and London & North Western Railways. It remained at Crewe until donated to the Science Museum in 1923. Science Museum inv. no. 1923-569.

174 Dr Alan Harris, 'The Tindale Fell Waggonway', *Transactions of the Cumberland & Westmorland Antiquarian & Archaeological Society*, N.S., LXXII (1972) pp227–247. Also Brian Webb and David A Gordon, *Lord Carlisle's Railways* (The Railway Correspondence & Travel Society, March 1978).

175 Letter from James Loch to the Earl of Carlisle, Wimbledon, Sunday 2 October 1836, Howard of Naworth Muniments, Palace Green Library, University of Durham, Box Item C591, Document 42.

176 Webb and Gordon, *op. cit.* (174), pp54–5.

177 Letter from John Ramshay to Earl of Carlisle, Stamford, 6 October 1836. Location of original letter not known. Typed copy retained in Howard Muniments, *ibid.*, C590, Bundle 1, Document 53.

178 Uncalendared petty payments 'To Bolton, Manchester, Liverpool … to buy *Rocket*', Howard Muniments, *op. cit.* (175).

179 Board minutes, *op. cit.* (172), p60, entry for 24 October 1836.

180 Accounts 'James Thompson in Accot with The Right Honorable the Earl of Carlisle…From Decr. 24th 1836 to & with Decr. 23rd 1837', Howard Muniments, *op. cit.* (175), C645, entry for 6 March 1837.

181 *Sun* and *Etna*, which were *Planet*-class locomotives, were sold for £200 and £250 respectively and *Goliath* of the *Samson*-class was sold for just £100. Sub-Committee minutes, *op. cit.* (139), p129, entry for 18 September 1835.

182 Advertisements, *Carlisle Journal*, 1836–7, *passim*.

183 The Newcastle & Carlisle Railway's Canal branch was not opened until 9 March 1837. *Carlisle Journal*, 4 and 11 March 1837.

184 Accountant's Journal 1834–1838, Newcastle & Carlisle Railway, PRO, Rail 509/97, p131, entry for 30 November 1836.

185 Accounts, *op. cit.* (180), entry for 28 December 1836. The entry is for £162. 12s. 2d for waggon wheels and 'repairing Locomotive Engine &c.'

186 'Sundry petty payments' for 1837, Howard Muniments, *op. cit.* (175), C590, Bundle 1, Document 66, 'Jany 24 Paid John Forster Carriage of Engine axle to Hexham 0" 18" 3'.

187 Letter from Thomas Thompson (son of James) to Wm Fletcher (of the Patent Office Museum), Kirkhouse, 22 October 1880, Science Museum *Rocket* technical file, 1862-5.

188 Obituary, 'The Late George Stephenson, Esq.', *Carlisle Journal*, 15 September 1848.

189 Carlisle Record Office, D/MBS/5/16/4.

190 'Memorandum of Agreement for a Lease of the Coal Mines and Limeworks, in working, of the Earl of Carlisle, near Naworth, in Cumberland', signed by James Thompson on 1 May 1838, Howard Muniments, *op. cit.* (175), C590, Bundle II, Document 72.

191 'Schedule and Valuation of the Stock [&c] upon the Earl of Carlisle's Colliery's [sic], Railways, Depots and Lime Kilns' &c, 11 May 1838. Howard Muniments, *op. cit.* (175), C590, Document 75.

192 *Ibid.*, Document 79.

193 Statement 'Coals, Lime and Coke Worked and Sold at the Right Honourable the Earl of Carlisle's Collieries and Lime Works for the year ending 11th May 1839', Howard Muniments, *op. cit.* (175), C646, Document 3.

194 Webb and Gordon, *op. cit.* (174), pp101–2.

195 Carlisle Record office, D/MBS/5/18/2, Invoice dated June 1850. A late 1999 publication (The People of Hartleyburn Parish, *The Gate: A Living History of Halton Lea Gate*) reproduces a letter written from the Colliery in 1906, when it was leased by the following generation of the Thompson family (Charles Lacy and James Thomas), showing that the vignette continued to be used until at least that date.

196 Obituary, *op. cit.* (188).

197 Mr Grant Thompson of Canberra, Australia.

198 Letter from Samuel Ford to F P Smith (Museum of Patents), Newcastle, 23 July 1862, Science Museum *Rocket* technical file 1862-5.

199 Letter from Robert Stephenson to Edward Starbuck, Suez, 1 January 1851, R Stephenson & Co. Collection, *op. cit.* (4), Folder 18.

200 Letter from Thomas Thompson to William Fletcher (Patent Office Museum), Kirkhouse, 22 October 1880, *Rocket* file, *op. cit.* (198).

201 Letter from Thomas Thompson to F P Smith (Patent Office Museum), Kirkhouse, 14 July 1862, *Rocket* file, *ibid.*

202 Webb and Gordon, *op. cit.* (174), p57.

203 Carlisle County Record Office, D/MBS/5/18/2.

204 Letter from William Walker to F P Smith (Patent Office Museum), London, nd, but letter written on paper with 1860 watermark, *Rocket* file, *op. cit.* (198).

205 Webb and Gordon, *op. cit.* (174).

206 Letter, Thomas Thompson, *op. cit.* (201).

207 Article, 'The Loan Collection of Scientific Instruments – History of the Steam Engine – No. IV', *The Engineer*, 30 June 1876, p481.

208 Jeremiah Head, Discussion following paper by Theodore West, 'An Outline History of the Locomotive Engine in England', *Proceedings of the Cleveland Institution of Engineers*, Middlesbrough, 1 March 1886.

209 John Hewish, *The Indefatigable Mr Woodcroft* (British Library, n.d. but 1979).

210 Letter from J D Wardale to Messrs Robert Stephenson & Co., Gateshead, 11 July 1913, R Stephenson & Co. Collection, *op. cit.* (4), Folder 16.

211 Letter, William Walker, *op. cit.* (204).

212 Letter, Thomas Thompson, *op. cit.* (201).

213 Letter from James Rouse (for R Stephenson & Co.) to F P Smith, Westminster, 18 July 1862, *Rocket* file, *op. cit.* (198).

214 Letter, Samuel Ford, *op. cit.* (198).

215 *Ibid.*

216 Letter from Samuel Ford to F P Smith, Newcastle, 28 July 1862, *Rocket* file, *op. cit.* (198).

217 Letter from Samuel Ford to F P Smith, Newcastle, 30 July 1862, *Rocket* file, *ibid.*

218 Letter from Samuel Ford to F P Smith, Wylam, 3 August 1862, *Rocket* file, *ibid.*

219 Letter from F P Smith to Capt. Brooke, South Kensington, 5 September 1862. Also letter from London & North Western Railway to F P Smith, 11 September 1862. Both *Rocket* file, *ibid.*

220 Copy letters, A Stuart Wortley to Major Donnelly, Patent Office Museum letterbook, Science Museum archive Z23/1, folios 590 and 595.

221 For example, *The Engineer*, 30 June 1876, p481.

222 Science Museum Archives Collection, references Z23/1 folio 941 and Z24/1 folios 1873, 1876, 1877.

223 Internal memoranda and quotation from H & S Barker & Co. Ltd, 12 April 1892, Science Museum letter file ScM60.

224 Proposal by E A Forward, undated, but endorsed 'Amended 1914', *Rocket* file, *op. cit.* (198).

225 Letter from H W Dickinson to *The Engineer*, vol.113, 23 January 1914, p107.

226 Reference Science Museum photograph dated 27 September 1922, negative no. 1648.

227 Reference Science Museum photograph dated 4 June 1923, negative nos 1838–1840. The Science Museum's Board of Survey file (ScM 7/370/1) notes that the Kirkhouse buffers and the replica connecting rods were disposed of in June 1933.

228 Science Museum files ScM60, ScM1631 and R427 contain extensive correspondence between Robert Stephenson & Co. Ltd, the Science Museum and Mr J G H Warren, formerly Chief Draughtsman, and then Consultant to the Stephenson Company.

229 Reference Science Museum photograph dated 20 January 1931, copy negative no. 547/96.

230 Reference Science Museum photograph dated June 1936, negative no. 8441. The Science Museum's Board of Survey file (ScM 7/471/1) notes that the replica chimney top and stays were issued to the 'scrap metal heap' in April 1936.

4 The Rocket survey

4.1 Survey methods and techniques

The *Rocket* survey was carried out in four phases, namely component removal, systematic recording, historical assessment and reassembly. Throughout the project, which was carried out in the National Railway Museum's Main Hall, requisite health and safety requirements were closely followed to protect the artefact, the consultants, other Museum personnel and visitors.[1]

Firstly, following a review of the benefits of dismantling, selected components were carefully removed with minimum risk to the artefact, in accordance with normal industrial archaeology practice and with procedures as recommended by the Museums and Galleries Commission.[2] Only those components that were to be of benefit to the survey were selected for removal. Photographs were taken of each assembly before dismantling. Easing oil was applied prior to removal of nuts, bolts and studs, and brass shims used within the jaws of spanners to avoid marking their heads. Components were carefully cleaned, labelled and weighed prior to survey. They were placed on view to Museum visitors in a locked display case, set up adjacent to the locomotive.

Secondly, a systematic programme of photographic recording and detailed examination was undertaken for each component, in order to ascertain:

- its material

- its dimensions

- the method of manufacture, machining and fitting

- the presence and dimensions of rivets, studs, bolts and nuts

- the presence and dimensions of redundant holes

- the presence and likely purpose of fitters' marks.

From this survey, drawings were prepared for each component using computer-aided design software. The drawings include all fittings, redundant holes and marks, as well as dimensions, to provide an aid to assessment of component history. A general arrangement drawing of *Rocket*, as now displayed, is shown as Drawing 4.1.

The survey's third phase was to develop an understanding of the likely history of each component using the drawings and photographs, in conjunction with the locomotive's career (Chapter 3). The findings from this phase, including an assessment of dynamic and thermodynamic characteristics suggested by the evidence, are discussed in the remainder of this chapter.

The final phase of the project followed the completion of the report, namely the reassembly of all components and the restoration of the limited areas of paintwork that had been affected by the survey and the component removal.

4.2 Main structural components

Rocket's main structural form has been built up from its original main frame to which was added, during its operating career on the L&MR, a supplementary frame and buffer at the front end, and large cylinder mounting plates and cross braces towards the rear (Drawing 4.2). Supplementary buffing timbers and braces, added during its time on the Naworth collieries railway, are no longer present.

4.2.1 Main-frame members

Rocket's main frame, shown as 'A' in Drawing 4.3, appears to be of original 1829 manufacture. It is largely of the same form as that which had been fitted to the earlier *Lancashire Witch* and *Pride of Newcastle* locomotives (Fig. 2.3), except for the step at the rear, which was forged to allow for the fitting of the firebox (Section 4.6.1).

Drawing 4.1 *Rocket* as in 1999
Scale: 1:32

A similar step was also later incorporated into *Invicta*'s frame (Fig. 2.9).

The longitudinal higher frame members are formed of 4 in. × 1 in. rolled iron, whilst the lower frame members were reduced to 2⅞ in. to accommodate the firebox (Drawing 4.4). The front and rear cross-members are made of 4 in. × 1 in. forged iron, rebated at their ends to allow for riveting to the main-frame bars. An eye for the draw-hook has been forged into the rear cross-member. The iron was also almost certainly supplied by the Bedlington Iron Company in 1829 (Section 3.3). The frames are not accurately aligned; the longitudinal members being not quite parallel and the frame width at the leading end being as much as ¼ in. narrower than the frame width measured at the leading horns.

There is significant accident damage to the left-hand longitudinal member, which has not only buckled but has broken 6 in. from the leading edge, at the point where there are two transverse holes (Drawing 4.5). It is likely that these holes, which feature only on the left side of the frame, had been for the mercurial gauge, fitted to meet the requirements of the Rainhill Trials (Appendix 1). It seems that major damage was incurred before the buffer beam and supplementary frame had been fitted (Section 4.2.2), when the main frame, which protruded beyond the smokebox, was vulnerable to impact damage. It appears that the leading left corner was bent back on itself, the severity of the impact suggesting that the damage may have been incurred by the accident in Olive Mount cutting in January 1831 (Section 3.7). During the locomotive's repair at the Edge Hill workshops, the frame was probably straightened by cold hammering which caused it to break, and which was thus braced by the supplementary frames. Further front-end impact damage was incurred on the Naworth collieries railway (below) which caused the buckling of the combined frame assembly, which is still evident.

The back end of *Rocket*'s frame has risen up, to the rear of the cylinder mounting plates, resulting in the footplate sloping towards the firebox. This was probably due to a lack of stiffening to counteract the weight of the firebox and the upward thrust of the rear wheel in motion. It is likely that two rear diagonal stays between the firebox back-plate and the rear frame cross-member, probably fitted following the Chat Moss accident (Section 3.7), provided stiffening to counteract any further movement of the frame. Although shown on the 'Thompson' and 'Stephenson' drawings at the end of the locomotive's working career (Fig. 4.1, p108), the stays had been removed by the date of its transfer to South Kensington.

Two pairs of redundant tapped holes on the front cross-member, holes 'C', are evidence of the former presence of the diagonal front tube-plate stays (Figs 3.2, 3.4 and 3.5), which were removed when the larger smokebox was fitted (Section 4.7.11). The rear cross-member also has two pairs of redundant holes, holes 'E', that may have been tapped, which were for the two rear diagonal frame-stiffening stays.

A number of other redundant holes in the frame reveal modifications that have been made during the working life of the locomotive. These include holes 'D' for the diagonal braces, which were originally fitted to stiffen the rear of the frame (Figs 3.2, 3.4 and 3.5), but were removed at some stage after the fitting of the cylinder mounting plates in 1831 (Section 4.2.8). Further redundant holes were for other modified components, as discussed in the relevant sections.

4.2.2 Supplementary frames

The two supplementary leading frames 'B' (Drawing 4.3), were probably fitted at the Edge Hill workshops in February 1831 following the Olive Mount accident (Section 3.7), by which date the need for *Rocket* to have a front buffer beam, to permit an increase in its operating flexibility, would have been apparent. They were to transmit buffing loads from the beam to the main frame and leading horns. They also strengthened the main frame, to which they were both riveted and braced through the horns.

These assemblies were made up from 4-in.-wide forged iron (Drawing 4.7). That forming the upper members is of ¾-in. thickness, whilst the diagonal braces between the front end and the leading horns are ⅝-in. thick. The lower ends of the braces are forged into keep-plates, which are strengthened to a thickness of ¾ in. A buffer-beam mounting pad has been forged onto each supplementary frame assembly.

Further braces at the front end were added when the locomotive went to Kirkhouse in 1836, probably by the fitters sent out from Newcastle by Robert Stephenson & Co. (Section 3.9). Additional wooden buffers were fitted on the underside of the main buffer beam to accommodate the lower buffing height of the chaldron waggons on the Naworth collieries railway (Section 4.2.3). The buffing loads were transmitted through to the main frame by these 'Kirkhouse' braces which were formed of iron pads, bolted to the buffer beam below the main pads, and upward-sloping diagonal members (Drawing 4.7). To prevent the upward buckling of the 1831 frames, vertical spacing-rods were inserted to secure the supplementary frames with the main frame (Fig. 4.2, p108).

Whilst operating on the Naworth collieries railway (and possibly contributing to its withdrawal from service), *Rocket* was involved in a front-end collision, probably with chaldron waggons, which appears to have fractured both left- and right-side

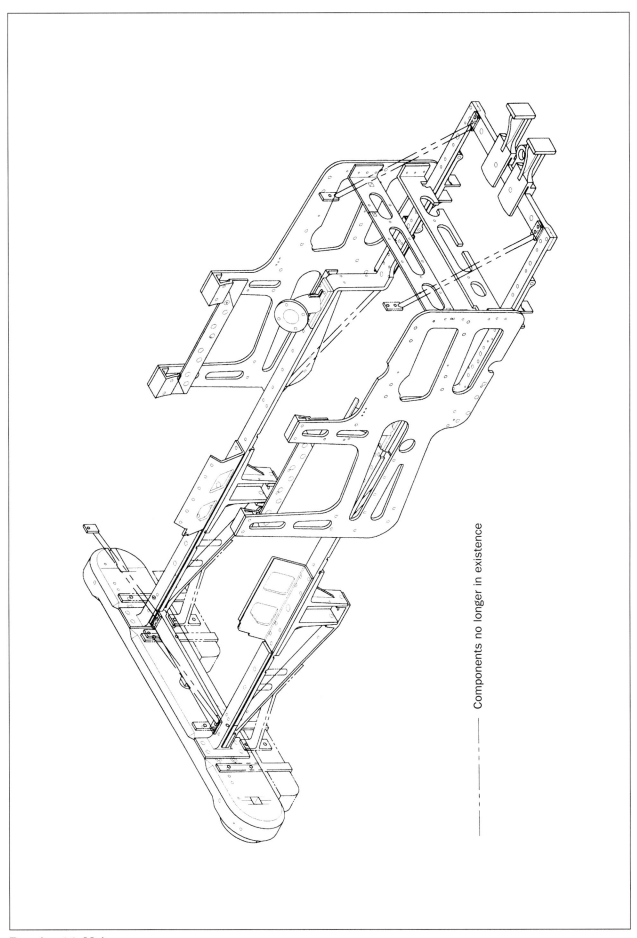

Components no longer in existence

Drawing 4.2 Main structure
Projection: isometric view, upper rear left *Scale:* 1:20

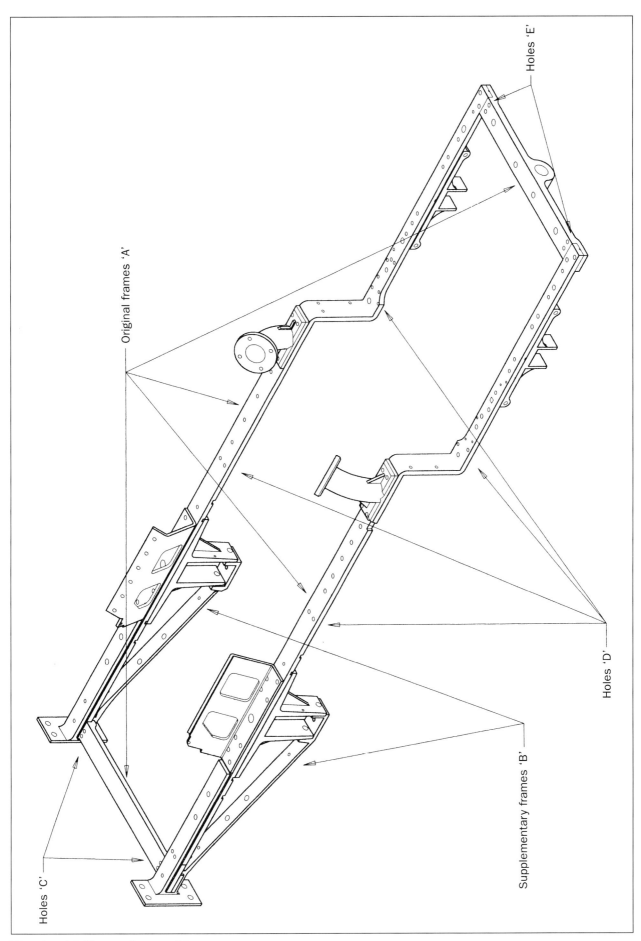

Holes 'E'

Original frames 'A'

Holes 'D'

Holes 'C'

Supplementary frames 'B'

Drawing 4.3 Frame (isometric)
Projection: isometric view, upper rear left *Scale:* 1:16

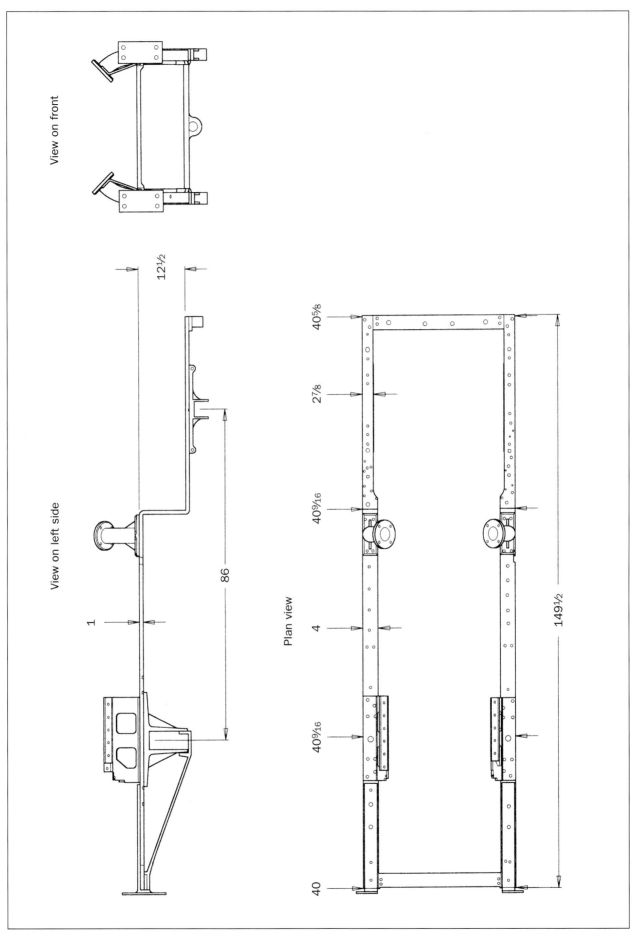

Drawing 4.4 Frame (orthographic)
Scale: 1:25 *Dimensions:* inches

Fig. 4.3 Detail of *Rocket* as seen in 1876, showing fractured 'Kirkhouse' braces
Source: 1876 'Wortley' photograph, Fig. 3.18

'Kirkhouse' braces, buckled the left-side main frame and supplementary frame,
(Section 4.2.1), and left the buffer beam with the downward tilt that it retains.
The remains of the lower buffers, their mounting pads and the fractured frame-braces
remained on the locomotive and were *in situ* when it was presented to the Patent
Office Museum in 1862 (Fig. 4.3).

Regrettably, the Kirkhouse braces and the tie-bolts were removed at the Science
Museum, in 1923 when the lower buffers were removed (Section 3.10). They were
apparently scrapped in 1933, but there is no file note to explain their removal.

4.2.3 Buffer beam, buffers and coupling eye

Rocket's 4¾-in.-thick oak buffer beam was fitted at the same time as its
supplementary frames, probably in February 1831 (Drawings 4.7, 4.8 and 4.9).
It retains good traces of the locomotive's L&MR running number (No. 1) which had
been painted, on two separate occasions, with a yellow topcoat on a green base
(Fig. 4.4, p108). The earlier numbering probably dated from the fitting of the beam
whilst the second application, which overpainted the first number, may date from
Rocket's second major overhaul in early 1833 (Section 3.7).

There is evidence that leather-bound, horsehair buffers have been fitted to the beam
on two occasions. This is indicated by two sets of perimeter nail-holes that were
probably used to secure the leather, using circumferential wrought-iron rings. The two
sets of holes and circumferential fitting marks made using a scribing compass are
evident in the timber (Fig. 4.5, p108).

At some stage during its L&MR career, possibly in 1833, *Rocket* appears to have been
fitted with horsehair buffers enclosing an iron buffer-plate with a square-section tail-
rod, possibly encompassing a spiral spring. Such an arrangement would serve to
explain the 2¼-in. square holes through the beam at the buffer centres. A square
wrought-iron contact plate rebated in a round wooden backing has survived from the
left-hand buffer. This suggests that this provided both guidance for a tail-rod and
contact for a spring, although there is no rubbing on the contact surface to confirm
this. Confirmation that such buffers were in occasional use by 1836 comes from the
description of those used on the Stephenson Company's later Patentee locomotives:[3]

> [the buffers] are strong leather cushions stuffed with horse-hair... those on the engines are
> sometimes made with a large spiral spring inside, that their action may be more perfect.

Large-size horsehair buffers were apparently fitted to *Rocket* by 1836, but there is no
confirmation that they included a spiral spring (Fig. 4.6, p108). The back of the buffer
beam has been burnt adjacent to the ash-box door.

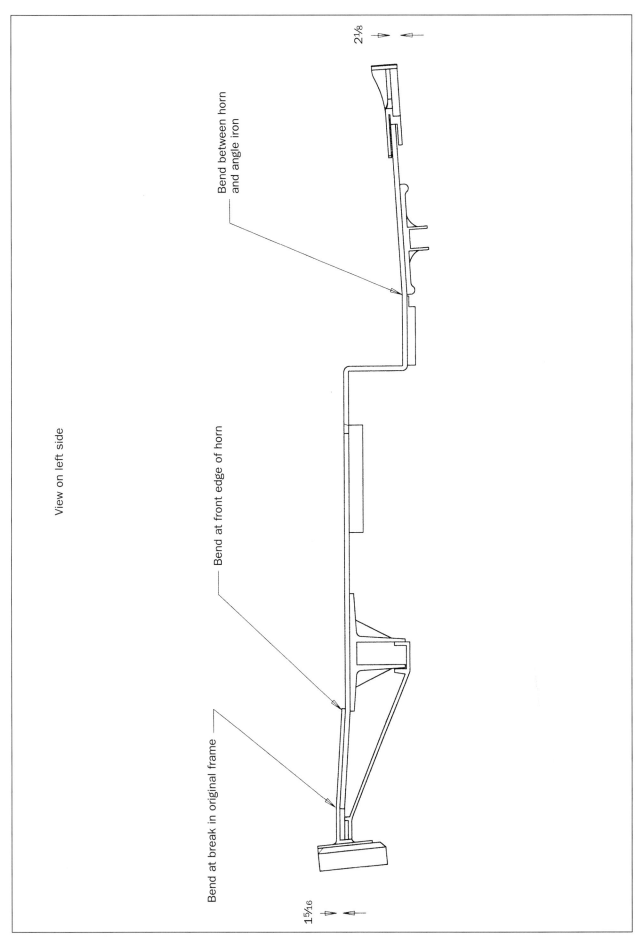

View on left side

Bend between horn
and angle iron

$2\frac{1}{8}$

Bend at front edge of horn

Bend at break in original frame

$1\frac{5}{16}$

Drawing 4.5 Left frame, showing bends
Projection: 1st angle *Scale:* 1:20 *Dimensions:* inches

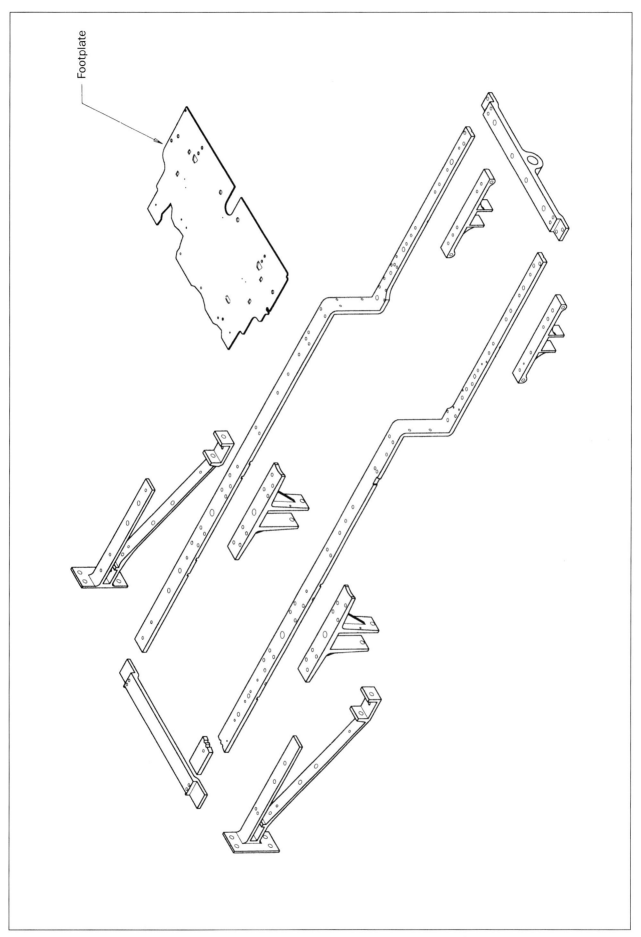

Footplate

Drawing 4.6 Frame, exploded
Projection: isometric view, upper rear left *Scale:* 1:20

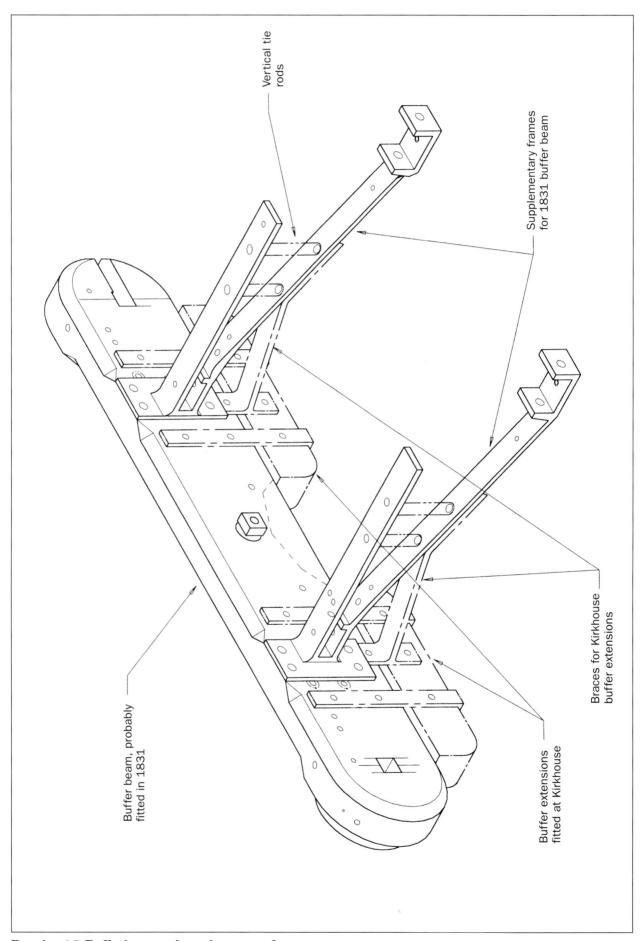

Vertical tie rods

Supplementary frames for 1831 buffer beam

Braces for Kirkhouse buffer extensions

Buffer extensions fitted at Kirkhouse

Buffer beam, probably fitted in 1831

Drawing 4.7 Buffer beam and supplementary frame
Projection: isometric view, upper rear left *Scale:* 1:10

Isometric view from upper front left

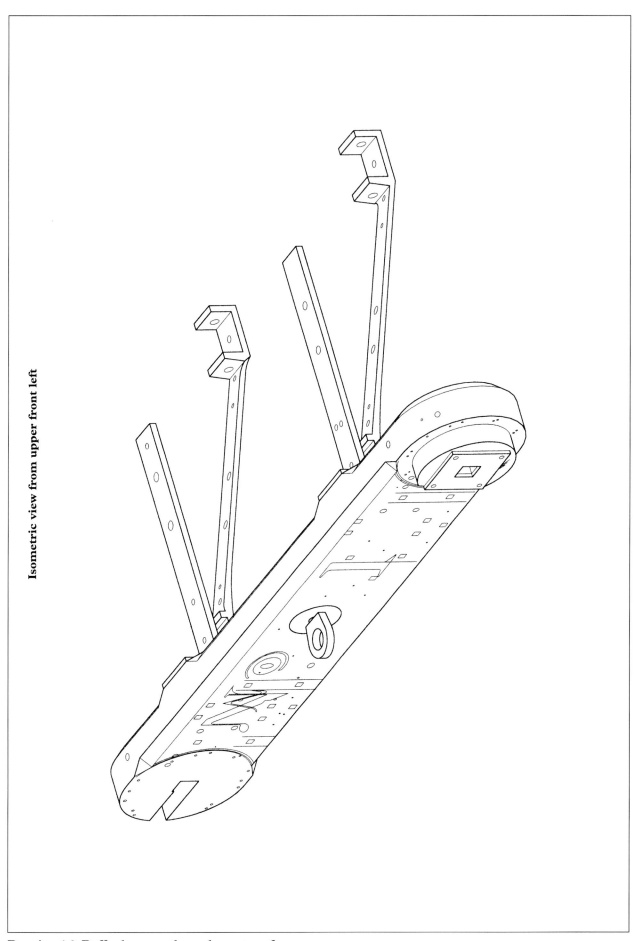

Drawing 4.8 Buffer beam and supplementary frame
Projection: isometric view, upper front left *Scale:* 1:10

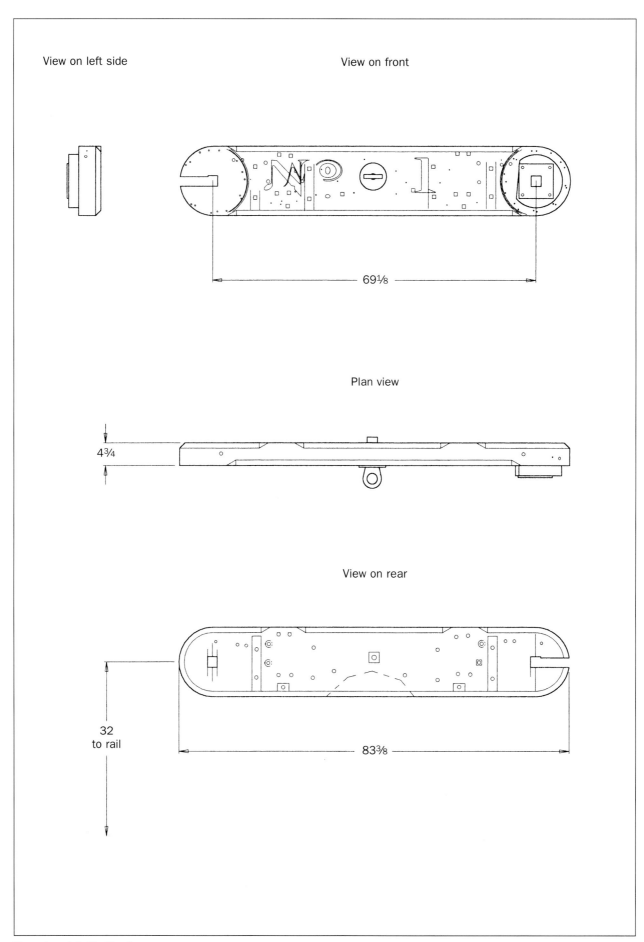

View on left side

View on front

69⅛

Plan view

4¾

View on rear

32
to rail

83⅜

Drawing 4.9 Buffer beam
Projection: 1st angle *Scale:* 1:10 *Dimensions:* inches

Fig. 4.7 Buffer beam showing supplementary buffers
Source: 1876 'Wortley' photograph, Fig. 3.19

When the locomotive was sold to the Naworth collieries railway in 1836, two supplementary buffer timbers, approximately 11 in. deep, were fitted, probably at Kirkhouse. They were placed immediately below the main beam to accommodate the lower buffing height and the reduced centres of the chaldron wagons used on that system. The timbers were each secured by two iron straps $10\frac{3}{8}$ in. apart. The buffing loads were transmitted by the 'Kirkhouse' braces (Section 4.2.2). These supplementary buffers (Fig. 4.7) remained in place until 1923, but were then removed (Section 3.10). There is no Science Museum file note to explain their removal, and they were discarded in 1933. The eight fixing holes through the main beam provide evidence of their location.

A coupling eye and washer remain in place in the centre of the buffer beam (Fig. 4.8, p108). Its date is uncertain but it may have been that present in 1836, to which a coupling chain and hook were attached (Fig. 4.6, p108). A further washer behind the buffer beam is missing; the hole has become worn and the eye bolt has become loose-fitting. To overcome this a hexagonal hollow-steel packing block has been inserted, probably at some time over the last fifty years, but there is no Science Museum file note to confirm the date of insertion.

4.2.4 Rear buffing pads

Two cast-iron buffing pads were fitted to the middle of the rear main frame member, to allow *Rocket* to propel its tender and trains (Drawing 4.2). The pads, which were not shown on the earliest drawings (Figs 3.2, 3.4 and 3.5), have been riveted through the footplate as well as the frame and, being a modification, may have been fitted in November 1830 following the Chat Moss accident (Section 3.7). As this accident occurred whilst *Rocket* was propelling its train, perhaps through the draw-bar alone, their fitting may have been prompted by the accident itself. The rectangular cross-section of the pad contact area allowed the locomotive to be coupled with tenders of varying frame heights then in use on the L&MR, thereby increasing its operating flexibility (Fig. 4.9, p108).

Between the buffing pads, a forged draw-bar eye is fitted, its tail passing through the forged eye in the rear-frame member, and secured by a tapered cotter. This arrangement suggests the use of an independent draw bar, pinned at both ends, which permitted the locomotive and its tender unhindered passage around sharply curved track, as well as tender frame-height variations.

4.2.5 Footplate

A ¼-in.-thick wrought-iron footplate is riveted to the rear of the locomotive's frame (Drawing 4.6). It is probably the original footplate, as it has been over-riveted by the

Isometric view upper rear left

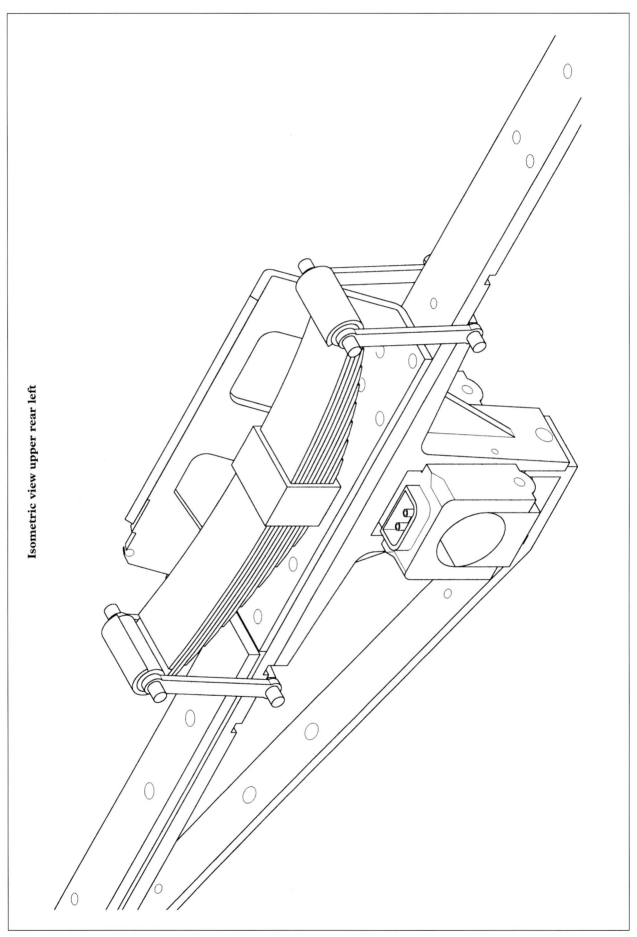

Drawing 4.10 Spring assembly, front left
Projection: isometric view, upper rear left *Scale:* 1:5

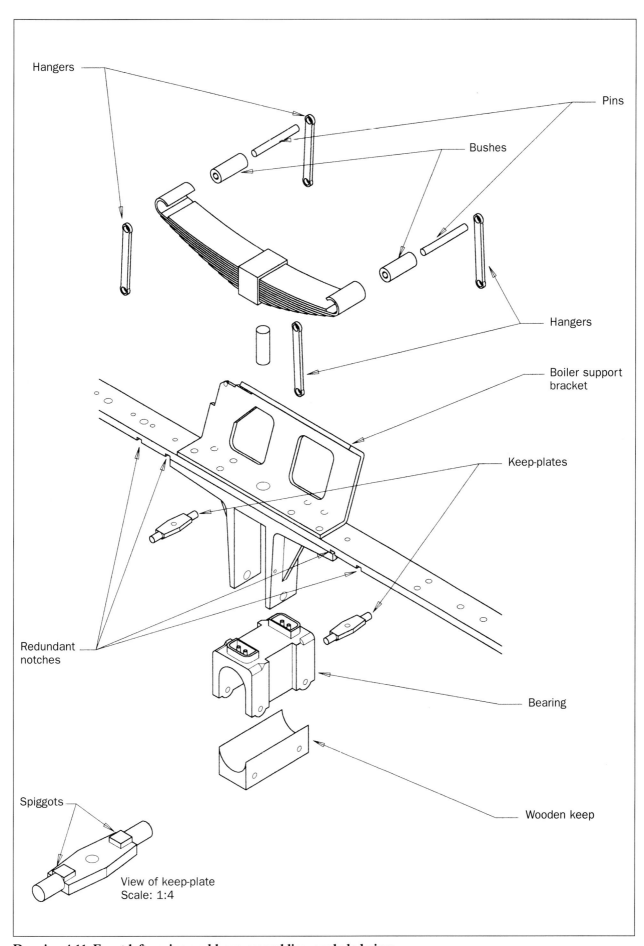

Hangers

Pins

Bushes

Hangers

Boiler support bracket

Keep-plates

Redundant notches

Bearing

Spiggots

Wooden keep

View of keep-plate
Scale: 1:4

Drawing 4.11 Front left spring and horn assemblies, exploded view
Projection: isometric *Scale:* 1:10

Isometric view upper left rear

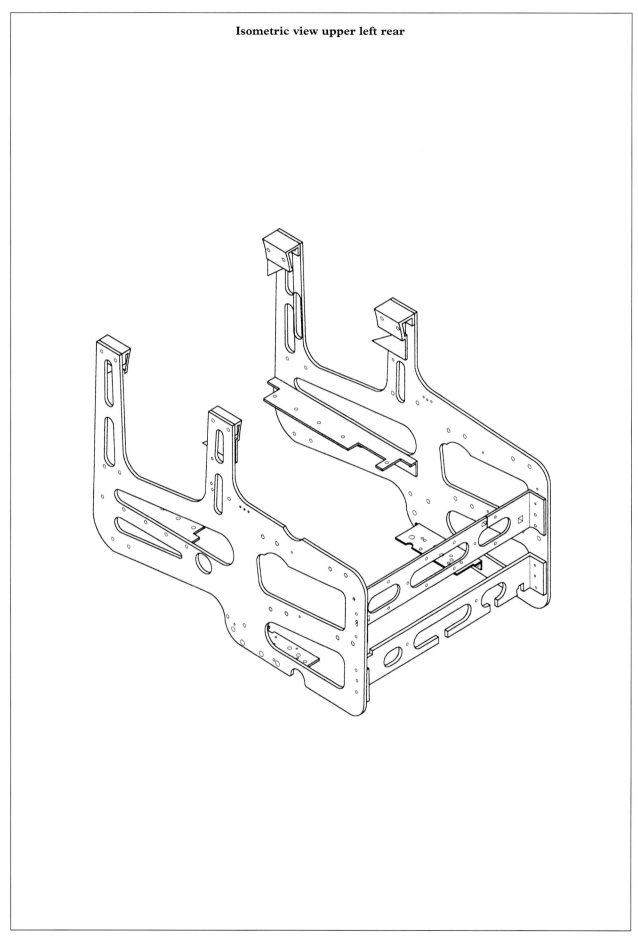

Drawing 4.12 1831 cylinder mounting plate assembly
Projection: isometric view, upper left rear *Scale:* 1:16

rear buffing pads, probably fitted in November 1830 (Fig. 4.9, p108). Its sides have, however, been cut away at its leading end, apparently *in situ*, to make room for the cylinder mounting plates.

The slip-eccentric reversing pedal (Section 4.10.6) is fitted through the footplate at the left front of the plate. There are a number of redundant holes in the plate, of which a pair on the front right were probably for a 'J'-form foot-pedal spring. Those above the rear frame cross-member were for the frame stiffening stays (Section 4.2.1). The holes on both sides were apparently for foot-board fixing bolts or hand-rail stanchions, the forward of which would have been lost when the front ends were cut away. The front edge of the plate is corroded, and there has been a significant loss of metal to the right of the centre-line.

4.2.6 Horns and springs

The horn and spring fittings to the main frame members are shown in Drawings 4.10 and 4.11. There have been a number of changes during the working life of the locomotive.

The cast-iron driving-axle horns were replaced early in *Rocket*'s career on the Liverpool & Manchester line. The original horns were made for the first axle, of 3¼-in. diameter, whilst the present pair, which are riveted to the main frame members, were fitted for its later 4-in. diameter axle (Section 4.3.4). These horns are longer than the first set, the evidence for which is the presence of notches under the frame which were probably used to locate and secure the original spring-hangers. The first horns were probably of the same length as the boiler support brackets above the frame (Fig. 4.10, p109).

It is possible that the horns were replaced shortly after the Rainhill Trials, if the original driving axle had been replaced at that time. It is more likely, however, that they were replaced in February 1831, following the Olive Mount accident, in which a driving wheel was broken and corresponding damage was no doubt incurred by both the axle and perhaps also the horns (Section 3.7).

Although both the driving-axle horns have single strengthening gussets, the right-side one is significantly more curved than the others, suggesting a replacement. These contrast with the rear, carrying-axle horns, however, which have double gussets. It is clear that the two pairs of horns were cast on separate occasions and from the work of a different patternmaker, and it is likely that the rear pair date from the construction of the locomotive.

The driving wheel-set springs are probably the third set to have been fitted to the locomotive. Evidence is provided by pairs of spring-hanger notches on either side of the undersurface of the main frame members. There are two unused sets of notches, the first (at 25-in. centres) now fouled by the present horns (above), and the second at 33-in. centres. Whilst the first springs appear to have been displaced by the larger horns, it is possible that the second set were found to be too soft.

The present driving wheel-set springs have returned to 26-in. centres, resulting in conflict between the spring-hanger keep-plate and the horn ends, the latter being profiled to accommodate the former. The keep-plates have been inverted and, in the absence of a third set of notches, are located under the frames by bolts (Fig. 4.11, p109).

The present spring-sets may be those in use at the end of service, as suggested by the 'Thompson'/'Stephenson' drawings (Figs 3.14 and 3.15, p107), but it is more likely that they are replacements of the same plate size, dating from the 1862 refurbishment. The steel spring leaves are in good condition, without the corrosion that would have been expected from a prolonged period of inactivity in less than ideal conditions (Fig. 4.12, p109).

A further indication that the driving wheel spring-sets may have been replaced in 1862 arises from the condition of the wrought iron spring-hangers. The right-side hangers differ from the left side in having a boss for the top hanger pin-fitting, and they are noticeably more corroded. It is thus possible that the left-side hangers were more

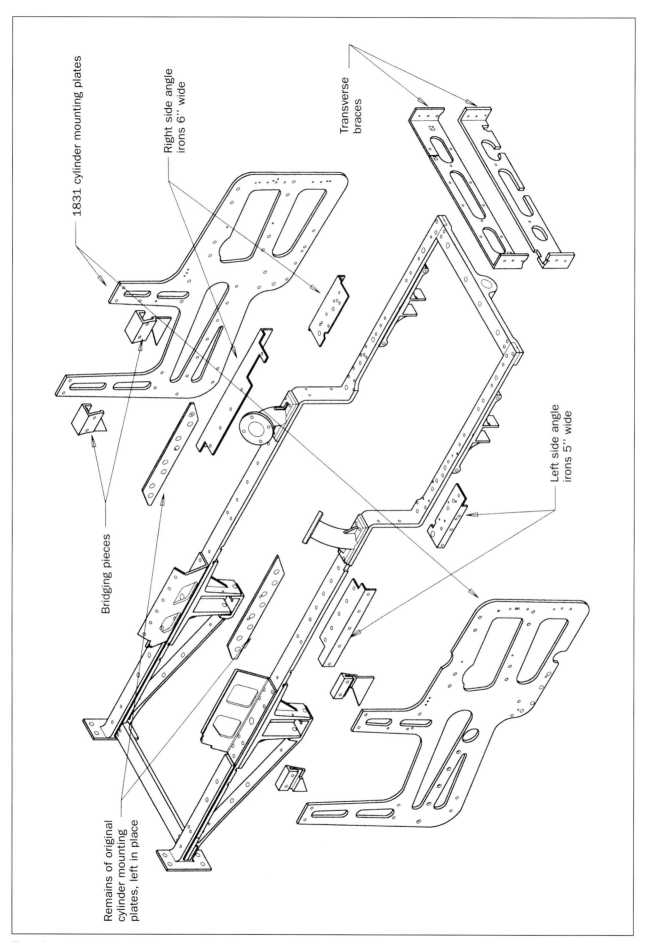

1831 cylinder mounting plates

Right side angle
irons 6'' wide

Transverse
braces

Left side angle
irons 5'' wide

Bridging pieces

Remains of original
cylinder mounting
plates, left in place

Drawing 4.13 1831 cylinder mounting plate assembly, exploded view

Projection: isometric *Scale:* 1:20 *Dimensions:* inches

badly corroded and had to be replaced to support new spring-sets during the 1862 refurbishment. The spring hangers on both sides are fitted with hexagonal pin-nuts, again indicating a later fitting.

It is notable that the rear spring-sets have been absent since the locomotive has been displayed at South Kensington. This suggests that they were badly corroded by 1862, but that there was insufficient justification for their replacement. The carrying axle is supported on wooden blocks, whilst the spring hangers are tied together by simple wrought-iron plates, bent under the axle.

4.2.7 Boiler-support brackets

The rear boiler-support brackets on *Rocket* appear to be original fittings and are similar, if not identical, to those previously employed by the Stephenson Company for *Lancashire Witch* and *Pride of Newcastle*, as shown in Fig. 4.13.

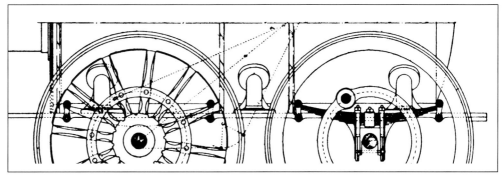

Fig. 4.13 Provisional scheme for cast-iron boiler brackets on *Lancashire Witch*
Source: R Stephenson & Co. Drawing Collection, Science Museum, inv. no. 1924-159

The cast-iron brackets, which were cast hollow for lightness, are of curved form, bolted to the frame with rectangular gusseted flanges and to the boiler barrel with circular flanges. The left-side bracket has been cut out to allow clearance for the valve gear cross-shaft levers.

The same form of brackets could not be used for the leading boiler-support brackets, because of the presence of the driving wheel spring-sets. These brackets have therefore been formed of ½-in.-thick and 21½-in.-long wrought-iron plate, the base of which has been forged into a flange and riveted to the main frame, whilst the forged top flange is bolted to the boiler barrel. Two lightening holes have been cut from each plate, which appear to be of 1829 manufacture (Drawing 4.11). The left-side bracket has been further cut away at the leading end of the boiler flange to accommodate two bolts in the boiler (Section 4.7.8).

In common with usual boiler-fitting practice on early locomotives, there is no allowance for expansion. Although this will have led to stresses being set up in the fixing bolts, there is no indication of failures or replacement bolts having been fitted.

4.2.8 Cylinder mounting plate assembly

The two large cylinder mounting plates (Drawings 4.12 and 4.13) were almost certainly fitted to *Rocket* at the Edge Hill workshops in February 1831 following the Olive Mount accident (Section 3.7). The ⅜-in.-thick wrought-iron plates, which accommodated the repositioned cylinders and slide bars, also served to stiffen up the rear of the locomotive's frame, making unnecessary the diagonal braces which were subsequently removed (Section 4.2.1). Eight lightening holes were cut from each plate, whilst smaller areas of metal were also removed to allow for the fitting of steam and exhaust pipes and the valve motion.

The plates were fitted by angle irons riveted to both the upper and lower lengths of the main frame, and by bridging pieces bolted to the boiler barrel. The rear of the locomotive was further stiffened by two transverse braces across the back of the

View on rear

View on left side

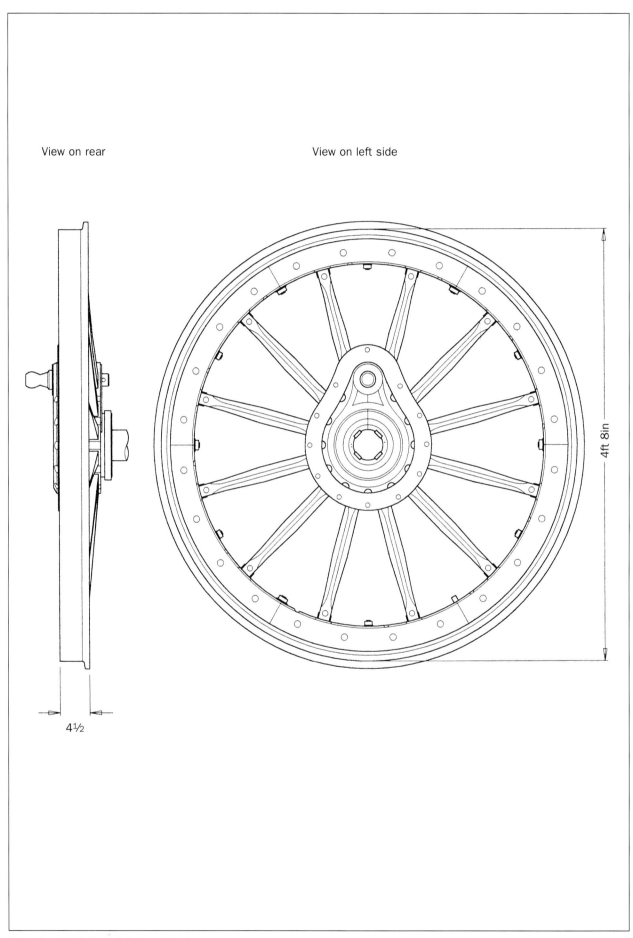

4ft 8in

4½

Drawing 4.14 Left driving wheel
Projection: 1st angle *Scale:* 1:12.5 *Dimensions:* inches

firebox, to which they were bolted. The flanged ends of the braces were riveted to the cylinder mounting plates.

The right-hand mounting plate has been fitted 1 in. further out from the locomotive frame than the left-hand mounting plate. This feature provides an important indication of the extent to which *Rocket*'s firebox was asymmetrical with its frame (Section 4.6.2). Robert Stephenson had noted that the firebox was 'not quite square built' when it was delivered (Section 3.3), and it therefore seems that this was a reference to it protruding beyond the main frame line on the right side. Compensating adjustments were made to the cylinder mounting pads towards a realignment of the cylinder centre lines with the wheel cranks (Section 4.8.8).

The alignment of the plates was achieved by the fitting of different-sized angle irons, the right side being 1 in. wider than the left. The upper angle irons were riveted to the mounting plates before assembly and, after adjustment for frame and firebox alignments, were drilled and bolted to the frame. The reverse was the case for the lower angle irons which, because of the need to replace the firebox before final assembly, were first riveted to the frame under the firebox and then bolted to the mounting plates. A comparison between the alignments of the two upper angle irons, illustrating the deviation of the right-side mounting plate, is given in Fig. 4.14, p109.

The upper angle irons are recessed at their leading ends providing a 'footprint' of the former diagonal brace (Section 4.2.1 above) that had remained in place for a period after the fitting of the cylinder mounting plates. The angle irons were also recessed at the rear, to accommodate the forward valve-gear rocking-shaft bearings, although the profile of these recesses indicates that an alteration has been made to this component (Section 4.10.3).

The upper arms of the cylinder mounting plates are bolted to iron bridging pieces which were forged to suit the gap to the boiler barrel, that on the right side being wider than the one on the left because of the asymmetric firebox.

4.3 Wheel-sets

4.3.1 Identification of the driving wheels

Rocket's surviving wheels, fitted to a 4-in. diameter axle, are probably the second or third set to have been fitted (Drawing 4.14). They are important survivors from the brief era between 1828 and 1833 when wooden wheels were adopted by Robert Stephenson & Co., as a short-term expedient to overcome the vulnerability and weight of cast-iron wheels, and before wrought-iron spokes had been successfully developed.[4] The wooden spokes and felloes were 'hooped' with wrought-iron bands, and further fitted with a wrought-iron flanged tyre. Nicholas Wood described them in 1831:[5]

> ...wooden spokes, on which was laid a malleable iron tire: wheels, thus hooped, though more expensive, seem quite necessary for the rapid rate at which some of those engines are propelled.

The five locomotives manufactured between March 1828 and July 1829 (Figs 2.2–2.4) had all been equipped with wooden wheels fitted with wrought-iron crank rings to which were fitted the crank pins.[6] *Lancashire Witch* was fitted with four replacement 4-ft-diameter wooden wheels in September 1829, with 'Wrought Iron Tires turned, with crank pins &c complete' which were charged out at £100.[7] Two 5-ft-diameter replacement wheels, made for *Dart* in November 1830, however, were charged out at only £42.[8]

Rocket's first driving wheels, which were 4 ft 8½-in. diameter and 3¼-in. wide when measured by John Rastrick in October 1829,[9] were, however, depicted on the earliest drawings without crank rings (Figs 3.2, 3.4 and 3.5). It is possible that the rings were omitted from the drawings, which portrayed the wheels as having twelve slender spokes, to one of which was fitted the crank boss. However, an indication that an alternative form of wheel was used is provided by James Scott Walker, who wrote that the connecting rod was:[10]

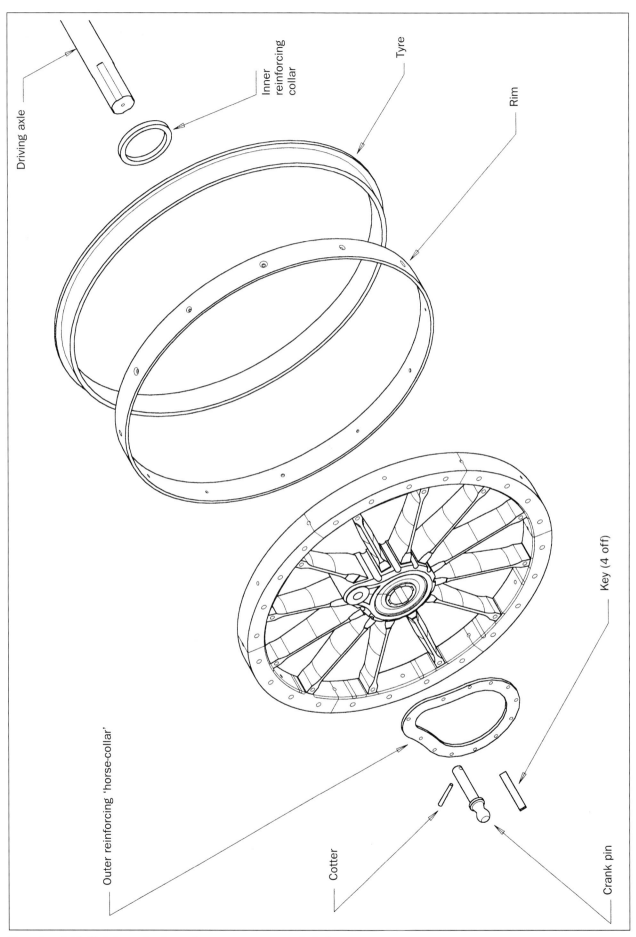

Driving axle

Inner reinforcing collar

Tyre

Rim

Key (4 off)

Outer reinforcing 'horse-collar'

Cotter

Crank pin

Drawing 4.15 Driving wheel, major components exploded
Projection: isometric view, upper rear left *Scale:* 1:15

attached to a strong spoke of the front wheel, at a short distance from the centre of the nave, and communicates the power on the principle of a crank, or, in other words, at every stroke of the engine, forces the wheel once round, as a common reel for yarn, is turned by a handle fixed to one of the spokes.

It is more likely that these original wheels, which were fitted to a 3¼-in.-diameter axle,[11] had wrought-iron straps fitted between the naves and the wheel rims, into which the crank pins were inserted. Such wheels were fitted, just four months later, to the four *Rocket*-type locomotives built for the L&MR (Fig. 2.8), and *Rocket* itself was depicted at the end of its service with such a wheel-set (Figs 3.14 and 3.15). The original wheels were either replaced soon after the Rainhill Trials, or remained in use until the Olive Mount accident of January 1831, when one wheel was reported to have been broken (Section 3.7).

Although preferable to cast-iron spokes, the wooden wheels were themselves vulnerable to breakage and the joints working, as well as drying out. The practice of supplying new locomotives with 'duplicate' driving wheel-sets became commonplace, in order to minimise the time a locomotive was out of service.[12] It is likely that *Rocket* was supplied with a duplicate strap-form wheel-set by Robert Stephenson & Co., probably in early 1830, shortly after it had been acquired by the L&MR, although evidence confirming this has not been found. Interchanging wheels with other locomotives was not possible as it was the only locomotive equipped with 4 ft 8½-in.-diameter driving wheels.

Rocket's surviving driving wheels, however, are of a later form, with the crank bosses formed from an enlarged cast-iron nave (Section 4.3.2). They appear to be a development from those fitted to the subsequent locomotives (*Phoenix, North Star, Northumbrian* and *Majestic*) delivered between June and December 1830 (Fig. 2.11). It is not known, however, whether the surviving wheels were made by the Stephenson company or by another contractor to the L&MR. Similarly, it is not known if they date from 1831, following the Olive Mount accident, or whether they were further replaced in 1833 following the Wigan Branch accident (Section 3.7). It is also possible that one wheel may have been re-spoked following the latter incident (Section 4.3.3). Thomas Hunt, who assisted with *Rocket*'s repairs and refurbishment in early 1833, later recalled that 'the crank-pin was in the boss of the driving-wheel, and not in a separate arm' at that time.[13]

The first deliveries of locomotives with driving wheels formed with wrought-iron spokes set into cast-iron rims and naves was in 1832, although only after many months of trial did their reliability become acceptable.[14] It may therefore be assumed that, had *Rocket*'s wheels been replaced later than 1833, this type of wheel would have been adopted. However, together with the patterns, the cost would have been difficult to justify for a locomotive nearing the end of its active service on the railway.

It is likely that when *Rocket* was sold to the Naworth collieries railway in 1836, its 'duplicate' wheel-set was supplied with it. Evidence suggesting that this was the case is provided by the purchase price of £295 19s 5d, rather than a round £300 (Section 3.9). It is probable that this figure included duplicate components, particularly a spare driving wheel-set, as well as the cost of the locomotive itself. Further evidence of the continued existence of the duplicate wheel-set arises from a comparison of the contemporary illustrations of the driving wheel-sets (Fig. 4.15, p109).

Whilst the locomotive was depicted in 1836 with probably the surviving driving wheel-set, it was further depicted in its end-of-service drawing as being fitted with crank-strap wheels. It is therefore probable that the surviving wheels were fitted to *Rocket* at the time of the locomotive's sale to the Earl of Carlisle. After a period of use, they may have become damaged or broken, and were replaced by the duplicate set for the remainder of its service. Although showing little sign of tyre wear, the surviving wheels have undergone prolonged use and maintenance and have both broken spokes and burnt felloes, either of which may have caused their withdrawal from service (Section 4.3.3).

It is not known what became of the duplicate set, but it would seem that the surviving wheels were returned to the locomotive, retaining the breakage, repairs and burn

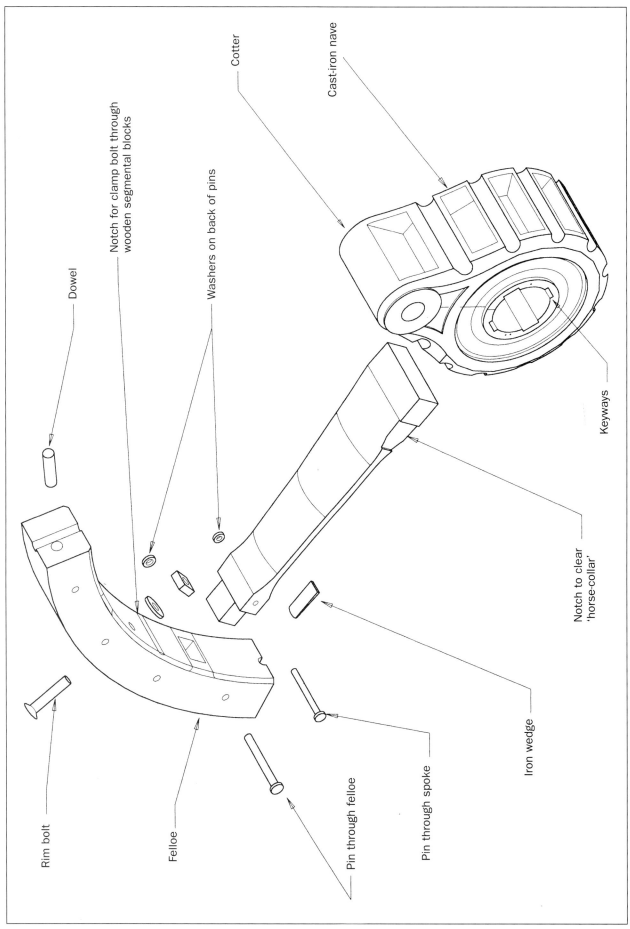

Drawing 4.16 Driving wheel detail
Projection: isometric view, upper rear left *Scale:* 1:6

marks, probably as part of the 1862 restoration. In its earliest years at South
Kensington, *Rocket*'s left-side driving wheel was braced with segmental wooden blocks
(Figs 3.18 and 3.19). These were probably inserted in 1862, as the wheel was
considered vulnerable (Section 4.3.3). The blocks appear to have been removed in
1892 (Section 3.10).

4.3.2 Description of the naves

The naves are each formed of a single casting, machined to be fitted to a 4-in. axle
(Drawing 4.16). In keeping with several, if not all, of the early 1830s-built Stephenson
locomotives, the naves are keyed to the axle with four $1\frac{1}{8} \times \frac{3}{8}$ in. rectangular steel
keys, to receive which keyways have been cut in both hub and axle. The wheels are
therefore a clearance fit to the axle and are supported by the keys, which also transmit
all the dynamic forces (Fig. 4.16, p110).

A similar method of fitting was in use by the Stephenson Company in 1836 with the
early locomotives of the *Patentee* type:[15]

> The wheels are entirely supported and held by these keys, as the naves do not touch the axle;
> and by this means a firm and uniform bearing can be obtained, and the wheels can also be
> fixed truly at right angles to the axle and at the proper distance from each other.

The castings include sockets for the rectangular spoke-ends. They also include crank-
pin holes at $8\frac{1}{2}$ in. centre distance from the axle centre (in accordance with the 17-in.
stroke). The forged ball-ended crank pins, inserted through the naves, are secured by
cotter pins.

Whilst the castings are substantial and able to withstand the piston forces, wrought-
iron reinforcing bands have been shrunk onto both their outer and inner faces. The
outer face reinforcing bands are profiled to include the crank bosses, and have been
formed into the shape of 'horse-collars'. The left-side band has $\frac{5}{8}$-in.-diameter holes
drilled between each spoke, probably for the bolts used to secure the wooden
segmental blocks in 1862 (Section 4.3.3). Following the removal of the latter in 1892,
the holes were filled with wooden plugs, some of which are now missing. The inner
reinforcing collars are simple rings around spigots on the back of the naves.[16]

4.3.3 Spokes and felloes

The spokes and felloes have been made and assembled by a wheelwright using ash
timber (Drawing 4.16). Unlike conventional road-carriage wheels, however, the wheels
do not have a concave form and the spokes and felloes remain in the same plain.
The full rectangular sections of the spoke timbers are inserted into the sockets, whilst
their outer ends are formed into tenons and mortised into the felloes. Each wheel is
built up with six felloes, apparently doweled with its neighbour and each mortised to
receive two spoke tenons. Full-width, $\frac{1}{2}$-in. thick, wrought-iron rims have been shrunk
on to the assembled wheels and secured by counter-sunk bolts through the felloes, mid-
way between each spoke, and tightened with nuts. Alternate bolts thus pass through the
felloe dowels. Wrought-iron flanged tyres have been shrunk onto the wheels.

The condition of the wheels reveals much about the maintenance practices that were
required to keep the locomotive operational. In addition to accident damage, the
stresses applied to the wheels in service conditions have weakened the mortise and
tenon joints, as well as putting strains on the spokes themselves. In addition, the left
wheel has received more maintenance than the right one, suggesting that it has run
more miles. The right-side spokes and felloes may have been replaced, as the profile of
the felloes differs from that of the left wheel, suggesting the work of another
wheelwright. If both wheels date from 1831, it is possible that the right one was
remade after the 1833 Wigan Branch accident.

Both wheels have $24\frac{1}{2}$-in.-diameter wrought-iron pins, with $\frac{7}{8}$-in.-diameter heads
and collars, inserted transversely through the felloes to minimise any warping
tendency that they may have had. On the left wheel, similar pins have been inserted
transversely through each spoke shoulder. These pins are not present on the right

wheel, and it is likely that this strengthening was carried out by the railway maintenance team. Over time, several iron wedges have been hammered into the weakened joints between spoke and nave, and between spoke and felloe, in order to stiffen them and prevent further misalignment. There are more wedges in the left wheel than in the right one.

Two spokes in the left wheel are cracked; one is in poor condition with a piece missing and another piece loose. The other has a bad split which has been secured with a common wood screw, probably during the twentieth century. The inside faces of both wheels have fire damage in the same orientation, suggesting that it may have been caused by careless ash removal or fire-dropping. The damage to the wheels could have resulted in *Rocket*'s withdrawal from service, or the substitution of the duplicate wheel-set (Fig. 4.17, p110).

When the locomotive was being prepared for exhibition in 1862, it appears that Robert Stephenson & Co. considered the condition of the left wheel to be of sufficient concern to require the insertion of wooden segmental strengthening blocks between the spokes. These were bolted to the 'horse-collar' reinforcing band (Section 4.3.2) and to additional circumferential bands located on either side of the spoke shoulders (Fig. 4.18). These latter bolts passed through the inner edge of the felloes.

The segmental blocks and their securing bands were removed in about 1892 by the South Kensington Museum curatorial staff. The ridges left in the felloes from the securing bolts have been filled using wooden inserts. There is no note in the Science Museum technical file relating to the removal of the segmental blocks.

The tyres on both driving wheels show signs of use. The wear on the left wheel is approximately ¼ in., whilst that on the right wheel is only ⅛ in. In the 1830s, the rate of wrought-iron tyre wear was said to be ⅛ in. per annum, but this figure was not related to any mileage.[17] The different amount of wear further suggests that the right

Fig. 4.18 Left driving wheel, as secured with segmental blocks in 1862
Source: 1876 'Wortley' photograph, Fig 3.18

wheel may have been remade after the Wigan Branch accident. The limited wear may be compared to the deep grooves on the tyres fitted to *Sans Pareil*, now displayed in the National Railway Museum.

4.3.4 Driving axle

The forged-iron driving axle has a constant 4-in. diameter, without variation for the journals or wheel-seats (Drawing 4.17). Four keyways at each end have been machined to accommodate the wheel-securing keys (Section 4.3.2).

Two impressions have been left in the axle by the left-hand valve-gear 'driver' pinch.-bolt (Section 4.9.5). A 1½-in. scar suggests that the valve-gear jammed whilst in service. In addition, however, there is a remarkable ¹⁄₁₆-in.-deep groove around the complete circumference, which demonstrates particularly bad handling when the locomotive was not in service. There is no evidence to indicate how or when the groove was created, but it is consistent with the locomotive having been dead-hauled by a strong locomotive force, whilst the valve gear was jammed in an immovable position (Fig. 4.19, p110). It is possible that this may have occurred when *Rocket* was being moved from Kirkhouse to Newcastle in 1851 (Section 3.10).

With the exception of fitter's marks for the dog-rings, there are no further marks on the axle, such as would be expected from the fitting of the Dundonald rotary engines (Section 3.8). These engines and a water pump would have required tapped or keyed fittings to secure them, and it is clear that the surviving axle is not that which was fitted to the locomotive at the time of the rotary engine trial. It is unlikely that a new axle was provided for the locomotive prior to its sale to the Earl of Carlisle, and it is therefore possible that *Rocket*'s duplicate driving wheel-set had been employed for the rotary engine trial.

4.3.5 Nave plates

The axle-end centres have been tapped to receive bolts for securing profiled brass plates to carry the engraved Stephenson company name and place (Fig. 4.20, p110). This type of 'builder's plate' was not a form adopted by the company in the early 1830s, and it is likely that the pair of plates were fitted to the axle-ends during the 1862 restoration.

4.3.6 Driving axle bearings

The two half-bearings are bronze castings (Drawing 4.17). They show signs of service wear, but it is not known whether they were fitted to the first 4-in.-diameter axle, or whether they were a subsequent fitting dating from, say, 1833 or 1836. The castings have been machined to provide an oil reservoir, feed-holes and distribution grooves (Fig. 4.21). The bearings are each secured to wooden keep-blocks by two keep-bolts. They may have been inserted during the 1862 restoration, but the keep-bolts are of early manufacture.

Fig. 4.21 Driving axle bearing running surface
Source: Science Museum View 1945, negative no. 155/45 – part

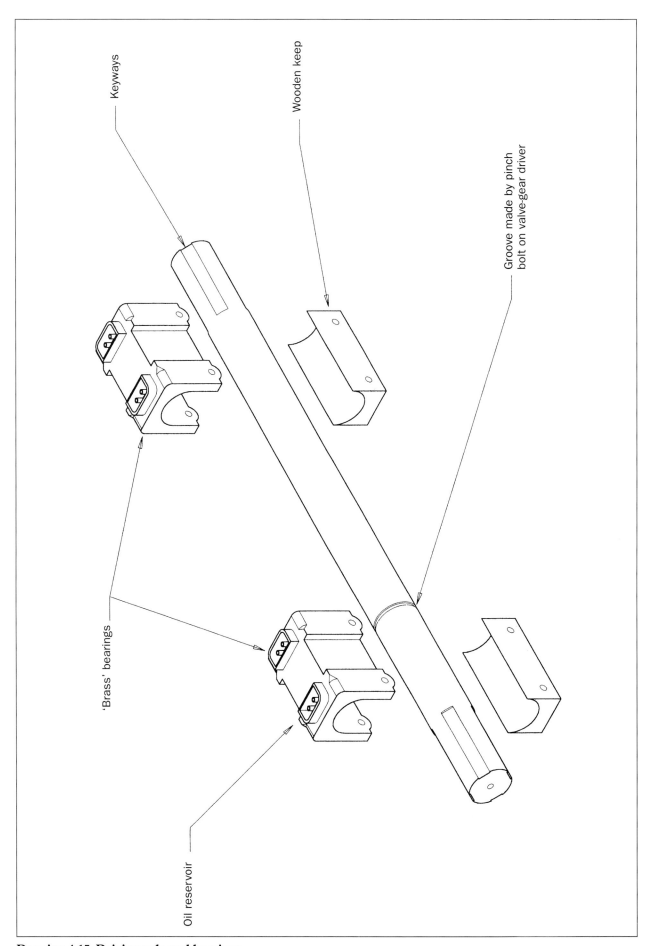

Keyways

Wooden keep

Groove made by pinch
bolt on valve-gear driver

'Brass' bearings

Oil reservoir

Drawing 4.17 Driving axle and bearings
Projection: isometric view, upper rear left *Scale:* 1:8

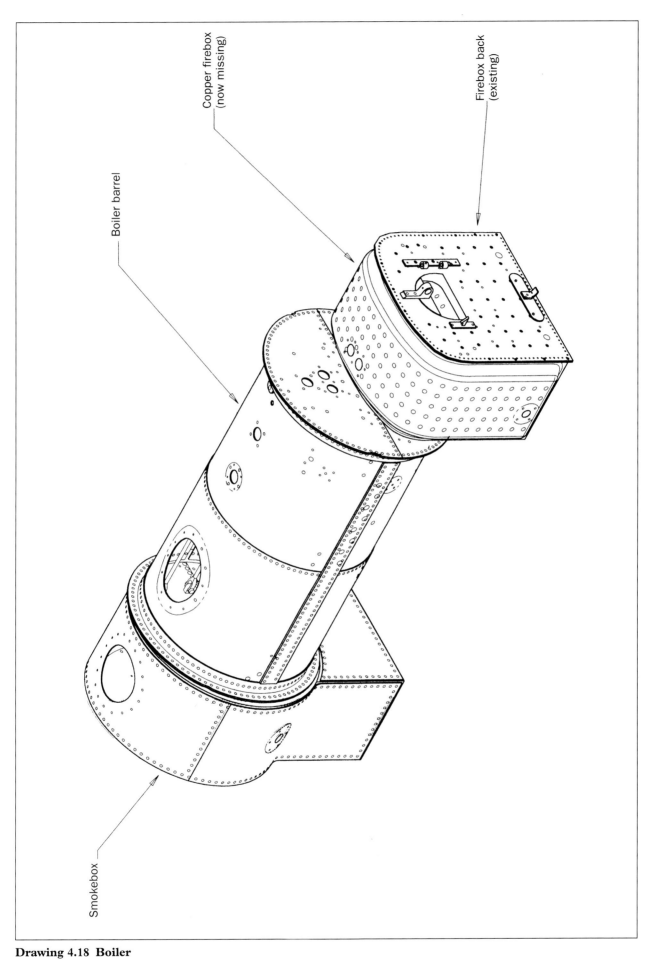

Copper firebox
(now missing)

Firebox back
(existing)

Boiler barrel

Smokebox

Drawing 4.18 Boiler
Projection: isometric view, upper rear left *Scale:* 1:20

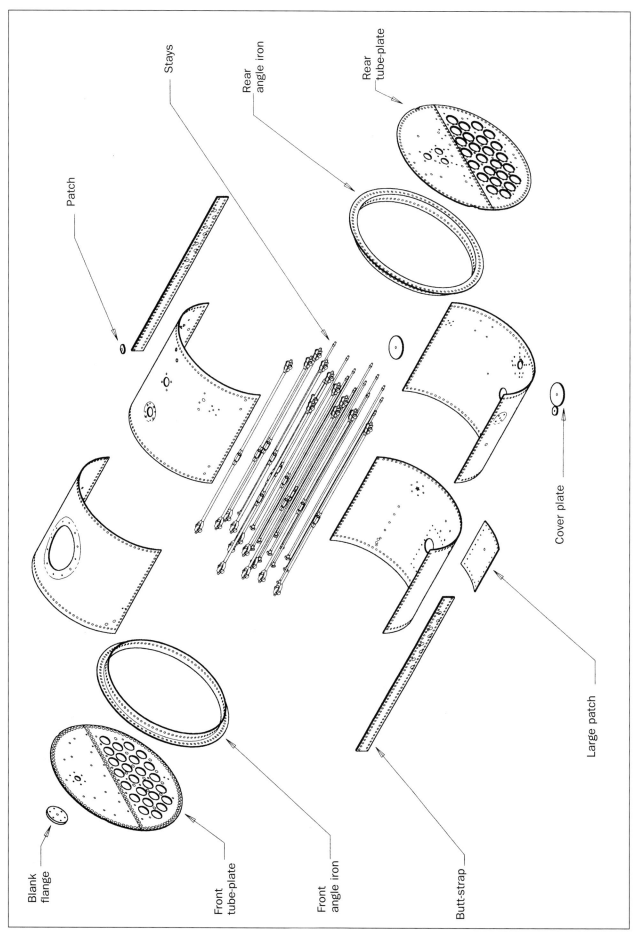

Patch

Stays

Rear
angle iron

Rear
tube-plate

Cover plate

Large patch

Butt-strap

Front
angle iron

Front
tube-plate

Blank
flange

Drawing 4.19 Boiler, exploded view
Projection: isometric, upper rear left *Scale:* 1:30

4.3.7 Rear wheel-set

Rocket's rear wheel-set did not survive through to 1862. It may well have been removed at Kirkhouse and reused as a replacement set for a wagon. As part of the 1862 restoration, Robert Stephenson & Co. fitted a spare wagon wheel-set with curved spokes, with which the locomotive was first displayed at South Kensington. In 1892, the South Kensington Museum replaced the wheel-set with another which was regarded as being more in keeping with the locomotive (Section 3.10). This cast-iron replacement set, now fitted to *Rocket*, was bought from H & S Barker & Co. Ltd, of the Don Iron & Wheel Works, Mexbro', South Yorkshire for £5.[18]

The Museum file note states that the wheels were nearly identical to the original ones. However, this set has eight-spoked ribbed wheels instead of ones with twelve unribbed spokes as portrayed on the 'Thompson'/'Stephenson' drawings (Figs 3.14 and 3.15, p107), and is therefore not an accurate portrayal. In the absence of the rear bearings and spring sets (Section 4.2.6), the weight is carried by simple wooden spacer blocks.

4.3.8 Splashers

The 'Crewe' drawing (Fig. 3.11 and detail Fig. 4.15, p109) shows that *Rocket* was fitted with splashers to both pairs of wheels at the end of its service on the L&MR. These had been removed by the end of its service on the Naworth collieries railway (Figs 3.14–3.15). The method of fixing them is uncertain, but surviving 'U'-bolts on the motion 'spectacle' brackets (Drawing 4.36) may be examples of the way in which they were secured.

4.4 Boiler

4.4.1 Boiler barrel

The surviving boiler is that which was made for *Rocket* in 1829 (Drawing 4.18). The 3-ft 4-in. diameter × 6-feet long barrel is formed of 'Best RB' rolled wrought-iron plate acquired from Joseph and William Bennitt of Dudley in Staffordshire (Section 3.3) at a cost of 11/- per hundredweight.[19] It has a composite formation of lap and strap riveting, which was common to the Stephenson company at this time. Other surviving boilers which have a similar formation are those on *Invicta* and 'John Bull'.[20]

The barrel is formed of four plates, each approximately 62 in. x 36 in., the two rear ones being riveted to the front plates with single-rivet lap joints (Drawing 4.19). The thickness of the plate is slightly more than $1/4$ in.[21] The top and bottom plates are riveted together, along the boiler centre-line, with a continuous butt-strap, with a 1-in. gap left between them. The straps are riveted with a single row to each plate. All the boiler rivets are 'cheese-head' on the inside, with hand-closed conical heads, between 1- and $1\frac{1}{8}$-in. diameter, on the outside. Whilst the forward end of the straps have conical rivets, those at the rear are probably counter-sunk rivets, being covered by the remaining lengths of the original cylinder-mounting plates (Section 4.9.1). The latter are bolted through the straps and the gap between the plate-ends and secured with nuts (Fig. 4.22, p110).

Because of the butt and strap formation, the completed barrel is not a true cylinder, the vertical dimension being $1/2$-in. greater than the horizontal diameter. A $3\frac{1}{4}$ in. x $2\frac{1}{2}$ in. angle iron is riveted to the front and rear edges of the barrel, to which the tube-plates were fitted (Section 4.4.2).

The hoop stress in the boiler-shell plates would have been about 1.79 ton/sq.in. In 1838 Fairbairn estimated that the ultimate tensile strength of Staffordshire plate to be about $19\frac{1}{2}$ ton/sq.in. in the direction of the fibre, and 21 ton/sq.in. across the fibre.

The factor of safety would therefore have been about eleven, a little lower than the normal for the time, which was twelve. Fairbairn, however, in calculating the strength of a boiler took into consideration the loss of metal due to the rivet holes and he would have rated a 3 ft 4-in.-diameter, single riveted boiler, with $1/4$-in. plates, at 35 lb/sq.in.[22]

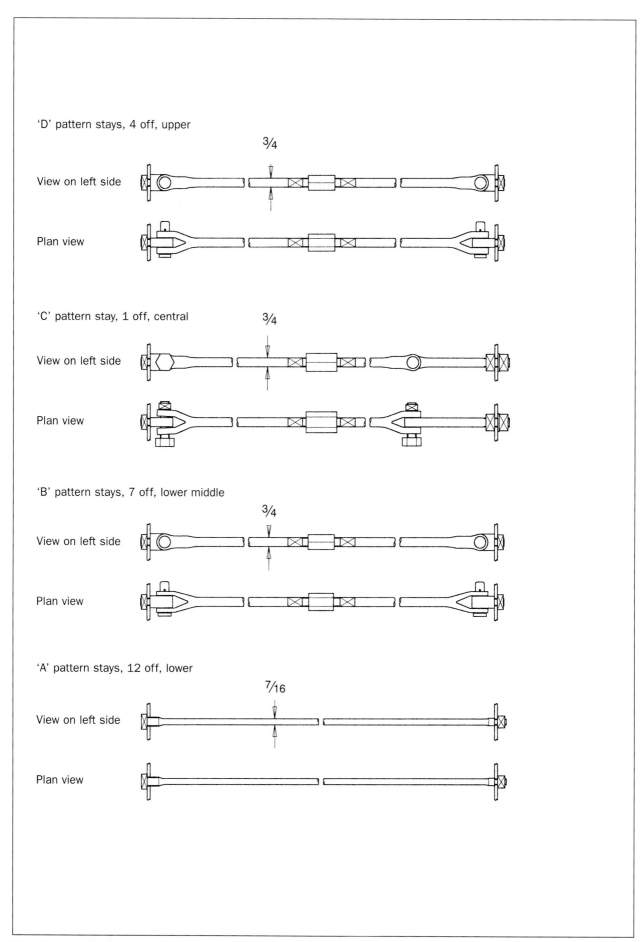

'D' pattern stays, 4 off, upper

View on left side

Plan view

'C' pattern stay, 1 off, central

View on left side

Plan view

'B' pattern stays, 7 off, lower middle

View on left side

Plan view

'A' pattern stays, 12 off, lower

View on left side

Plan view

Drawing 4.20 Boiler stays
Projection: 1st angle *Scale:* 1:8 *Dimensions:* inches

Writing near the end of the wrought-iron era of boilermaking, Burgh would have rated such a boiler at 55 lb/sq.in.[23]

The barrel is mounted onto the frame on two forward wrought-iron plate brackets and two rear cast-iron brackets (Section 4.2.7). Whereas the forward brackets are secured by bolts into tapped holes in the boiler plate, the rear bracket bolts are secured by nuts on the boiler interior (Fig. 4.23, p110). No allowance was made for thermal expansion.

4.4.2 Tube-plates

The front and rear tube-plates are each formed of two wrought-iron semi-circular plates, also slightly more than 1/4-in. thick (Drawings 4.32 and 4.33 *post*).[24] The plates were again supplied by Joseph and William Bennitt.[25] The front and rear bottom semi-circles were probably clamped together in order to drill, simultaneously, the 25-in. x 3-in.-diameter tube holes. The plates were then riveted to the upper semi-circles to form the 44-in.-diameter front and rear tube-plates, which were, in turn, riveted to the angle irons around the ends of the boiler barrel. Each plate had a number of fittings (Sections 4.7.10 and 4.7.11), in addition to the tubes and boiler stays, as shown in Fig. 4.24, p111.

4.4.3 Boiler stays

There are four kinds of longitudinal stay-rods fitted to *Rocket*'s boiler, indicating separate events in the strengthening of the tube-plates (Drawing 4.20).

The twelve stays in the lower part of the boiler, within the tube cluster ('A' pattern), are probably those inserted by Robert Stephenson and his team at Newcastle following the deflection of the tube-plate during the testing of the boiler in August 1829 (Section 3.3). The 7/16-in.-diameter stays were forged to form 'bolt-heads' with screwed shanks at the smokebox end, whilst the firebox end was secured to its tube-plate against forged 'shoulders'. A threaded extension from these shoulders, which passed through the tube-plate, was tightened with a nut.

The remainder of the surviving stays are similar to those employed on most subsequent locomotive boilers, being removable when required for maintenance. There is no evidence to indicate when they were fitted, but they were probably inserted in Liverpool, either by Foster & Griffin (Section 3.7), or by the L&MR itself after 1832, when its Edge Hill workshops were equipped to carry out the work. It is also possible that some replacements were carried out at Kirkhouse in the latter part of *Rocket*'s working life.

These later stays, which are 3/4-in. in diameter, were forged in two lengths, each with jaws at the outer end and threaded at the centre. Eyes with threaded tails were inserted through holes in the tube-plates and held with nuts on the exterior. The stays were fitted to the eyes with round-headed clevis pins inserted through the jaws and secured with cotter pins. The threaded ends were joined and adjusted with turnbuckles.

These stays, which are substantially stronger, were either replacements for those of the earlier 'A' pattern, or were additional stays which were found to be necessary. There are three variations of pattern, indicating that they were inserted on different occasions. The four 'D' pattern stays have thicker jaws than the seven 'B' pattern ones, whilst the sole example of the 'C' pattern has a much longer eye at the firebox end, a larger turnbuckle and hexagon bolts and nuts in place of the clevis pins. The four different patterns of stays are shown in Fig. 4.25, p111.

4.4.4 Boiler cladding

It is likely that *Rocket*'s boiler was clad with wood when first manufactured. Robert Stephenson was still considering the options for boiler cladding whilst the locomotive was being built when, on 3 August 1829, he wrote: 'The barrel might be covered with something like the body of a coach' (Section 3.3).

When James Scott Walker wrote about the railway and its locomotives in August 1830, he commented that:[26]

The boiler, a cylinder placed horizontally and longitudinally, and cased with wood or copper, occupies nearly the whole length and bulk of the machine.

The use of copper cladding is a reference to *Northumbrian*, thus inferring the use of wood on *Rocket* and the later *Rocket*-type locomotives. Clayton's *c*.1830 sketch (Fig. 3.3) suggests the use of cladding, but the earliest confirmed illustration of slatted-wood cladding is the 'Crewe' drawing (Fig. 3.11). The only surviving evidence of *Rocket*'s cladding, which could have been inserted when built or during its career, are single holes on the leading end of the front boiler-support brackets, which were used to secure the forward cladding band (Fig. 4.45, p113). This suggests that cladding was omitted from the underside of the boiler, which would, in any case, have provided only about 1 in. of clearance above the eccentrics before allowance for spring movement.

A small, charred piece of wood lagging was found on *Rocket* during the research which preceded the design for the 1929 'Ford' replica (Appendix 6).[27] It was grooved on each edge for the insertion of a 'slip' tongue, and when cleaned was found to be painted green. Regrettably, the whereabouts of this piece are not now known.

4.5 *Boiler water level and steam collection*

4.5.1 *Priming*

A principal defect of the earliest main-line locomotives, including *Rocket*, was their propensity to 'prime', due to the regulator drawing water as well as steam directly from the open steam-space in the boiler. In 1838, Robert Armstrong, who had much experience of boilers, wrote of 'the many curious contrivances adopted from time to time to prevent the priming of the boilers' on the Liverpool & Manchester locomotives.[28] He went on to expand on the problem:

> ...if we attempt to use the steam at a moderate pressure, although fully equivalent to a reasonable speed, there is the constant liability of the water to prime over into the cylinder, from whence it is forced, by successive blows of the pistons, through the funnel of the chimney, to the great detriment of the whole of the machinery... in fact, when the boiler primes, the piston is acting for some time like the ram of a powerful force pump or water engine, and the resulting effect must depend upon the acquired momentum or velocity of the engine at the time, and the strength of the parts. Any one may observe the effects of a locomotive engine priming, in a fine shower of spray from the top of the funnel, immediately on reaching the bottom of any considerable inclined plane, unless the speed is previously slackened or the regulator used with extreme care.

Rocket's boiler barrel was similar to that of the preceding Stephenson-built locomotives, notably *Lancashire Witch*, save for the substitution of the multiple tubes for a single return or twin flues (Fig. 2.3). Their relatively slow rate of steam generation had, however, also limited the priming of their boilers.

With all the development work carried out in great haste to achieve a reliable boiler for *Rocket* during 1829, it is likely that efforts to minimise priming, which would arise from its much higher rate of steam generation, were limited to the fitting of a short steam 'riser'. This was probably fitted just inside the rear tube-plate, to which it would have been bolted with the regulator fixing bolts (Section 4.7.9).

To understand the measures that were taken by the L&MR to overcome the priming problem, evidence was obtained during the survey of the improvements that were made to the means by which the steam was conveyed to the regulator, and the further benefits that were derived from the raising of the water level in the boiler.

4.5.2 *Inspection hole, dome and internal steam pipe*

The top centre-line of *Rocket*'s leading barrel-plate has an oval inspection hole, 14¾ in. long x 11¾ in. across. It is surrounded by the witness of a 4¾-in.-wide flange and by twelve tapped holes. Four studs and one nut remain in place, whilst a further eight broken studs are also present. It is most likely that the hole and its door were inserted, at the time of the locomotive's manufacture, in order to provide access to the interior

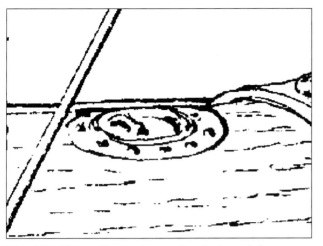

Fig. 4.26 View of boiler inspection hole and door on *Northumbrian*

Source: James Nasmyth sketch

Fig. 4.28 Detail of boiler-top in 1829, showing safety-valve locations

Source: Nicholas Wood, Fig. 3.6

for maintenance and modification. A contemporary view of the inspection hole and door on *Northumbrian*[29] shows the form that may have been taken on *Rocket* (Fig. 4.26).

A similar inspection hole, but of smaller dimensions, can be seen on the front barrel-plate of *Invicta*. A comparison between the two holes is shown in Fig. 4.27, p111.

The inspection hole on *Invicta* is now built up with an unusual circumferential ring to which the door is bolted, but this may be a replacement from some unknown period during its many years of preservation. There is no evidence that such an arrangement was used on *Rocket*, whose oval hole suggests that the original door may have been inserted and turned through 90° to form an inner seal, as was common practice for mud-hole doors. There is, however, no witness of the use of bridge-bars. Although lacking detail and accuracy, the earliest drawings of *Rocket* show that the forward of its two safety valves was first fitted in what would seem to be the inspection-hole door (Fig. 4.28).

Although a number of later locomotives (for example the L&MR's *Lion* of 1838) had safety valves fitted to inspection-hole doors, such a feature on *Rocket* would have been an early example of such practice. This safety valve was probably the 'lock-up' valve required by the 'Stipulations and Conditions' of the Rainhill Trials (Appendix 1) to be 'completely out of the control of the engine-man', and which was referred to, but without description, by John Rastrick in October 1829.[30]

Rocket was not fitted with a dome when first built. The portrayal of 'as-built' replica *Rocket* locomotives with a brass dome first arose·from the use of the incorrect Wardale drawings of 1858 (Figs 3.16 and 3.17) which were adopted for the first replica, built in the London & North Western Railway's Crewe workshops in 1881. The aesthetic appeal of the dome has led to its inclusion on all subsequent replicas, including the 1979 version.[31]

There is no evidence to suggest that the four *Rocket*-type locomotives constructed by the Stephenson company in early 1830 (Fig. 2.8) were fitted with domes. However, perhaps arising from the priming problems on these Liverpool & Manchester locomotives, *Invicta*, manufactured by Robert Stephenson & Co. for the Canterbury & Whitstable line and delivered in April 1830, appears to have been fitted with the earliest form of external 'riser', being a manifold above the boiler, feeding dryer steam to the cylinders (Fig. 4.29, p112).

The earliest drawing of a dome and internal steam pipe on a locomotive on the L&MR was that fitted to *Phoenix*, delivered in June 1830 (Fig. 4.30). The subsequent locomotives were all fitted with domes (Figs 2.11 and 2.12), and it would seem that, after five months experience of significantly reduced priming, *Rocket* was also fitted with a dome in November 1830. Rather than cut another hole in *Rocket*'s boiler-top, it

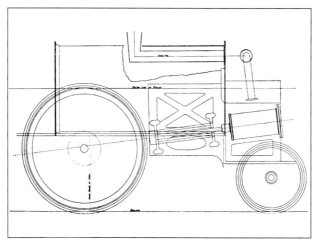

Fig. 4.30 Drawing of *Phoenix* as built in June 1830
Source: as for Fig. 2.10

was decided to remove the inspection-hole door and safety valve and fit a conversion collar on which to locate the round dome. In the absence of secondary fixing holes, it would seem that the collar was bolted in place, as now determined by the surviving studs and stud-holes.

Within the dome there would have been a steam 'riser', being the forward end of a steam pipe feeding steam directly to the regulator, replacing the earlier short riser. The remains of a support bracket within the boiler survive on the rear two inspection-hole studs. The steam pipe would therefore have been similar to that shown on the *Phoenix* drawing. The dome and the internal steam pipe, were probably fitted by Foster & Griffin of Liverpool (Section 3.7).

The dome may have been made of cast- or wrought-iron as, following the Wigan Branch accident of November 1832, John Melling was reprimanded for having adopted 'unnecessary ornamental Brass Work' in the repairs he supervised the following month. This may have been a reference either to the replacement of the first dome, or by its being covered, by one made of brass. The first illustration of *Rocket* after these repairs was not until the 'Crewe' drawing of 1836. Both this and the 'Thompson'/'Stephenson' drawings of *c.* 1840 (Figs 3.14 and 3.15) show identical brass dome-covers, which was presumably that fitted at the end of 1832 (Fig. 4.31, p112).

4.5.3 *Water sight-gauges and gauge cocks*

The evidence relating to the boiler water level is provided by the positioning of its gauge cock (try-cock) and sight-gauge holes. *Rocket* may have been fitted with a sight gauge, as well as gauge cocks, when it was first constructed. The early use of a sight gauge was noted by a contemporary observer, possibly referring to *Rocket*:[32]

> ...and there was a small glass tube affixed to the boiler, with water in it, which indicates by its fullness or emptiness when the creature wants water...

The *Northumbrian* was fitted with a sight gauge when sketched by James Nasmyth in September 1830 (Fig. 4.32).[33] However, Isaac Boulton 'was inclined to think that glass water gauge was not in existence; most certainly it was not on the Rocket in the form shown [by Nasmyth]'.[34]

There are twin sets of holes for a sight gauge and its flanges on the right side of the boiler which have been plugged and painted over. They are difficult to see from the exterior (Fig. 4.33, p112), but the residual studs and plug are prominent on the inside of the barrel.

The corresponding twin gauge cocks were located at the leading end of the boiler on the left side. Although this would have been beyond the reach of the fireman when the locomotive was in motion, it may perhaps have provided an additional means with which to check on water level when it was stationary for long periods, and was required to run up and down the track to activate the feed-water pumps. Twin gauge cocks had similarly been fitted into the front boiler-plate on *Lancashire Witch* (Fig. 4.34).

It would seem, however, that *Rocket*'s sight gauge and gauge cocks were replaced by a new sight gauge and gauge-cock cluster to provide for a higher water level, probably in November 1830, at the same time as the installation of the steam dome. The replacement sight gauge was fitted to the left side of the locomotive. Although the 'Crewe' drawing of 1836 (Fig. 3.11) strangely omits this fitting, it is shown on the *c*.1840 'Thompson' / 'Stephenson' drawings (Fig. 4.35, p112).

A trio of gauge cocks was fitted to the right side of the boiler (Fig. 4.33, p112), probably at the same time.

4.5.4 *Water level*

The evidence from the survey suggests that priming had been anticipated when *Rocket* was built, as the working range of the water in the boiler, as determined by the original left-side gauge cock fittings, was between 3 in. and 5 in. above the boiler's centre-line (Drawing 4.21). It must be noted here that the positioning of the bottom flange of the original right-side sight gauge was restricted from being centrally located, in relation to

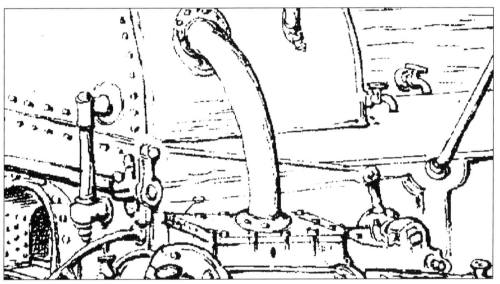

Fig. 4.32 Sight and gauge cocks fitted to *Northumbrian* in September 1830
Source: Nasmyth sketch

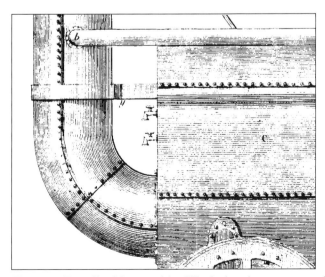

Fig. 4.34 Detail of *Lancashire Witch* showing gauge cocks on front boiler-plate
Source: Coste and Perdonnet, 'Sur les chemins a ornières', *Annales des Mines*, Vol. VI, 1829
Fig. XXX, plate IX, p288

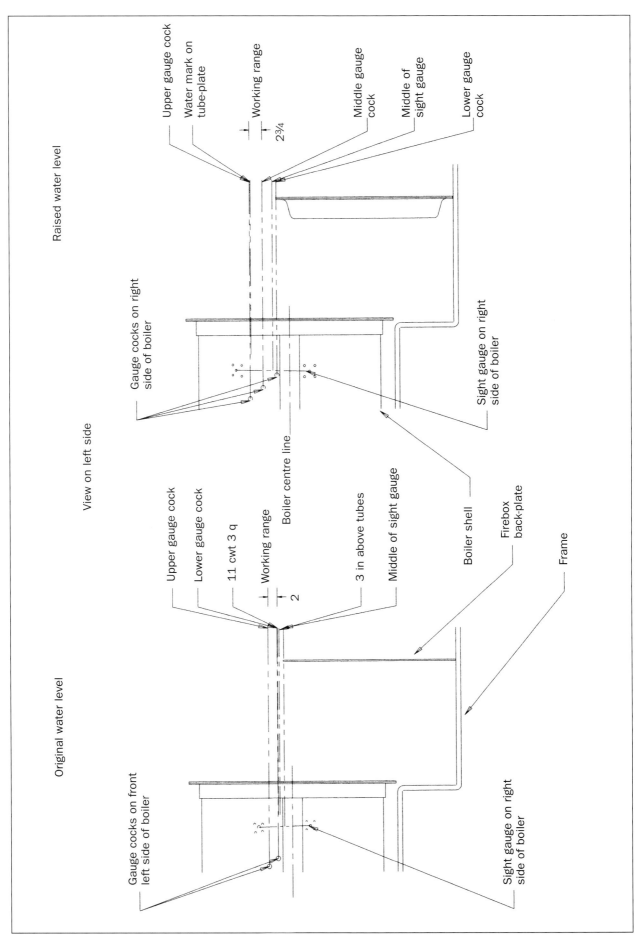

Drawing 4.21 Water levels in boiler
Scale: 1:20 *Dimensions:* inches

the water level, by the boiler strap. The mean level, 4 in. above the boiler's centre-line, would therefore have appeared in the upper part of the gauge rather than the middle.[35]

When John Rastrick inspected the boiler in October 1829, he estimated that 'the highest row [of tubes] is about three Inches below the surface of the Water when the boiler has its complement of Water in it.'[36] Three inches would place the water level at about the same as that of the lower gauge cock. Further confirmation is provided from Robert Stephenson's estimate of the weight of the water in the boiler at 11 cwt. 3 qr., which he made on 3 August 1829 (Section 3.3). The level of water equivalent to this weight is approximately in line with the lower gauge cock.

It is thus evident from the later fitting of the three gauge cocks on the right side of the boiler, that the working range of the water level was raised to between $5\frac{3}{4}$ in. and $8\frac{1}{2}$ in. above the boiler centre-line. This would have been undertaken to ensure a greater depth of water over the firebox crown, which suggests that there had been fears in this regard during *Rocket*'s initial period of operation. The higher range, resulting in an increase of 3in. to the mean water level to about 7 in. above the centre-line, was also covered by the replacement water gauge on the left side of the barrel. However, as with the earlier sight-gauge, the boiler strap prevented its central fitting, and the waterline would have appeared in the upper part of the gauge.

The opportunity to raise the water level was probably taken in November 1830 after the Chat Moss accident (Section 3.7), when the priming problem appears to have been reduced with the fitting of the dome and internal steam pipe, and the water-jacketed firebox back-plate was fitted (Section 4.6.3).

The survey also revealed a 'waterline' on the front tube-plate, $8\frac{3}{8}$ in. above the boiler centre-line, about the upper working level during the latter part of the locomotive's career. This line would seem to represent the limit of the turbulent water, however, rather than the nominal upper level of still water (See Fig. 4.50, p114).

4.6 Firebox

4.6.1 Configuration

When *Rocket* was being manufactured and assembled in the summer of 1829, the requirement to provide a separate fireplace outside the boiler barrel was met by making a 'box' from three component parts, bolted to both the barrel and the rear of the main frame. The latter was stepped down by $12\frac{1}{2}$ in. to accommodate a larger heating surface and to place the grate below the bottom tube-line (Drawing 4.22).

To achieve primary heating of the water, before the flue gases passed through the boiler's multiple tubes, the external 'box' required a water jacket to receive the radiant heat from the fire, water feed-pipes from the boiler and steam pipes to communicate the generated steam back into the boiler's steam space. With the limited time available to achieve this requirement, George and Robert Stephenson limited the water jacket to a form of 'saddle' encompassing the crown and two sides only.

The front and back plates of the box were plain wrought-iron 'dry' plates, the former fitted beneath the boiler tube-cluster, whilst the latter fitted the profile of the 'saddle'. Heat loss from both these plates was limited by a firebrick lining, being a practice then regularly employed in stationary steam engine boilers. The saddle was bolted to the rear tube-plate, and to the firebox front and back-plates, by angle irons. The fire rested on bars placed over cross-bearers between the frame members.

4.6.2 Firebox saddle

Following the Stephensons' discussion in Liverpool on its form, the saddle was ordered from James Leishman and John Welsh, coppersmiths of Redcross Street, Liverpool (Section 3.3). It was delivered to Newcastle in August 1829 for a cost of £58 2s 0d.[37] The saddle was formed of two copper plates, being either $\frac{3}{8}$-in. or $\frac{1}{4}$-in. thick, chosen because of their good heat conductivity. Copper plate of this thickness was not normally available at this time and would have had to have been specially produced.[38]

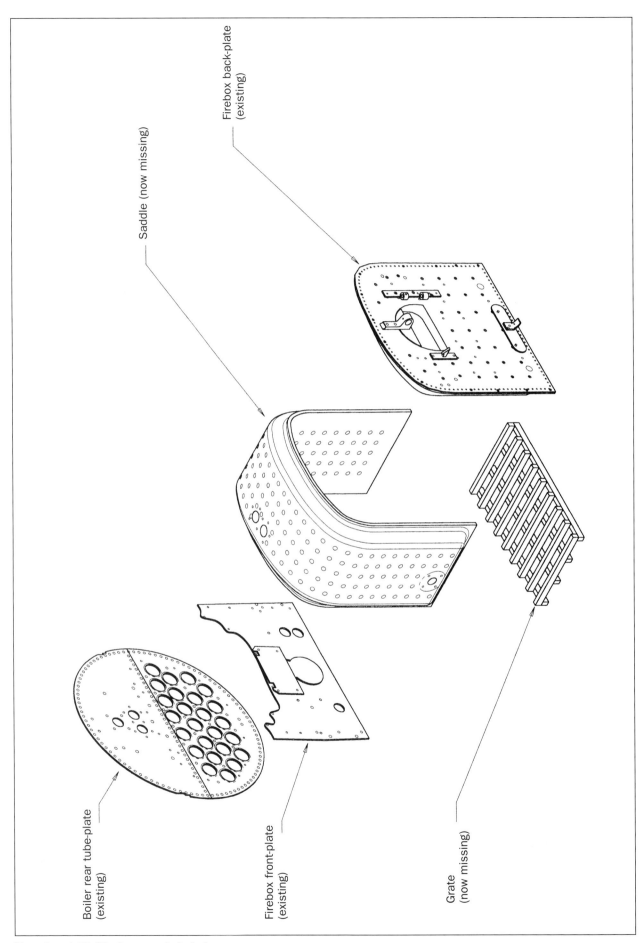

Saddle (now missing)

Firebox back-plate
(existing)

Boiler rear tube-plate
(existing)

Firebox front-plate
(existing)

Grate
(now missing)

Drawing 4.22 Firebox, exploded view
Projection: isometric view, upper rear left *Scale:* 1:20

There is a tradition in BICC Limited that one of its Group Companies, Thomas Bolton & Sons, established in New Street, Birmingham in 1823, supplied the copper plate for the firebox. Although Boltons would have been a likely source, it has not been possible to verify this claim.[39]

Rastrick described the saddle as having a 3-in. water space, with stays being fitted with a pitch of 3 in.[40] Nearly thirty years later however, J D Wardale wrote that the water space was 2½ in., the inference being that 3 in. was the external dimension, which some other authors have copied.[41] The saddle had, however, been closely examined and described by John Rastrick in his notebook when he saw *Rocket* in October 1829:[42]

> The Rocket has a small Boiler of the figure and dimentions annexed in the Margin, which is constantly kept full of Water this serves for the Fire Place, the Grate being three feet wide and two feet long, with an area of six feet square, which gives 6/10 of a square foot of firegrate for each horse Power. The surface of this Boiler exposed to the action of the fire is 18 square feet. It is made of Copper and the flat sides are strengthened by distance Pieces and Rivetts at every three Inches, in each direction. By this means a large fire surface is obtained and a great strength is given to the Boiler, the principal objection to this construction is the difficulty of getting at the inside to clean it out. The sediment from the Water will mostly settle to the Bottom into the narrow part where it is rivetted together, but the Scurf or calcarious encrustation will affix itself to all parts of the Inside of the Boiler.
>
> It is proposed to clear out the sediment by making a small Hole on each side towards the Bottom to get the hand in, but as the distance between the Sides of the Boiler is only three Inches, and as there are so many distance pieces in the way, the withdrawing of the Sediment will be a tedious and difficult operation and the Scurf cannot be effectually scaled from off the inside of the Boiler, without taking it to pieces. How often this may require to be done must depend entirely on the nature of the Water, with which the Boiler is fed and can only be learned from experience.

The evidence from *Rocket*'s surviving components shows that the saddle was fitted by an angle iron to the rear tube-plate, and to both sides of the firebox front-plate. In addition, the rear frame members show evidence that the bottom of the firebox had also been attached to angle irons, each being secured to the outer edge of the frame members by three bolts. The angle irons and bolts were shown on the earliest drawings of *Rocket* (albeit with four bolts not three), as seen in the detailed view (Fig. 4.36).

The saddle has not survived and was probably removed for scrap during the period *Rocket* was laid up at Kirkhouse (Section 3.10). Since the locomotive's preservation and display, the precise appearance of the firebox has been the subject of much debate. The most considered view was formed by the three consultant historians and Robert Stephenson & Co. Ltd, prior to the manufacture of the 'Ford' replica locomotive in 1929.[43] Evidence relating to the firebox was brought together and assessed in a typed, limited-circulation report that was written by the Stephenson company to accompany the first replica to the Henry Ford Museum in 1929.[44]

In the knowledge that the plates were riveted together along their edges, the debate on the shape of the plates centred on whether the outer, the inner, or both of the plates were arched to provide the stayed water-space. The latter form was selected for the Henry Ford and subsequent replicas, including the 1979 replica now employed at the National Railway Museum. The reasons for selecting the 'double arch' form, which are outlined in the 1929 report, were based on a consideration of the boiler water level and the outline form of the surviving back-plate (Drawing 4.23).

The consultants' conclusion is, however, at variance with the form of the firebox as seen and sketched by John Rastrick in October 1829 when the locomotive was newly constructed. The sketches show that the inner plate was flat around the crown and two sides. The outer plate, however, was formed into an arched shape to provide the water space and edge-riveting to the inner plate (Fig. 4.37).

Having misread the evidence relating to the water level (Section 4.5.4, Note 35), the consultants sought to place the firebox crown too low. They correctly took the profile of the surviving back-plate, to which the saddle had been bolted with an angle iron, as

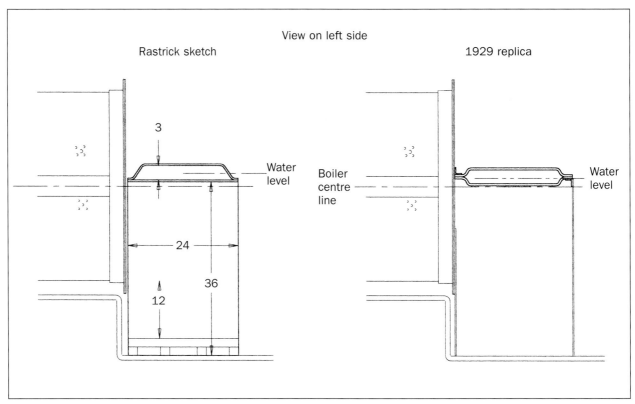

Drawing 4.23 Firebox, Rastrick sketch and 1929 replica
Scale: 1:20 *Dimensions:* inches

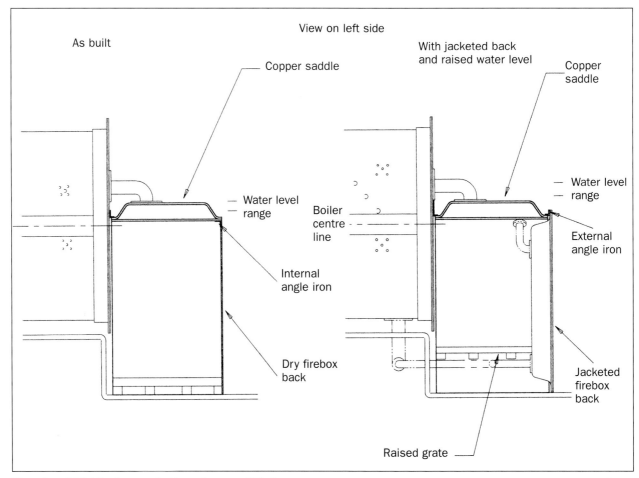

Drawing 4.24 Firebox, as built and as modified
Scale: 1:20

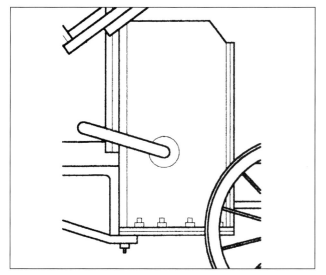

Fig. 4.36 Detail of 1829 drawings of *Rocket*'s firebox
Source: Re-drawn from *Mechanics Magazine* 1829, Fig. 3.4

Fig. 4.38 Detail view of *Rocket*'s firebox
Source: Henry Booth, Fig 3.5

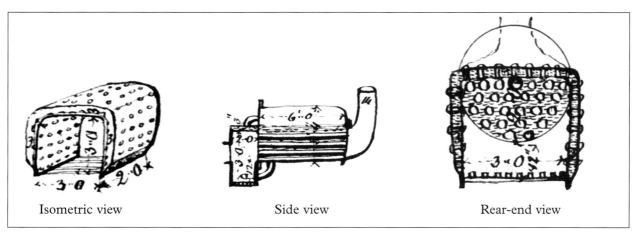

| Isometric view | Side view | Rear-end view |

Fig. 4.37 *Rocket*'s firebox as sketched by John Rastrick, 5 October 1829
Source: Notebook, Science Museum, inv. no. 1945-108

one of the constraints in deciding on the shape and position of the saddle. In order to reconcile the crown level with the higher back-plate, however, they reasoned that both saddle-plates were arched, each by 1½ in. This shape did not conform with Rastrick's sketches, which the consultants therefore believed to be in error through their interpretation of the surviving evidence.

Taking Rastrick's sketch and data to be correct, the firebox saddle would have taken the form shown in Drawing 4.24, namely a flat inner plate and arched outer plate. The water gauge evidence confirms that the crown would have been covered by a minimum of 1¾ in. of water. It is likely that the original 'dry' back-plate was fitted to the back edge of the saddle with an angle iron set inside the firebox.

An important conclusion, confirmed by this drawing, is that the rear arched face of the crown rose by the full 3 in., thus giving rise to a pronounced back-head slope, further emphasised by the small back-plate. Although this relationship accords well with the earliest drawings of *Rocket* (Fig. 4.36), the slope became exaggerated in Booth's 1830 volume on the L&MR (Fig. 4.38).

This would appear to be the origin of the 'sloping back' which some of the older members of staff of Robert Stephenson & Co. had recalled in later years.
The preparation of the 1858 drawings by J D Wardale (Figs 3.16 and 3.17) was dependent upon memories dating back twenty-nine years, which, like Booth's book, had apparently exaggerated the extent of the slope, and which has led to much confusion since that time.

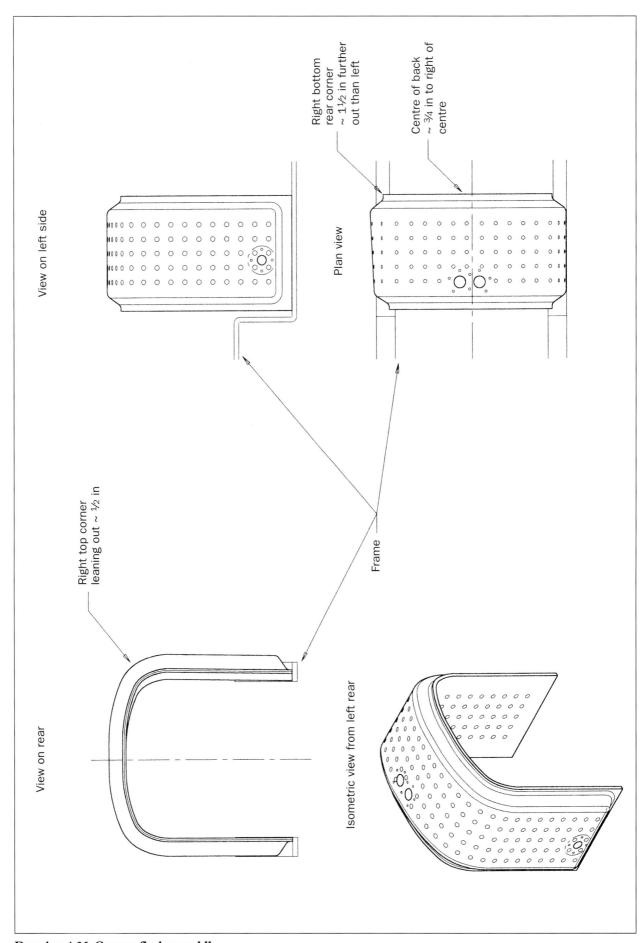

View on left side

Plan view

Right bottom rear corner ~ 1½ in further out than left

Centre of back ~ ¾ in to right of centre

Right top corner leaning out ~ ½ in

Frame

View on rear

Isometric view from left rear

Drawing 4.25 Copper firebox saddle
Projection: 1st angle *Scale:* 1:20 *Dimensions:* inches

When the replacement back-plate was fitted, probably in February 1831, it was made to a higher profile than the original dry back-plate. To be fitted to the saddle edge, therefore, would have required an angle iron on the upper face of the saddle and the inner face of the back-plate (Drawing 4.24). The later views of the firebox shown in the 'Crewe' (Fig. 3.11) and 'Thompson'/'Stephenson' drawings (Figs 3.14 and 3.15), suggests that cosmetic bands were fitted at some stage over both the back-plate and tube-plate angle irons.

There are two arcs of studs (the upper set having nuts on the inside) on the rear tube-plate providing evidence of an alteration to the fitting of the saddle's leading edge angle iron. It would appear that the lower arc was for the first fitting, the possible failure of which may have prompted its replacement by the upper arc, for which a larger angle iron would have been required. The possibility that the saddle had been raised at some stage is not, however, feasible as it would have resulted in insufficient water over the crown. The two arcs of studs are shown in Fig. 4.39, p112.

When the saddle was delivered to Newcastle in August 1829, Robert Stephenson reported that it was 'not quite square built' (Section 3.3). From the evidence of the surviving back-plate, which was made to fit the saddle's profile, and the later placement of the cylinder mounting plates (Section 4.2.8), which now provide a 'footprint' of the missing saddle, it is possible to determine the extent of this misalignment (Drawing 4.25). It is apparent that the rear of the saddle was offset to the right of the locomotive's centre-line by 1 in. It is also apparent, from the two steam pipe holes and the saddle angle-iron holes in the rear tube-plate, that the saddle leaned to the right at the front by between $1/2$ in and $3/4$ in. The asymmetry of the firebox in turn affected the fitting of the right-side cylinder mounting plate, probably in February 1831, which was correspondingly fitted further from the centre-line than the left-side plate.

4.6.3 Back-plate

The surviving wrought-iron, water-jacketed back-plate was probably made and fitted to *Rocket* by Foster & Griffin in November 1830, following the Chat Moss accident (Section 3.7). The back-plate is of riveted construction, formed as a stayed water-jacket, the back-head being flat and the inner plate being arched (Drawing. 4.26). It is biased to the right side, having followed the profile of the saddle, to which it was attached with an angle iron around its two sides and crown (Fig. 4.40, p112).

Some of the peripheral rivets have been drilled out to accommodate the angle-iron fixing bolts. Most of these holes now contain lead plugs, being the remains of lead rivets probably inserted during the 1862 restoration to secure a sheet iron replica of the missing saddle. The locomotive was exhibited with this sheet until it was removed, prior to 1922, by the Science Museum apparently cutting through the lead rivets. There is no file note in the Museum's technical file to confirm the date of removal (Section 3.10).

The semi-circular fire-hole rim is formed of riveted angle irons and a forged collar. The upper portion of the hole was fouled by the valve gear rocking-shaft, which was probably repositioned in February 1831, only three months after the new back-plate had been fitted (Section 4.10.3). The top of the firehole was blanked off with an iron sheet, which was bolted into place (Fig. 4.41, p112).

The fire-hole door, which was reduced in size to clear the rocking-shaft, is a simple iron plate with a latch and two riveted hinge-pieces. The hinge-eyes and catch-plate are both riveted to the back-head, the hinge-pin being made of iron. The two cross-braces between the cylinder mounting plates (Section 4.2.8), also probably fitted in February 1831, were bolted to the back-plate, the upper one fouling the lower part of the hinge eyes. There is evidence of a previous hinge and catch-plate close to that of the surviving fittings.

The water space is 3 in. and the back-plate is stayed at 5-in. intervals. There is a central horizontal mud-hole door at the bottom of the rear face of the back-plate. On either side are two wash-out holes, the left-hand one retaining its screw plug.

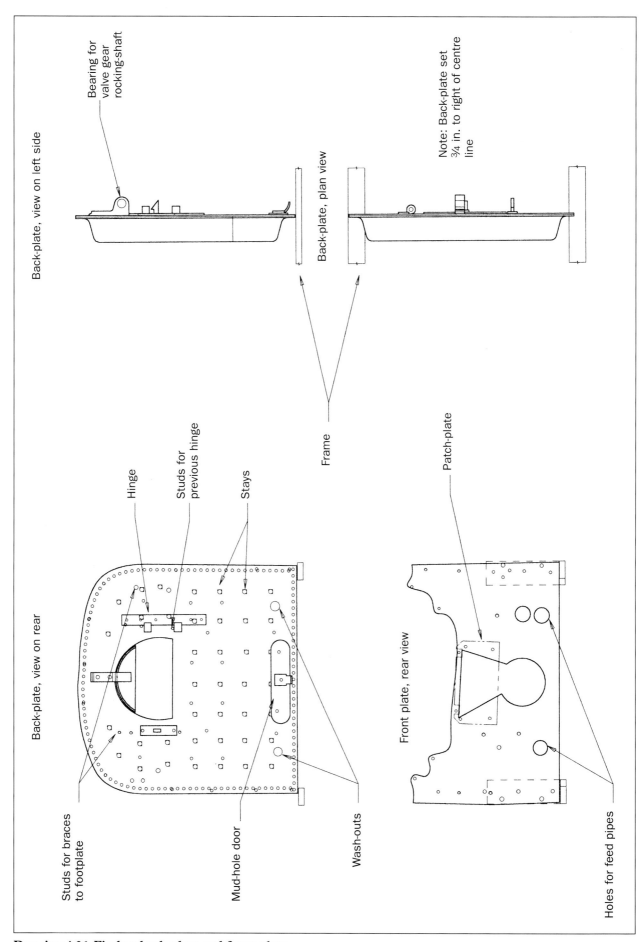

Drawing 4.26 Firebox back-plate and front-plate
Projection: 1st angle *Scale:* 1:16

The water space is remarkably free of scale, indicating the use of soft water on the Naworth collieries railway, as well as on the L&MR (Section 3.7).

Two 1¼-in.-diameter flanged holes, at 2-ft centres, were inserted in the bottom of the inner face of the back-plate. These were for feed-water pipes, which would have been routed under the raised fire-grate (Section 4.6.4). Two further holes of the same diameter and spacing were inserted at the top of the back-plate, to continue the water flow into the saddle-crown (Drawing 4.27).

4.6.4 Firebars and ashpan

No trace of the firebars or cross-bearers remain. However, from the cross-sectional view shown in John Rastrick's sketches (Fig. 4.37 above), it would seem that there were four or five cross-bearers between the frames resting on, and probably fixed to, support irons at both ends. These support irons were probably an inch wide and just rested on the inner edge of the frames, as there are no redundant holes or fixing bolts that can be attributed to them. The firebars would then have been placed over the cross-bearers to form the assembled grate. The grate was probably raised by approximately 6 in. in November 1830, to allow the water feed-pipe from the boiler to reach the bottom of the new back-plate. In the absence of any evidence on the frames, it is presumed that the support irons were correspondingly increased in height (Drawings 4.22 and 4.24).

The earliest locomotives on the L&MR were not fitted with dampers or ashpans. A fortnight before the opening of the railway, a three-train convoy of inspection was operated for the Directors and their guests. The convoy arrived back after dark, and the trains were reported to be visible 1000 yards before their arrival at Edge Hill 'by the glare of the engine fires and the issuing of burning sparks from the chimneys.'[45]

Although there was a constant danger of fires to vehicles and line-side, not until January 1833 did the railway undertake to fit 'ash-boxes' to their locomotives.[46] There was a slow response, which prompted the railway six months later to reissue their instruction to fit ash-boxes 'where practicable, and where that was not the case to fasten a wire screen behind the Tender to intercept hot cinders before they should reach the Waggons.'[47]

There is no evidence on *Rocket*'s frame of an ashpan or firebox damper fitting, and it may be the case, therefore, that by mid 1833, it was not considered worth a further modification and that, when it was employed in service, a wire screen was fitted to the tender.

4.6.5 Firebox front-plate and water feed-pipes

The firebox front-plate, which has an irregular top to fit beneath the tube cluster, was fitted by bolts into tapped holes in the rear tube-plate (Drawing 4.26). In the absence of any evidence to suggest that refitting has taken place, it was almost certainly fitted in 1829 and is, therefore, the only surviving component of the original firebox. The nominally ⁵⁄₁₆-in.-thick plate, probably supplied by the Bedlington Iron Company, has considerable wastage down to typically ¹⁄₁₆ in. and in some areas has corroded away completely. A 14-in. × 7-in. patch, which has been bolted over the corroded upper-mid-section of the plate, was probably fitted during the working life of the locomotive (Fig. 4.42, p113).

The front-plate contains three 2½-in.-diameter holes, as well as a large 8-in.-diameter hole, providing evidence of several applications. As discussed below, some of these applications may have been related to one or more of the thermodynamic experiments conducted by the L&MR in the early 1830s (Section 3.8).

When *Rocket* was first manufactured, a water feed-pipe was fitted from the boiler to the exterior of the saddle sides. Two of the earliest drawings (Fig. 4.36 and 4.38) suggest that these feed-pipes were fitted to the sides of the boiler barrel, but there is no evidence of such a fitting in those locations. It is most likely that a manifold serving the feed-pipes was fitted to the bottom centre-line of the boiler, where a

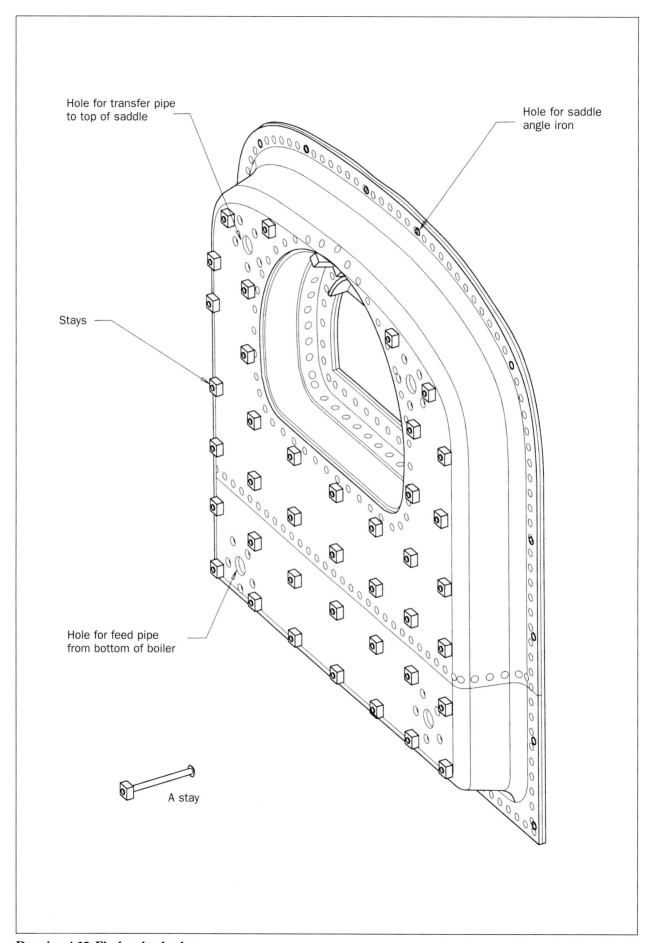

Hole for transfer pipe
to top of saddle

Hole for saddle
angle iron

Stays

Hole for feed pipe
from bottom of boiler

A stay

Drawing 4.27 Firebox back-plate
Projection: isometric view, upper front left *Scale:* 1:6

2½-in.-diameter hole (Drawing 4.29 – Section 4.7) shows evidence of an early flange fitting.

When the new back-plate was fitted, these two outside feed-pipes were probably removed and replaced by two new feed-pipes routed through the lower two of the 2½-in.-diameter holes in the firebox front-plate, and underneath the raised fire-grate. These pipes, which would have avoided some heat loss, were probably routed into the forward end of the saddle sides, with additional elbow pipes taking the water from the rear end of the saddle sides to feed the two 1¼-in.-diameter flanged holes in the bottom of the back-plate. Alternatively, the pipes may have fed the saddle-side and back-plate with a 'T'-piece.

The purpose of the large central hole and the third 2½-in.-diameter hole are not known. It is possible that they were in some way associated with the thermodynamic experiments which were undertaken in the early 1830s, but no evidence is available to support this. There is no evidence, for example, that *Rocket* was used as one of the trial locomotives for Jacob Perkins' patent water circulators of 1832 (Section 3.8). The circulators were inserted within the boiler barrels of those locomotives used for the trial to promote water movement, but there was no apparent necessity to modify the fire space. In the same year, John Melling, the Edge Hill workshop superintendent promoted his own 'improved Fire Place for a Loco motive Engine, with hollow bars, and ash pit constructed so as to form part of the Boiler.' Melling's proposal, which was eventually incorporated into his patent of 1837,[48] was a form of water pre-heater in a tank fitted under the fire bars, but *Rocket*'s configuration was too confined for this purpose and the holes in the firebox front plate were inconveniently placed for such a function. Although *Rocket* was modified for the trial of Lord Dundonald's rotary engine in 1834 (Section 3.8), there was again, by the nature of the trial, no necessity to modify the water space. In 1835 John Gray was promoting his 'Improved Furnace for Consuming Smoke and Economizing Fuel'[49], this being a form of partitioned firebox, burning coal on the main grate and coke (to consume smoke particles) on an intermediate water-tube 'shelf'. There is no evidence that such a form of firebox was ever taken up by the L&MR and, in any event, *Rocket*'s firebox was too small to incorporate even a trial of such an arrangement.

4.7 *Boiler fittings*

The steam regulator is the only boiler fitting remaining *in situ*. All other fittings have been removed, probably whilst *Rocket* was laid up at Kirkhouse, either for scrap or to be used on the other locomotives operating on the Naworth collieries railway. Drawing 4.28 shows a representation of the boiler opened out into a two-dimensional representation and showing the many holes which provide evidence of the boiler fittings. From the evidence of these holes and flange fittings, together with the early drawings of the locomotive, it is possible to ascertain the location and form of each fitting. These are considered starting from the upper part of the boiler and working down to those on the underside of the boiler, concluding with the rear and front tube-plate fittings.

4.7.1 *'Lock-up' safety valve*

Rocket was fitted with a 'lock-up' safety valve, apparently in the inspection-hole door (Section 4.5.2). According to Wardale, it was 'covered by a tin dome fastened down to the boiler by two small padlocks',[50] but this cannot be confirmed from contemporary descriptions. The valve was almost certainly spring-loaded.

Prior to *Rocket*'s completion, the Stephenson Company built the *Twin Sisters* (Fig. 2.4), which was fitted with two safety valves apparently to try out the arrangement in anticipation of the Rainhill Trial requirements. It was reported as being a safety improvement, which was:[51]

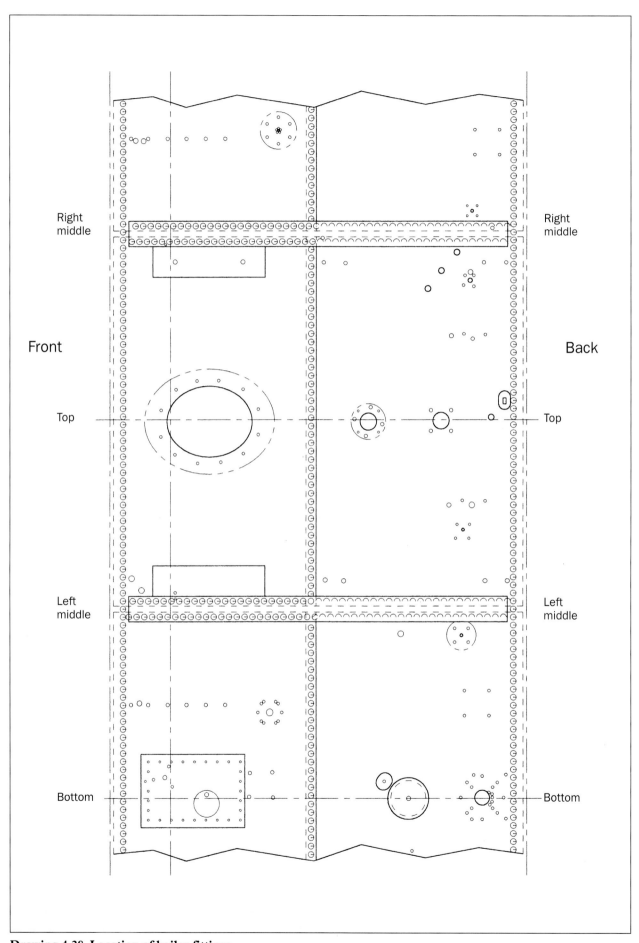

Right
middle

Right
middle

Front

Back

Top

Top

Left
middle

Left
middle

Bottom

Bottom

Drawing 4.28 Location of boiler fittings
Projection: developed *Scale:* 1:16

effected by means of two safety-valves, one of them of the ordinary kind, but the other acting by a spring, and not liable to be effected by any thing that is done by the engine-man; it is not all under his control, but will immediately remedy any carelessness of which he may be guilty.

Lancashire Witch was also fitted with a spring-loaded safety valve in September 1829, which was probably of the same design as that fitted to *Rocket*. The Stephenson Company supplied: '1 Cross Head, 2 Side Rods for Spring Safety Valve' weighing 8 lb., "12 Steel Springs for Valve" weighing 4 lb. and charged out at 4/-, and '1 Brass Safety Valve' weighing 9¼ lb. and charged out at 10/9d.[52]

When the locked safety valve was displaced from the inspection-hole door, probably in November 1830, it was relocated to a point 15 in. from the rear of the boiler (Drawing 4.29). The 2½-in.-diameter hole, flange witness and bolt holes are shown in Fig. 4.44, p113. The earliest illustration of the valve in its later position is that shown on the 'Crewe' drawing (detail in Fig. 4.43). It appears to be a simple upright cylinder, and was probably secured with a padlock. In July 1831, William Allcard, then Locomotive Superintendent, had been ordered to 'prove the correctness of the Safety Valves, on all the Locomotive Engines, and that he lock up & retain the Key of one of the Valves on each Engine...'[53] By the time *Rocket* completed its service on the Naworth collieries railway, however, the locked valve had gained a more decorative cover, apparently made of brass or copper (Fig. 4.43).

4.7.2 Lever safety valve

The second of *Rocket*'s original safety valves, fitted in the middle of the boiler-top, was a weight-loaded lever valve, of the type used on earlier Stephenson-built locomotives (for example *Lancashire Witch*, Fig. 2.3). It was drawn by John Rastrick in October 1829 as shown in Fig. 4.43. Weight-loaded valves were unsatisfactory in main-line service because they lifted and released steam with each vibration, a problem accentuated by the increased speeds of the early 1830s. The weight-loaded valve was replaced, possibly as early as November 1830, by a lever-arm spring-balance valve, being a type first fitted to *Northumbrian* in July 1830.

The first illustration of the spring-balance valve on *Rocket* is that shown on the 'Crewe' drawing of 1836. The spring-balance, shown as being fitted to the right side of the boiler barrel, seems to have been incorrectly drawn by the draughtsman as being adjacent to the rear angle iron. It is more likely to have been some 9½ in. from the boiler back-plate, however, as there is a redundant, plugged hole on the side of the boiler, above the boiler centre-line, which appears to have been the anchor point for the spring balance (Fig. 4.33, p112). A longer lever arm, with a spring balance fitted to the rear tube-plate, appears to have been fitted during the locomotive's service on the Naworth collieries railway.

The 2⅞-in.-diameter hole in the boiler-top, together with a flange witness, shows where the lever safety-valves were fitted. There are two sets of securing boltholes, confirming the substitution of the original fitting (Fig. 4.44, p113).

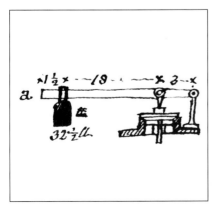  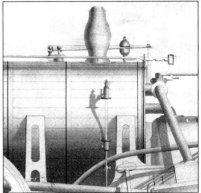

Fig. 4.43 *Rocket*'s **lever safety-valve as shown in 1829, 1836 and** *c.***1840**
Source: Rastrick's drawing, 1829; 'Crewe' drawing, 1836 and 'Thompson'/'Stephenson' drawings *c.*1840

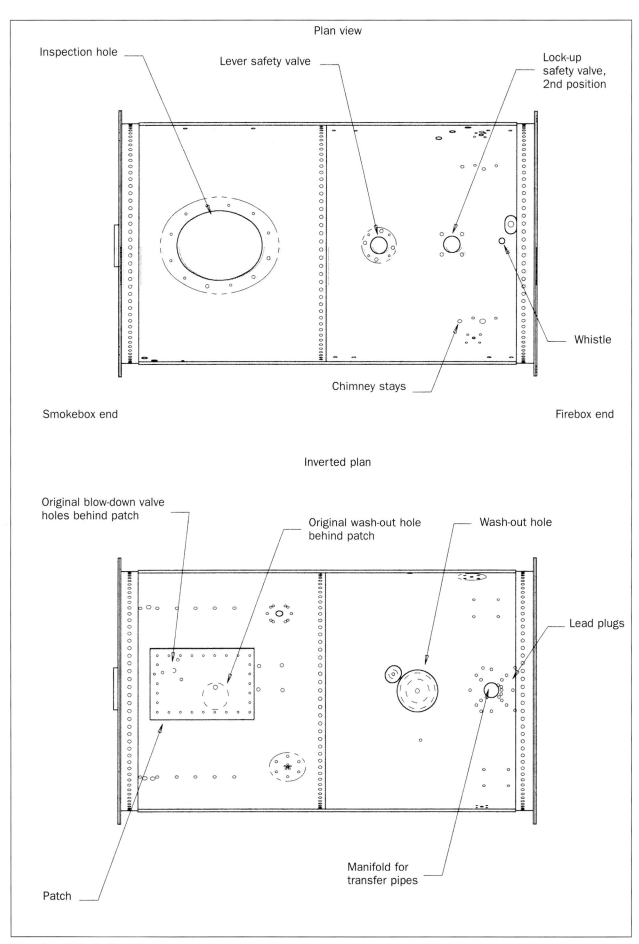

Drawing 4.29 Boiler plan views
Scale: 1:16

Fig. 3.11 *Rocket* **in 1836 – the 'Crewe' drawing** (formerly in the possession of the London & North Western Railway Co., now retained in the Science Museum, inv. no: 1923-569)

Fig. 3.14 *Rocket c.*1840 – the 'Stephenson' drawing** (formerly in the possession of Robert Stephenson & Co., now in the archive of the National Railway Museum, York)

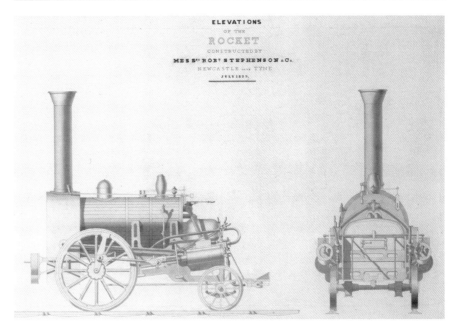

Fig. 3.15 *Rocket c.*1840 – the 'Thompson' drawing** (formerly in the possession of James Thompson, now privately owned)

Fig. 4.1 Rear view of *Rocket* in its end-of-service condition, showing diagonal frame stiffening stays
Source: 'Thompson' drawing, Fig. 3.15

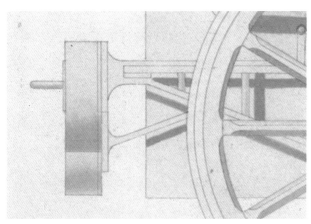

Fig. 4.2 Supplementary frame, 'Kirkhouse' brace and vertical spacing-rods
Source: 'Thompson' drawing, Fig. 3.15

Fig. 4.6 Detail of *Rocket*'s buffer-beam and horse-hair buffer as depicted in 1836
Source: 'Crewe' drawing, Fig. 3.11

Fig. 4.4 Detail of buffer beam, showing surviving paintwork

Fig. 4.5 Left-hand buffer remains, showing scribe lines, nail holes, contact plate, backing timber and tail-rod hole

Fig. 4.8 Front coupling eye and washer

Fig. 4.9 Footplate, rear buffing pads and draw-bar bracket

Fig. 4.10 Left-hand driving axle horn

Fig. 4.11 Under-view of right-side driving wheel-set spring-hanger keep-plate, showing profiled horn-end and redundant notches

Fig. 4.12 Left-hand spring set, showing good condition of leaves

Under-view of left-side frame

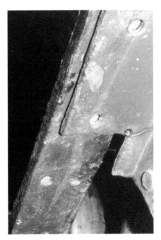

Under-view of right-side frame

Fig. 4.14 Comparison of upper-angle iron and cylinder mounting plate alignments

1836 Secondhand sale view
Source: 'Crewe' drawing, Fig. 3.11

Fig. 4.15 Driving-wheel comparison, 1836 and *c.* 1840

*c.*1840 End-of-service view
Source: 'Thompson' drawing, Fig. 3.15

109

Fig. 4.16 Driving axle end and nave, showing keys and keyways

Fig. 4.17 Detail of left wheel-nave, showing broken and cracked spokes, 'horse-collar' with plugged holes, crank-boss and pin

Fig. 4.19 Detail of axle, showing deep groove, shorter scar and fitter's mark for the left-hand valve-gear 'driver'

Fig. 4.20 Builder's plate in right wheel-nave

Fig. 4.22 Interior view of right-side rear plate join, showing gap between plates, cheese-head strap rivets, and original cylinder-mounting plate securing bolts

Front left-side bracket

Rear right-side bracket

Fig. 4.23 Interior views of boiler bracket securing bolts

Front tube-plate exterior

Fig. 4.24 Tube-plates showing tube holes and stays

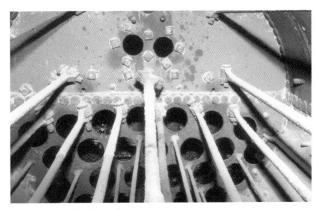

Rear tube-plate interior

Front tube-plate

Fig. 4.25 Boiler interior showing four stay patterns

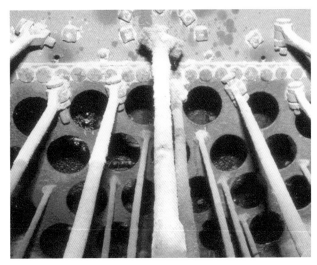

Rear tube-plate

Rocket – rear view

Fig. 4.27 Comparison of inspection-holes on Rocket and Invicta

Invicta – rear view

Fig. 4.29 Contemporary view of *Invicta* showing its steam manifold

Source: detail from C Hullmandel's lithograph of
T M Baynes' painting of the opening of the Canterbury &
Whitstable Railway in May 1830

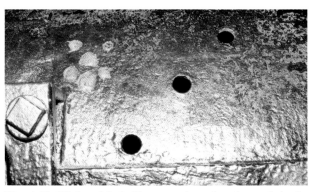

Fig. 4.33 Right-side boiler exterior, showing original upper sight-gauge location, and later try-cock hole cluster; also original spring-balance anchor

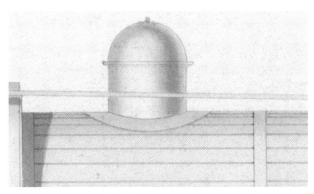

Fig. 4.31 Detail of boiler-top showing brass dome, *c.*1840

Source: 'Thompson' drawing, Fig. 3.15

Fig. 4.35 Detail view of left-side showing water sight-gauge

Source: 'Thompson' drawing, Fig.3.15

Fig. 4.39 Interior detail view of rear tube-plate, showing early and later angle-iron fittings for the firebox 'Saddle'

Fig. 4.40 Exterior view of firebox back-plate

Fig. 4.41 Interior view of firebox back-plate

Fig. 4.42 Inner face of firebox front-plate

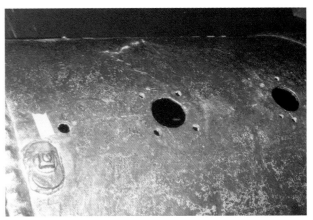

Fig. 4.44 Boiler-top showing (left to right), unknown fitting, whistle hole, lock-up and lever safety-valve holes

Fig. 4.45 Detail of front left of boiler bracket showing cutaway, plugged hole and cladding-band securing point

Fig. 4.46 Interior view of the leading end of boiler bottom (through boiler stays), showing bracket bolts, plugged holes and patch-plate bolts

Fig. 4.47 Steam regulator body and plug, showing sediment deposit and grooving

Exterior view

Interior view

Fig. 4.50 Front tube-plate, upper part detail, showing blank flange

Fig. 4.48 Detail of rear tube-plate fittings *c.*1840
Source: 'Thompson' drawing, Fig.3.15

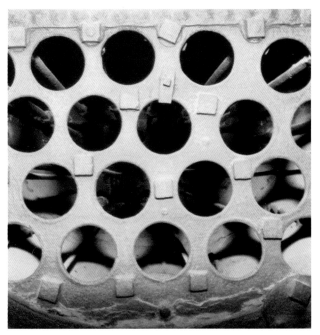

Fig. 4.51 Detail of front tube-plate exterior, showing beads around the tube-holes

Fig. 4.49 Front tube-plate exterior view

Fig. 4.52 Interior of ash-box, showing bottom, rear and side-plates

Pride of Newcastle (1828)

Fig. 4.53 Smokebox crown and left-side plate, angle iron and tube-plate tabs

Rocket (1829: inverted 1831)

Invicta (1830)

Fig. 4.55 Development of the Stephenson cylinder 1828–31

Fig. 4.54 Left side of *Invicta*, showing cylinder mounting frame

Front view   Rear view

Fig. 4.56 Left-side cylinder assembly, showing steam-port protrusion, valve-chest, mounting feet and cylinder-end cover

Fig. 4.58 *Rocket*'s left-side piston boss and rear end-plate, compared with piston arrangement on *Patentee*-type locomotives
Source: W P Marshall, Description of the Patent Locomotive Steam Engine of Messrs. Robert Stephenson and Co. (London, 1838) p.28

Lancashire Witch (1828)   *Pride of Newcastle* (1828)   *Rocket* (1829)   *Invicta* (1830)

Fig. 4.59 Development of piston-rod fittings to cross-heads
Source: *Lancashire Witch* – Coste and Perdonnet, 'Sur les chemins à Ornièrs', Annales des mines, Vol. VI, (1829) pp.199–201, plate X, Fig. a. *Pride of Newcastle* – Smithsonian Institution, Washington DC, photograph ref. 5279A

Fig. 4.60 Gudgeon pin showing knurl marks, and cotter

Spherical boss big end
Source: 'Crewe' Drawing Fig. 3.11

End of service connecting rod with strap boss
Source: 'Thompson' Drawing Fig. 3.15

Fig. 4.61 Left-side cross-head showing worn guide-way surfaces

Invicta's little end

Fig. 4.62 Comparison of connecting rod fittings

Fig. 4.65 Left-side valve-face and steam-chest, valve and rod (inverted)

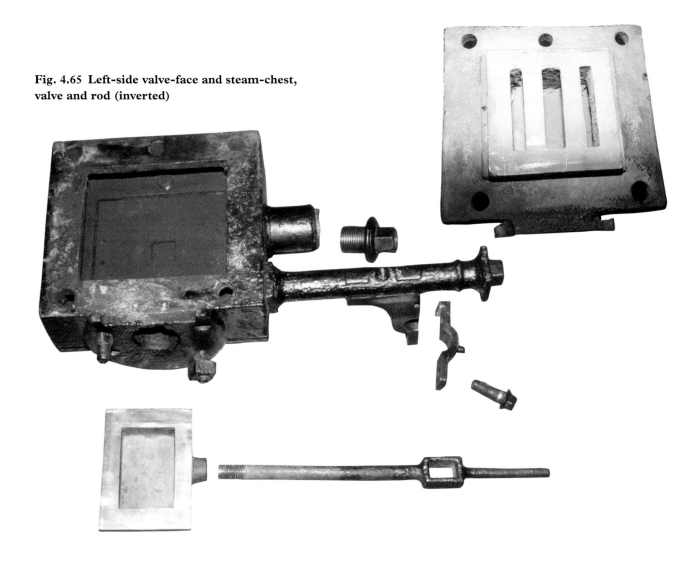

Fig. 4.66 Valve motion, with back-head rocking-shaft, valve-levers, side-rods and side-rod levers
Photograph: P A Davidson

Fig. 4.67 Forward rocking-shaft and levers, with eccentric-rod knuckle-joints

Rocket

Invicta

Fig. 4.68 Eccentric assembly comparison between
Rocket* and *Invicta

**Fig. 4.69 Eccentric sleeve-half, showing ribs,
keyways, screws, and redundant and plugged holes**

**Fig. 4.70 Right-hand eccentric sheaves and left-hand
broken eccentric sheave, showing tongue and groove
joints and fitting bolts, key-ways and bolt-holes**

Fig. 4.71 Eccentric
cheek-plates
showing valve-gear
driving slots

Fig. 4.72 Eccentric strap details showing
identification numbers and fitting marks

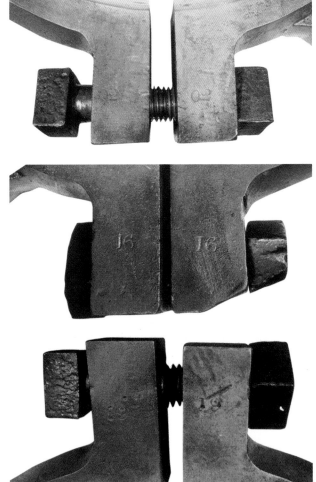

Left-hand driver and dog

Right-hand driver and dog

Fig. 4.73 Views of drivers showing dogs, hinges, clamp-bolts and axle-bolts

Rocket's slider and 'yoke'

Invicta's 'yoke'

Fig. 4.74 Comparison of reversing 'yokes' on Rocket and *Invicta*

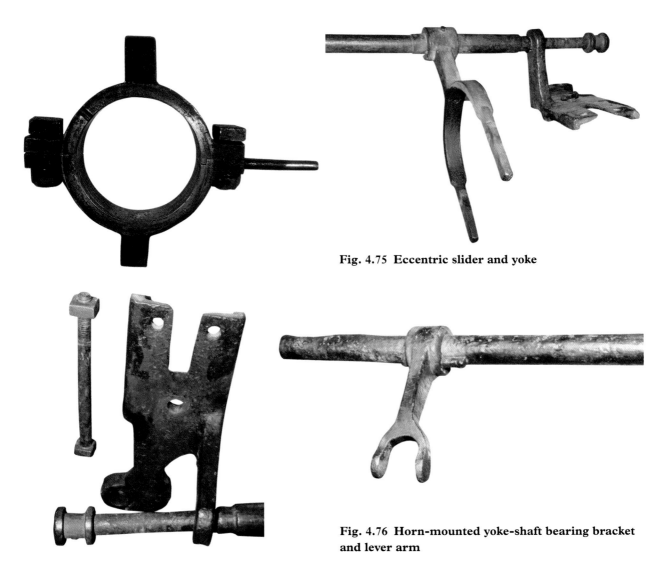

Fig. 4.75 Eccentric slider and yoke

Fig. 4.76 Horn-mounted yoke-shaft bearing bracket and lever arm

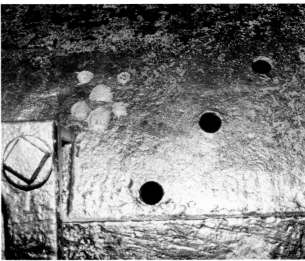

Fig. 5.1 Detail of boiler plate showing mottled surface and rust where paint has been removed from former sight-gauge and spring-balance fittings

Fig. 4.77 Reversing rod, pedal shaft and pedal

4.7.3 Steam whistle

There is no evidence that a steam whistle was fitted to *Rocket* during its later service with the L&MR. It appears to have been fitted with a brass 'cup and cone' whistle during its time on the Naworth collieries railway. The whistle was fitted into a tapped hole 6 in. from the rear of the boiler and just to the right of its centre-line (Fig. 4.43).

Close to the whistle, and immediately adjacent to the rear angle iron, there is a rectangular hole, sealed and made pressure-tight by a cover-plate sandwiching a lead gasket. It is secured by a 'T'-headed bolt inserted headfirst into the hole, with the purpose (not fully carried out) of being turned through 90° and tightened by an external nut and washer. As other redundant holes in the boiler have been skilfully plugged by the L&MR maintenance teams, this unusual form of sealing a redundant hole may have been undertaken by the Kirkhouse colliery maintenance men. Although no purpose has been identified for this hole, it is possible that it was an earlier attempt to provide a form of steam whistle.

4.7.4 Chimney stays

Rocket's original chimney was braced by two stays which were apparently led back to the rear shoulders of the boiler. A pair of plugged holes on each side of the boiler indicate the location of the stay feet. The pair on the left side had been secured by bolts inserted into tapped holes, whilst the pair on the right were additionally secured with nuts and washers.

An additional pair of holes on both sides, each in close proximity to the original pair, are not plugged. From the precision of their threads, it would seem that they were drilled and tapped at a much later date, almost certainly as part of the 1862 restoration, when replica stays were provided to support the replica chimney. The stays, which were erroneous for the locomotive in its end-of-service condition, were removed by the Science Museum in *c*.1935.

4.7.5 Cylinder mounting-plate arms

The two upper arms of the cylinder mounting plates (Section 4.2.8) are secured through bridging pieces to each side of the boiler, to which they are bolted through tapped holes into the plate. The left-side rear bolt has snapped through, possibly as the result of fatigue from the reciprocating stresses of the piston action.

4.7.6 Nameplates

Only the right-side nameplate survives, and that is in poor condition. It appears, at some stage, that an attempt has been made to remove it by prising it away from its backing timber. It is broken and a small piece is missing. It is been flattened and secured to the backing timber with common wood screws. The left-side nameplate is missing. A plaster replica, possibly cast from the right side, has been substituted at some unknown time. The backing timbers have been bolted to the boiler with latter-day bolts, possibly in 1862.

4.7.7 Boiler clack valves

Water was fed into the boiler through two clack valves fitted to its underside, to the rear of the leading boiler-support brackets (Drawing 4.30). The feed inlets and witnesses of the flanges indicate that they were not of the same pattern and appear to have been fitted at different times. The left-side 1³⁄₁₆-in.-diameter hole has two series of flange boltholes tapped into the boiler, indicating a refitting of the clack valve at some stage.

The right-side fitting, however, has only one set of tapped holes for its flange, and its inlet hole has been drilled into the boiler plate as a cluster of six ³⁄₈-in.-diameter holes. This suggests that the facilities available to drill a comparable 1³⁄₁₆-in.-diameter hole were either not available or, more probably, the hole, which is behind the driving

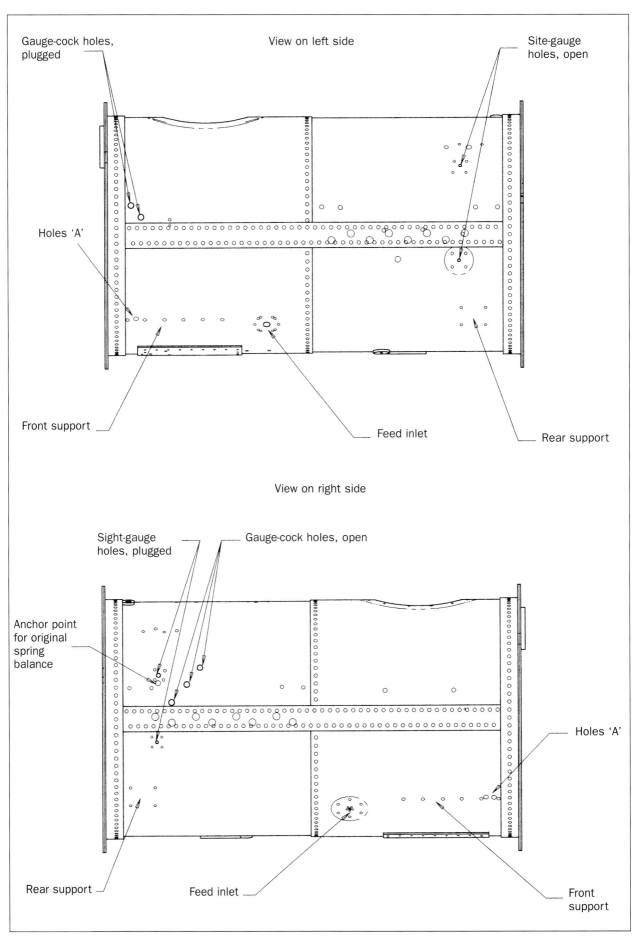

Gauge-cock holes,
plugged

View on left side

Site-gauge
holes, open

Holes 'A'

Front support

Feed inlet

Rear support

View on right side

Sight-gauge
holes, plugged

Gauge-cock holes, open

Anchor point
for original
spring
balance

Holes 'A'

Rear support

Feed inlet

Front
support

Drawing 4.30 Boiler, elevations

Scale: 1:16

wheel, was inaccessible for a large drilling apparatus. This, in turn, suggests that the work was carried out by a maintenance depot, rather than in the Stephenson factory.

It is likely, therefore, that *Rocket* had only the left-side clack valve to begin with, and that, perhaps finding this inadequate, the second was added later. The cross-head driven water-pumps, which were fitted behind the cylinders (Section 4.9.7), have not survived.

4.7.8 Boiler-bottom holes and patches

The bottom of the boiler has several holes and patches (Drawing 4.29). On both sides of the boiler, there is a pair of holes ('A' in Drawing 4.30) of $^7/_8$-in.-diameter, in front of the line of bolts securing the leading boiler-support brackets. The brackets appear to have been cut back to accommodate the holes. The holes are now plugged with studs secured on both the interior and exterior of the plate by washers and nuts, whilst one of those on the left side is a 'T'-headed bolt (Fig.4.45, p113). The purpose of these holes is not known.

At the leading end of the barrel, and centrally located along the bottom centre-line, there is a large exterior rectangular patch, 18 in. long and 12 in. wide. It is bolted to the boiler plate through twenty-eight tapped holes. There is a $^3/_4$-in.-diameter hole in the boiler, (within the patch-plate area), surrounded by three flange-fixing boltholes, which is offset to the left of the bottom centre-line. This may have been for a blow-down valve for daily clearing of boiler sediment. Access to the valve would have been from the front of the locomotive using an extension handle.

Also within the patch-plate area, there is a further $4^1/_2$-in.-diameter hole in the boiler, without evidence of a flange, offset to the right of, but encompassing, the boiler centre-line. It is likely that this hole was provided for a periodic washing-out of the boiler, although it was probably soon found to be a poor location, being very close to the eccentric cluster and thus injurious to its working. To seal the hole would have required an internal plate, approximately 6 in. in diameter, bolted to a cover plate of similar dimension.

The fitting of an ash-box beneath the smokebox, probably in November 1830 (Section 4.8.1), would have prevented access to the blow-down valve. It would seem that this prompted the abandoning of both the blow-down valve hole and the wash-out hole. At some stage, therefore, the area of the boiler incorporating both holes was covered by the patch plate. The interior view of the patch-plate bolts is shown in Fig. 4.46, p113. To the rear of the patch plate, and offset to the left of the bottom centre-line, are four plugged boltholes in a square pattern. Their purpose is unknown.

On the bottom centre-line, $15^3/_4$ in. from the rear of the boiler, is a hole, possibly also $4^3/_4$ in. in diameter. It has been sealed with a cover plate and lead gasket on the outside and a further plate and gasket on the inside, and secured with a $^3/_4$-in.-diameter bolt and exterior nut. It is probable that it was inserted as the replacement wash-out hole when the earlier hole was abandoned. Just in advance of this hole, but offset to the left side, is a small hole sealed with an oval patch-plate, approximately 3 in. by $2^1/_2$ in., and packing secured with a 'T'-head bolt and an exterior nut. The purpose of this hole is not known.

Seven-and-a-half in. along the bottom centre-line from the rear of the boiler is a $2^1/_2$-in.-diameter hole surrounded by two sets of flange boltholes. This would have been for the firebox water-feed manifold (Section 4.6.5). The original manifold fed water to the outside of the saddle side-plates through copper pipes. The manifold was probably replaced in November 1830 with the installation of the new firebox back-plate and water feed-pipes. A new blow-down valve may also have been fitted to the manifold when the original valve became inaccessible. Six of the redundant flange-fixing holes were filled with threaded lead plugs, which remain in place.

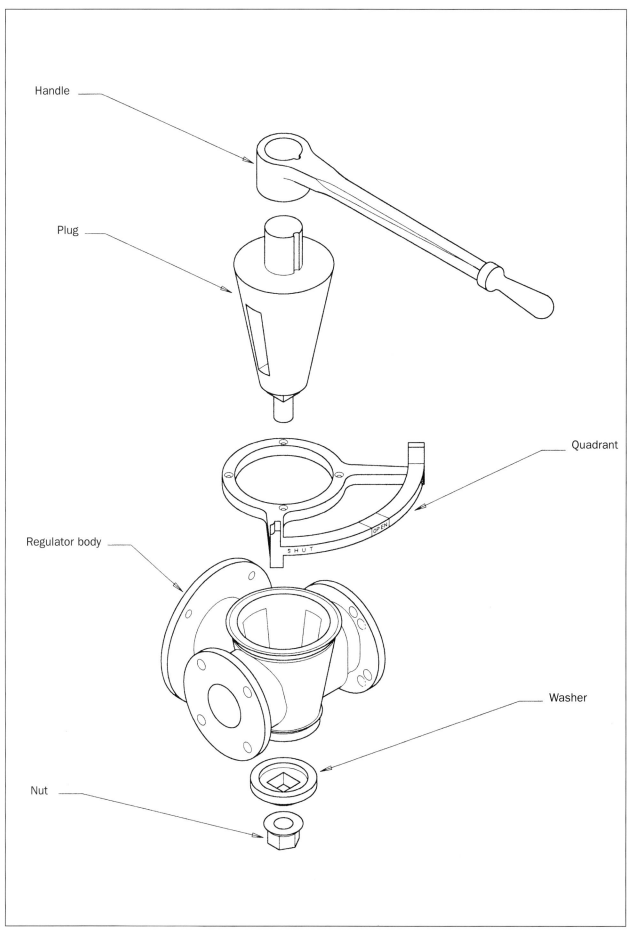

Handle

Plug

Quadrant

Regulator body

Washer

Nut

Drawing 4.31 Regulator
Projection: isometric view, upper rear left *Scale:* 1:25

4.7.9 Steam regulator

The survival of the regulator is probably due to its basic design, which, unlike the other boiler fittings, would not have been readily reuseable on other locomotives on the Naworth collieries railway (Drawing 4.31). It was fitted to a 2⅜-in.-diameter hole in the rear tube-plate, between the upper boiler-stays, with four bolts through tapped holes (Drawing 4.32). It is fitted ½ in. to the right of the vertical centre-line, a bias which arose from the asymmetrical firebox saddle and its two steam communicating pipes fitted directly underneath. Initially, the steam may have been fed to the regulator via a short riser, or the inlet was shielded by a baffle, either of which could have been fitted to the inside of the regulator's fixing bolts. However, with the fitting of a dome, probably in November 1830 (Section 4.5.2), steam was fed to the regulator through an internal steam pipe, also flange-fitted over the regulator fixing bolts and secured with nuts.

The regulator body is a bronze casting, with a flanged inlet and a separate flanged outlet for each cylinder. The conical plug has rectangular steam passages, and is retained in the body with a washer and nut at the bottom. It was rotated by a regulator handle fitted to its top, and moved through a one-eighth turn, from a left or right-side shut position to a central, fully open position, allowing driving from either side of the footplate.

It is possible that the regulator is the original 1829 fitting, but there is no evidence on it to confirm this. If of original Newcastle make, it is likely to have been cast and machined by either John Abbot or Henry Marshall, both of whom supplied non-ferrous castings to the Stephenson company during 1829 (Section 3.3). The housing and valve are in very good condition, but exhibit the signs of considerable use. There are deposits of sediment within the housing, and the sealing surfaces are badly grooved from sediment ingress (Fig. 4.47, p114).

There is a bronze quadrant fitted to the body, which is engraved or stamped with 'SHUT' at the extremities and 'OPEN' in the middle. The latter word is on a replacement brass insert.

4.7.10 Other rear tube-plate fittings

In addition to the steam regulator, the rear tube-plate retains the evidence of other fittings (Drawing 4.32). Some of these can be identified from the 'Thompson'/'Stephenson' drawings (Fig. 4.48, p114).

Two 2½-in.-diameter steam communicating pipes from the firebox crown were fed into the boiler steam space directly under the steam regulator. They were fitted with contiguous flanges; the centre two of their eight bolts, fitted to tapped holes in the tube-plate, being common to them both. Although located on either side of the boiler centre-line, the holes are biased to the right by ½ in., suggesting that they were drilled to suit the asymmetrical firebox saddle (Section 4.6.2). Between the upper boiler tubes and the steam communicating pipes are the two arcs of fixing bolts, being the original and later fitting points for the firebox saddle angle irons.

A simple vertical bracket was bolted to the upper-left side of the tube-plate, apparently during the locomotive's time on the Naworth collieries railway. Its purpose was to provide a firm location for the graduated notches in a chimney damper operating rod (Fig. 4.48, p114), which was not shown on the 1836 'Crewe' drawing. The bracket has been removed and the sheared remains of its studs left *in situ*.

The anchor point for the relocated safety-valve spring-balance (Section 4.7.2) was on the right side of the tube-plate. The disused hole retains the sheared remains of its stud.

There are two indications on the tube-plate of the original 38° cylinder mounting-plates to which the cylinders had been fitted between 1829 and February 1831 (Figs 3.2–3.6). A pair of holes at the top of the tube-plate, immediately adjacent to the rivets securing the boiler angle iron, were probably for transverse stays to the mounting plates. The sheared remains of the studs are left *in situ*. On either side of the

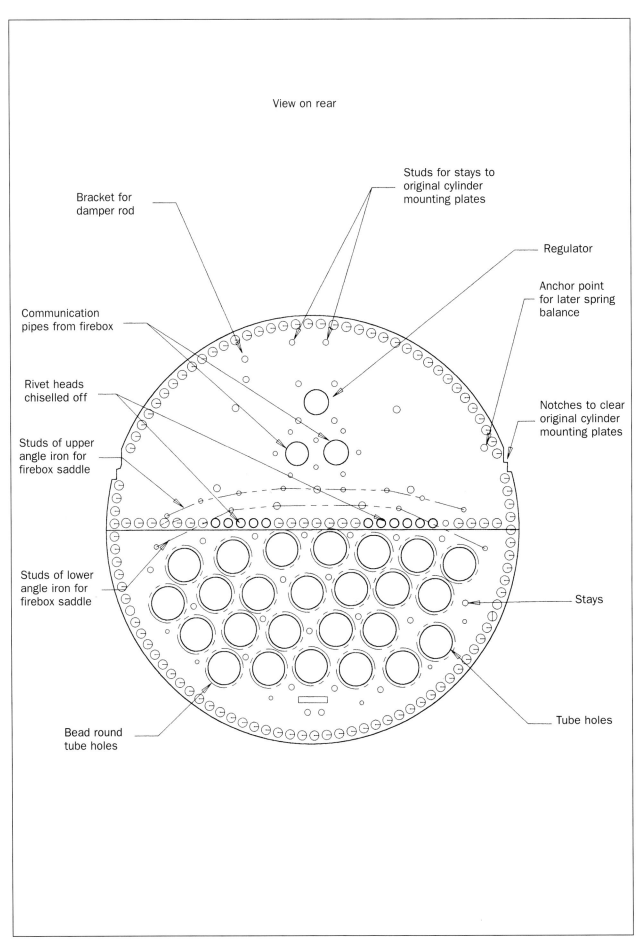

View on rear

Studs for stays to
original cylinder
mounting plates

Bracket for
damper rod

Regulator

Anchor point
for later spring
balance

Communication
pipes from firebox

Rivet heads
chiselled off

Notches to clear
original cylinder
mounting plates

Studs of upper
angle iron for
firebox saddle

Studs of lower
angle iron for
firebox saddle

Stays

Bead round
tube holes

Tube holes

Drawing 4.32 Rear tube-plate
Scale: 1:10

tube-plate, just above the waterline, there are double notches in both the tube-plate circumference and the angle iron. The adjacent rivet-heads are missing. These notches were necessary, in order to provide clearance for the mounting plates.

There is also a rectangular hole 1½ in. above the bottom of the plate, 3 in. wide by ⅝ in. high, with a wrought-iron protruding tongue. Below this are two ⅝-in.-diameter bolts. The purpose of these fittings, which are covered by the firebox front-plate, is not known.

4.7.11 Front tube-plate fittings

The front tube-plate shows evidence of several early fittings (Drawing 4.33). There is a series of six broken-off studs ('A') above the tubes which fixed the upper part of the original smoke-collecting chamber (Figs 3.2–3.6). Below the centre-line and at the bottom of the tube-plate are three further broken-off studs ('B') that would have been used to fix the lower part of the chamber. There may have been further studs around the periphery for fixing the chamber, which are now obscured by the angle iron for the surviving smokebox.

Two pairs of boltholes, in the left and right shoulders of the tube-plate ('C'), are now used for fixing the two largest pads for the smokebox angle iron, but may originally have been used for the upper feet of the diagonal tube-plate stays, which had been fitted to the main frame cross-member (Section 4.2.1).

Seven further bolts in the periphery of the tube-plate ('D') complete the support ring for the surviving smokebox angle iron (Section 4.8.1).

There are two broken-off studs, either side of the centre-line, in the upper half of the tube-plate ('E'). It is possible that they were used for securing a blast-pipe at some stage during the locomotive's career. There are four further broken-off studs in the lower half of the tube-plate ('F'), one of which is fitted with a small rectangular 'clamp'. Their purpose is not known. The bolts and broken-off studs are seen in the exterior view of the tube-plate (Fig. 4.49, p114).

At the top of the tube-plate, but offset to the left side by ⅜ in. from the vertical centre-line, there is a 7-in.-diameter blank flange. It is retained by six bolts through holes tapped into the tube-plate and has a copper plug at its centre. The plate covers a 2-in.-diameter hole, apparently for a steam pipe (Fig. 4.50, p114).

This hole was possibly made for the Dundonald rotary engine experiment, making it the only surviving evidence (Section 3.8). The steam hole suggests that steam was drawn from the dome by diverting the steam pipe through the front tube-plate. Assuming bifurcation in the smokebox, the two steam pipes, routed round its perimeter in a similar manner to the contemporary *Planet* locomotives, would then have been routed to the rotary engines through the rear of the ash-box (Section 4.8.1).

4.7.12 Boiler tubes

All the boiler tubes have been removed and the tube holes left vacant. The manner in which the original copper tubes – of 3-in. outside diameter and probably made in Newcastle by John Abbott,[54] – had been fitted to the tube-plates was the subject of some erroneous statements in the nineteenth century.[55] Both Smiles and Jeaffreson relate that the tubes were soldered or brazed to brass screws in the tube-plate. The Stephensons' draughtsman, George Phipps, however, later recalled that this was:[56]

> …quite erroneous and that such a method was never tried. There was much discussion as to the best method for securing the tubes, and quite probably the above was discussed but it was not actually tried. Indeed, to have done so, and then changed to the ferrule system would have implied the formation of new boiler ends which certainly was not done. The ferrules were originated at Newcastle at Messrs. Stephensons.

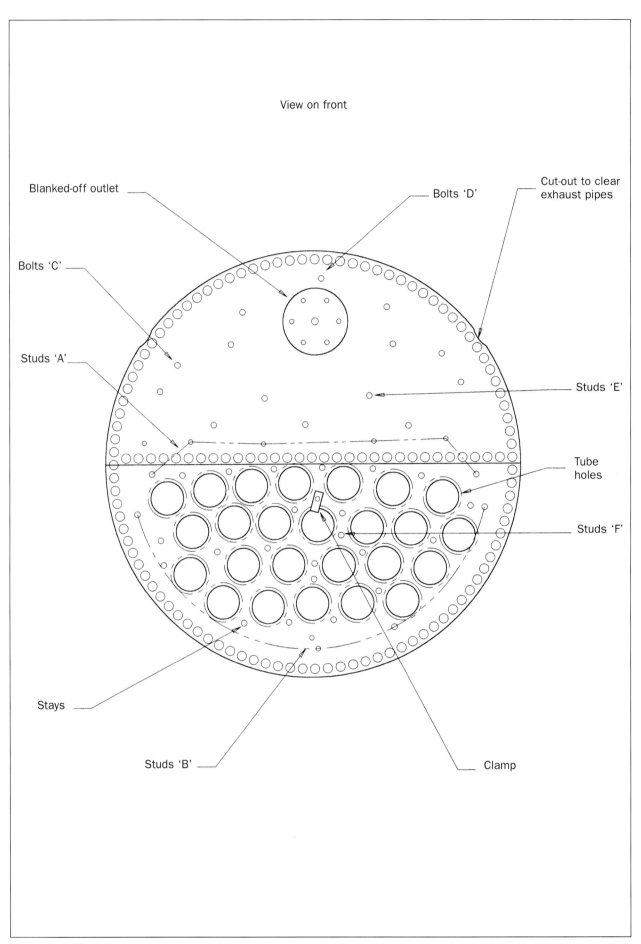

View on front

Blanked-off outlet

Bolts 'C'

Studs 'A'

Bolts 'D'

Cut-out to clear
exhaust pipes

Studs 'E'

Tube
holes

Studs 'F'

Stays

Studs 'B'

Clamp

Drawing 4.33 Front tube-plate
Scale: 1:10

The ferrules had earlier been described by David Stevenson, each being a steel ring:[57]

> ...about one-eighth of an in. in thickness, one inch in breadth, and slightly tapered. This ring is driven into the brass tube, after it is fitted into the boiler plate, by which means the tube is wedged against the plate, and thereby rendered water and steam tight. The tubes are proved by means of a water pressure of 50 lb on the square inch, and, notwithstanding this, they frequently burst. When this accident happens, the engineer stops both ends of the broken tube with wooden plugs.

Rocket's tubes were made from $3/32$-in.-thick copper sheet,[58] formed over a mandril and soldered or brazed. Each weighed 21.01 lb. according to Robert Stephenson's letter of 3 August 1829 (Section 3.3). The copper tubes of 2-in. and $1^5/8$-in.-diameter, fitted to later locomotives on the L&MR, were made of $1/32$-in.-thick copper sheet, no doubt to effect a considerable saving on cost. They were badly scoured by coke particles, however, and had to be replaced every few thousand miles, in some cases adopting $1/16$-in.-thick sheet in an attempt to give them a longer life.[59] Stevenson reported that 'The mechanics connected with the railway prefer the large tubes of three in. bore to the small ones, which are more apt to get choked with soot and ashes...'[60]

Rocket was re-tubed in January 1833 after the Wigan Branch accident (Section 3.7). In view of the thickness of its tubes and its relatively light workload during its career, it is possible that its tubes lasted longer than those of the other locomotives. Being a non-standard size, the railway had to obtain a particular quote for replacement tubes. Their potential expense led to the divisional engineer, William Allcard, being:[61]

> instructed to ascertain whether Copper Tubes 3 inches diameter could not be obtained at a lower rate per lb. than tubes $1^5/8$ inch-diameter.

The re-tubing just preceded the railway's switch to brass tubes, which was generally adopted from April 1833.[62] The tube-holes now measure $3^1/2$ in. in diameter and are surrounded by beads which are $3/32$-in. thick and have a $4^1/8$-in. outside diameter. This indicates that they were enlarged during the life of the locomotive, partly by cutting to fit larger tubes and partly as a consequence of the wedging action of the ferrules. *Rocket* may therefore have been re-tubed more than once after its 1833 refurbishment, possibly including an occasion at the Kirkhouse workshops, and possibly switching to brass tubes. The enlargement of the holes has removed the opportunity to find any evidence to confirm or deny that screw-fitting or brazing had originally been attempted (Fig. 4.51, p114).

4.8 Smokebox assembly

4.8.1 Smokebox and ash-box

Rocket's smokebox is probably the third to have been fitted. The first was a simple smoke-collecting chamber to divert the flue gases, exiting from the tubes, up the chimney. There is no contemporary front view of this chamber other than Clayton's sketch (Fig. 3.3), but the side views (Figs 3.2 and 3.4-3.6) illustrate it as being the bottom part of the chimney. Rastrick recorded in his Notebook that:[63]

> The Caloric and heated Air from the Fire Place and small Boiler passes through these Tubes into the Chimney which is enlarged at its Bottom to embrace the whole of the five and twenty Copper Tubes.

It is assumed that there was a small door in the confined base of this chamber through which to remove ash, which would have been a frequent requirement in the absence of any form of ash-box, and a constraint on operations. Robert Stannard later recalled that *Rocket* was modified by the addition of a smokebox and shorter chimney in November 1830 after the Chat Moss accident (Section 3.7).[64] However, the two Bury drawings, published in early 1831 (Figs 3.7 and 3.8), which illustrate *Rocket* on passenger service, apparently following its November 1830 rebuild, suggest that a small ash-box had been added to the base of the smoke collecting chamber rather than its replacement by a smokebox. They do, however, show a shorter chimney, and Stannard may have mis-remembered the provision of a smokebox at that time.

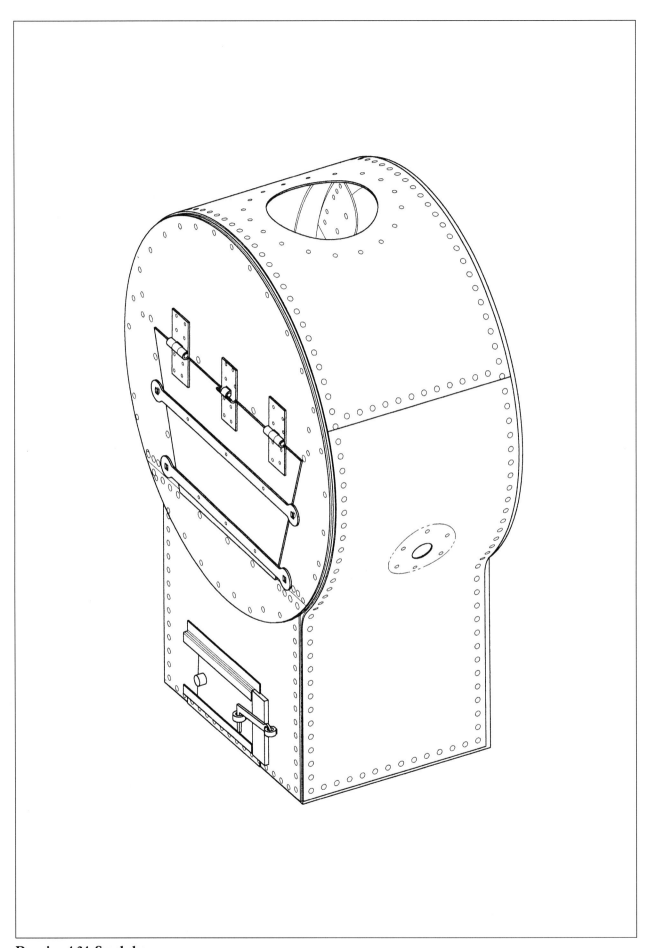

Drawing 4.34 Smokebox
Projection: isometric view, upper front left *Scale:* 1:10

The demonstrable benefits of a smokebox had been apparent since the arrival of *Phoenix* in June 1830, and all subsequent locomotives were so fitted. It is therefore most likely that a second smokebox was fitted, prior to the surviving one, although there is no evidence, on the front tube-plate or from any surviving illustrations, of what form it took. It is probable that one was fitted in February 1831, following the Olive Mount accident (Section 3.7), when its front end appears to have been damaged and its frame buckled (Section 4.2.1). It is possible that this smokebox was fitted with the same boltholes as those latterly used.

It is likely that by the date of the Dundonald rotary engine trial in October 1834 (Section 3.8), a smokebox would have been fitted and that a bifurcated steam pipe was routed through it. It is assumed that the steam pipes were fitted around the periphery of the tubes, before passing through the rear of a deep ash-box, and under the boiler barrel to reach the rotary engines. The surviving smokebox assembly, however, shows no evidence that pipes had been routed through the back of its deep ash-box. The smokebox is, furthermore, in remarkably good condition, without any of the characteristic sulphuric acid corrosion that is usually associated with smokeboxes that have been used for a number of years. The ash-box is also in good condition and was clearly well cleaned-out when the locomotive was taken out of service. It is notable that such a deep ash-box was provided, quite beyond the requirements of a main-line locomotive, let alone one destined for duties on a colliery railway (Fig. 4.52, p115).

It is possible that an inner ash-box was used, which had corroded and has since been discarded, but access to it would have been required through the front-end sliding ash-hole door. The latter does show signs of extensive use and has survived in a slightly distorted state, which prevents it opening along the upper and lower runners. A flat iron plate cut to size now lies on the bottom of the ash-box.

The smokebox sides and top are formed of three 3/16-in.-thick wrought-iron plates lap-riveted together; the crown-plate incorporating the chimney-fitting, and the side plates incorporating the ash-box sides (Drawing 4.34). The two side-plates have 2½-in.-diameter holes, surrounded by 6 boltholes, as well as the witness of flanges, originally for the exhaust pipes and blast-pipe fitting. None of this is now present.

The front face is formed of a 44-in.-diameter main plate to the lower sill of the access hole, a small plate below that completing the circle, and a separate ash-box front plate which incorporates the ash-hole door opening. The three plates are butt-riveted. The smokebox access hole has been cut into the face-plate. The smokebox door has three hinges on its top edge, (the centre one is broken), riveted to the face-plate and door. Two wrought-iron cross-bands extend beyond the door's sides and are secured, with nuts, to four bolts in the face-plate. When fitted, the cross-bands would have secured the door to minimise loss of vacuum.

The smokebox sheets are supported by an angle-iron framework (Drawing 4.35). The whole assembly is supported by the front tube-plate, to which it is bolted using irregular tabs riveted to the angle iron (Fig. 4.53, p115). The topmost tab is squeezed in above the steam pipe blanking-plate, confirming the latter's pre-existence (Fig. 4.50, p114). With the assumption that this steam hole was employed for the Dundonald experiment, this indicates that the smokebox was fitted after this time. The formation of the smokebox is the same as that shown on both the 1836 'Crewe' and the *c.*1840 'Thompson'/'Stephenson' drawings (Figs 3.14 and 3.15). It is most likely, therefore, that the surviving smokebox was fitted to *Rocket* in the summer of 1836, when the L&MR's Edge Hill workshops prepared the locomotive for sale on the second-hand market (Section 3.8).

4.8.2 Chimney and blast-pipe

Rocket's chimney, the top of which stands 13 ft 6 in. above rail level, is at least the sixth to have been carried by the locomotive:

- The first, with a petalled top, was that illustrated in 1829 and 1830 (Figs 3.2–3.6)
- the second, with a round top, was probably fitted in November 1830 after the Chat Moss accident (Figs 3.7 and 3.8)

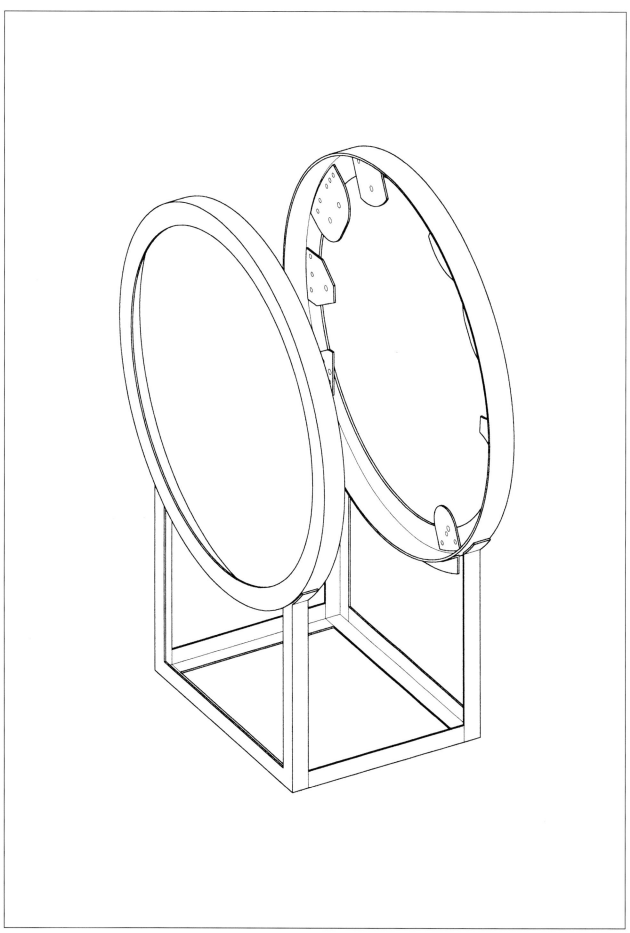

Drawing 4.35 Smokebox frame
Projection: isometric view, upper front left *Scale:* 1:10

- the third was that shown mounted on top of the smokebox on the 1836 'Crewe' drawing, and fitted with a spark-arresting screen (Fig. 3.11)

- the fourth was that shown on the 'Thompson'/'Stephenson' drawings with a partial inverted-cone top and a damper controlled by an operating rod from the boiler back-plate (Figs 3.14 and 3.15). The chimney was apparently missing when the locomotive was prepared for display in 1862

- the fifth (made to replace chimney no. 4) was made by Robert Stephenson & Co., attempting to replicate the original version with a petalled top, but mounted onto the smokebox. Two new stays were also fitted to the rear of the boiler (Section 4.7.4). This was inappropriate for the locomotive in its end-of-service condition, but it remained on display in the Science Museum with this appearance for about 70 years. It was removed, probably in 1935, to coincide with the arrival of the sectioned replica of *Rocket* in its original condition.

- the sixth chimney, fitted in *c*.1935, sought to recreate the outline of the third chimney, depicted in the 'Crewe' drawing. A framework, made for the spark-arresting screen, was installed but, for unknown reasons, the screen itself was not fitted. There is no note in the Science Museum technical file to explain this omission.

The chimney is fitted to a collar, replicating that shown on the 'Crewe' drawing, which sits over the smokebox crown and to which it is bolted by eighteen present-day nuts and bolts. Some or all of the holes in the smokebox crown were those used for the 1862 chimney, there being no evidence of any redundant holes in the plate.

The original exhaust pipes were routed from the cylinders along the shoulder-line of the boiler and into the base of the chimney barrel. The pipes were first turned into a 'double blast-pipe' with contracted orifices, but after the Rainhill Trials Robert Stephenson had the blast-pipe modified by the insertion of a contracted union-piece to convert the fitting into a single blast-pipe (Section 3.4). The smokebox shown in the 'Crewe' drawing (Fig. 3.11) shows the exhaust pipes to have been relocated to a rising route from the lowered cylinders to the base of the smokebox. The 1862 attempt to replicate the exhaust pipes resulted in an erroneous course along the upper boiler into the base of the replica chimney. These were removed by the Science Museum between 1924 and 1931.

4.9 Cylinders and driving motion

4.9.1 Cylinder and motion arrangement

Rocket's cylinders and motion slide-bars are mounted, at 8° to the horizontal, on the mounting plates towards the rear of the locomotive (Drawing 4.36). It is most likely that the two cylinders are those that were fitted to *Rocket* when it was manufactured in 1829. The patternmaking, casting and machining would have been carried out by Robert Stephenson & Co., which had its own foundry at that time.[65] The cylinders were cast and machined with an 8-in. bore, the original piston-stroke being 16½ in.[66] The stroke was increased to 17 in., probably in February 1831, when the cylinders were repositioned and replacement wheels were fitted (Section 4.3.1).

The cylinders were originally mounted on plates set at 38° to the horizontal and bolted to the boiler along its centre-line strap (Section 4.4.1).[67] These plates, which were stayed to the top of the boiler's rear tube-plate (Section 4.7.10), were probably similar to those now seen on *Invicta* (Fig. 4.54, p115). There is, however, no evidence on *Rocket* that they were stayed to the frame, as is the case with *Invicta*.

Rocket's initial unsteadiness, particularly at the higher speeds at which it was tested (Section 3.5), arose from the reciprocating piston action alternately depressing the left- and right-side springs, and the vertical component of the out-of-balance forces. The problem was immediately apparent and the four *Rocket*-type locomotives, ordered from the Stephenson Company in November 1830, had cylinders fitted at 8° (Fig. 2.8). However, *Rocket* was not immediately rebuilt to lower its cylinders and it continued to operate, mostly on slow-speed ballast duties, with elevated cylinders. The cost of the modification would perhaps have been a deterrent, and even when the

Isometric view upper front left

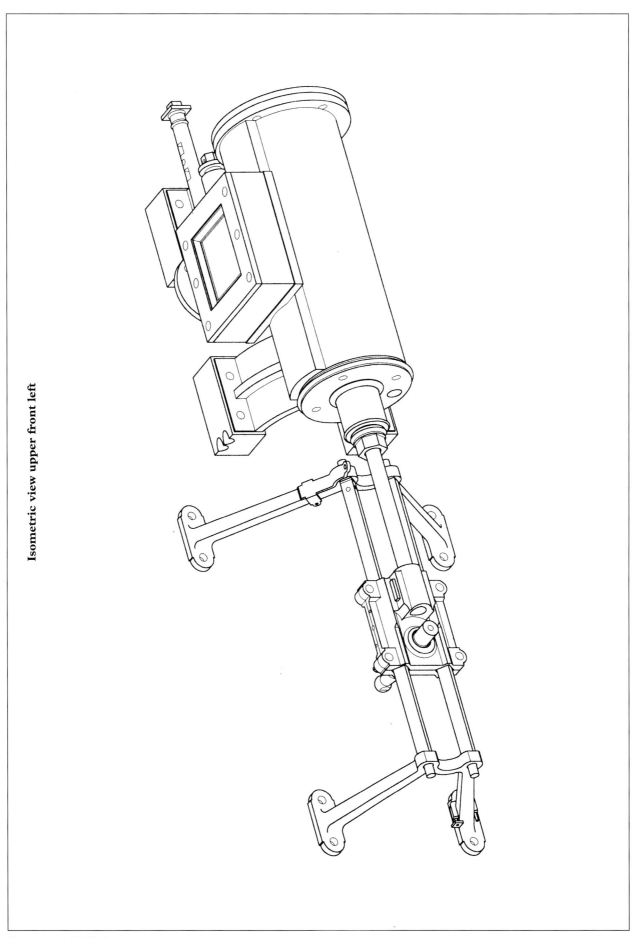

Drawing 4.36 Driving motion
Scale: 1:8

water-level modifications were made, probably in November 1830 (Section 4.5), the cylinders remained elevated.

The lowering of the motion line from 38° to 8° seems to have been undertaken during the repairs which followed the Olive Mount accident of January 1831, although there is no evidence that *Rocket*'s unsteadiness contributed to that accident. Since the water-level modifications made three months previously, the locomotive appears to have been transferred to main-line passenger duties to relieve a shortage of locomotives (Section 3.7) and its unsuitability for this work, because of the unsteadiness, may have determined the decision.

In common with several previous Stephenson locomotives, such as *Lancashire Witch* and *Pride of Newcastle*, *Rocket*'s cylinders originally had the valve chests located on the underside of the bore. This was almost certainly a means of alleviating the priming and condensation problems which characterised *Rocket*'s first year of operations (Section 4.5.1). To prevent damage to the cylinders and drive motion from the presence of water in the steam, as well as the condensate from the cylinder walls, the steam passages, being underneath, allowed the water to clear more effectively and be exhausted to the chimney. A spring would have been required to return the valve to the valve face (Section 4.10.2).

The introduction of the steam manifold on *Invicta*, and the experience of dryer steam gained from the domes of *Phoenix* and the later locomotives, including *Rocket* from November 1830, then made it possible for its cylinders to be inverted to bring the valves onto their upper face. The left- and right-side cylinders were accordingly exchanged and inverted, the primary objective being to simplify the alignment and fitting of the valve motion.

The surviving Stephenson cylinders, fitted to *Pride of Newcastle*,[68] *Rocket* and *Invicta* can be compared (Fig. 4.55, p115), from which it may be seen that the main castings are generally similar, but that the valve-chest arrangements have been modified.

4.9.2 Steam pipes

The two $2^5/_8$-in.-diameter external steam pipes, that delivered steam from the regulator to the valve chests above the cylinders, are made of copper sheets formed over a mandril with a soldered join, with flanges attached at each end. There is no evidence to indicate their date of manufacture, which could have been in February 1831, when the cylinders were probably refitted to their present position, or at any later time. The steam pipes would have been removed at Kirkhouse, in order to remove the firebox, and it is possible that the original pipes were not returned, the surviving ones thus being replacements dating from the 1862 refurbishment.

4.9.3 Cylinders

Rocket's cast-iron cylinders each have a partially 'blind' leading end, save for a $4^3/_4$-in.-diameter hole, in which is located the front cover boss (Drawing 4.37). The rear end is enlarged to form a flange for the cylinder-end cover. The steam passages were cast into a protrusion along the (now upper) part of the cylinder, in the centre of which was located the 11 in. × 10 in. valve-chest base, incorporating the valve-port face. Each casting includes four ribbed feet which are fastened, through spacer blocks, to the cylinder mounting plates with two bolts.

Cast-iron front covers, incorporating the piston-rod glands, are fitted to the 'blind' end of the cylinders with four bolts into tapped holes. A bronze gland nut is screwed into a $3^3/_4$-in.-long extension to each cover. The packing would probably have been hemp. A bronze cylinder drain-cock with a quarter-turn tap is inserted in the bottom of the covers.

Each of the rear cylinder-end covers has a register to provide a precise fit within the bore, and is secured to the flange with five bolts in tapped holes. The register is fitted with an iron ring which confirms that the cylinders have been re-bored (Section 3.7). There are six tapped holes, 'A', on the inside of the cover which would have held a disc

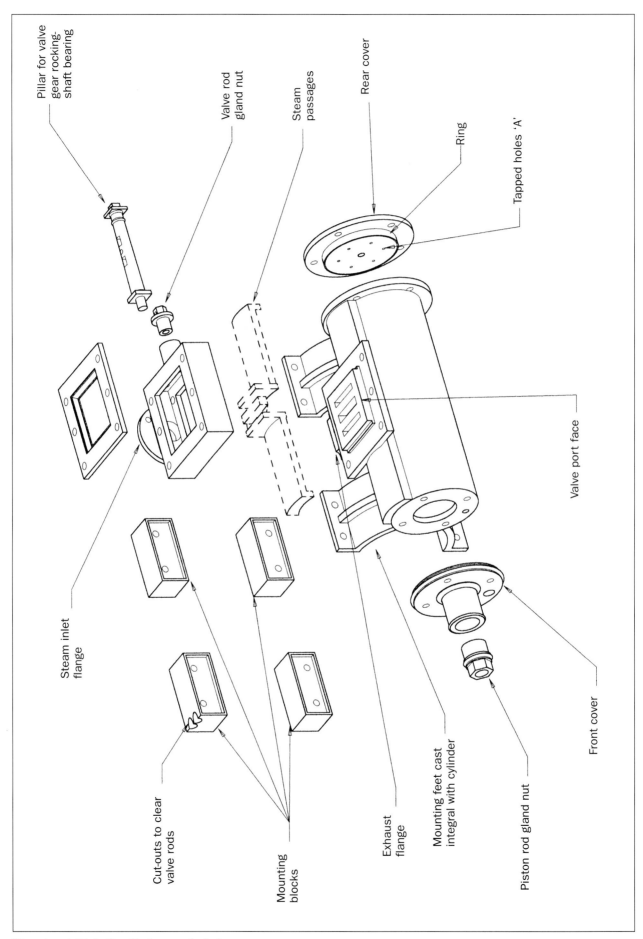

Drawing 4.37 Left cylinder, exploded

Projection: isometric view, upper front left *Scale:* 1:10

to reduce the clearance volume (Section 4.9.8). Bronze cylinder lubricators remain *in situ* in the centre of both plates, but they are of different patterns and one, at least, appears to be a replacement. The right-side cover has a notch in its circumference, but its purpose is not known. The left-side cylinder assembly is illustrated in Fig. 4.56, p116.

The valve-port area of the left-side cylinder is 2.5 sq. in., whilst the area of each port
cylinder is 2.2 sq. in. which would have resulted in some
passing through the valve. The right-side cylinder was not
med that a similar ratio applied to it.

e was enough wear in the cylinders to warrant a re-bore when
erhaul in the Edge Hill workshops following the Wigan Branch
The information provided by Robert Daglish & Co. of the St
ey had supplied new pistons of 8¼-in.-diameter at that time
ers were re-bored to at least that dimension. However, the left-
ne piston travel at the rear, has a re-bore of only 8³/₁₆ in., from
ned that Daglish's records, when consulted in 1907, were not as
their letter to the Science Museum (Section 3.7, Note 140).

that the cylinders were not subsequently re-bored, and that the
he cylinder bore was incurred by the locomotive's operations
e wear is typically 0.020 in., being slightly more at the rear than
e is only a very small variation between the vertical and

iston-rods

n of pistons and rings *Rocket* was first fitted with. It is possible
ere iron, such as were in regular use on stationary engines by
equally likely that the pistons were fitted with hemp rings, as in
that:[70]

first applied to locomotives by Messrs Murdoch and Aiken of Glasgow,
them for the Monkland and Kirkintilloch Railway, which was set to
ere can be no doubt of the economy and great utility of these pistons;
ver the old method of packing has been so fully established, that they
al use.

n rings had been used, the wear from which might have given
e 1833 re-bore, is suggested from an examination of the
the 1828-built *Pride of Newcastle*. This is fitted with iron rings,
cut at an angle of 60° with the edges of the rings, and which

Fig. 4.57 Piston from *Pride of Newcastle*
Source: The Smithsonian Institution, Washington DC

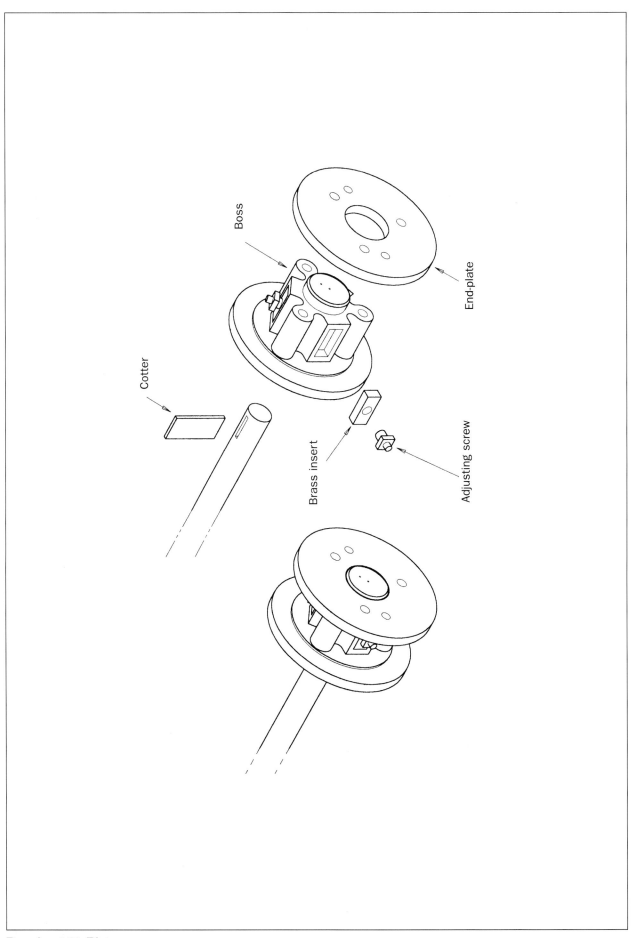

Drawing 4.38 Piston

Projection: isometric view, upper rear left *Scale:* 1:5

assume a diameter no larger than the edges of the piston plates. The rings are packed with hemp, however, which may have been rammed in tight while dry, but when wet from the condensation in the cylinder, would cause the rings to expand against the cylinder wall (Fig. 4.57).[71]

The two surviving 4-in.-long pistons, made by Robert Daglish & Co. in 1833, are each built up from a front end-plate, cast integrally with a 'clover' boss, to which is bolted a rear end-plate (Drawing 4.38). The plates are 8⅛-in.-diameter, being an ⅛-in. smaller than claimed by the Daglish company in 1907 (Section 3.7), and had a 1/32-in. clearance within the cylinder bore. The rear plates are fitted by three bolts into tapped holes in the boss.

The 2⅞-in.-long boss has three radial adjusting screws, which compressed three piston-ring expansion springs. The Daglish company letter referred to the fitting of brass rings and steel springs, but none has survived. The arrangement was similar to that used by the Stephenson company in 1835 for its *Patentee*-type locomotives (Fig.4.58, p116).

Marshall's description of the piston-rings provides a detailed contemporary description of the manner in which *Rocket*'s piston-rings were fitted and maintained:[72]

> The inner ring is three-eighths of an inch thick, and is the same width as the space between the plates: the two outer rings are half an inch thick, and of half the width; and on of them has a projecting ring or rebate upon its edge, fitting into a corresponding groove in the other to keep them steady. The rings are turned exactly to fit the cylinder and each other, and cut through in one part, having been first hammered a little all round on the inside, which gives them a tendency to expand, and causes them to fly open on being cut; when, therefore, they are put in their places in the cylinder, they press against the cylinder by their elasticity, and keep in close contact with it, so as to make a steam-tight joint during the motion of the piston. The divisions in the rings are placed in opposite positions, or break joint, in order to prevent the escape of steam through them; for if they were to coincide, a passage would be left for the steam through the piston.
>
> The elasticity of these rings is found to be quite sufficient to keep the piston steam-tight when moved in the cylinder, and it continues so for a long time; when, however, the rings become so much worn by the friction as to have expanded nearly to the utmost, some other means is necessary to press them against the cylinder. For this purpose, the three steel springs are placed in the piston; they are of the same width as the inside ring, against which they bear, and one-eighth of an inch thick in the middle, and a pin is put through each of them, having a collar bearing against the spring, and screwed at the other end into the centre boss of the piston; by unscrewing the pin a little the spring can be made to press harder against the ring when required, and the pin is then fixed by screwing up the set-nut upon it against the boss. When the piston is first made and the rings are new, these springs are not required, and they are set so as only to touch the rings; but as the rings wear and become too loose in the cylinder, the springs are screwed up more and more, and made to press harder against the rings; and when they are very much worn they are kept tight to the cylinder by the springs only, as they have expanded to their utmost.

The Stephenson company was reported still to be using this form of piston in 1846, when the advantages of using brass rings was described:[73]

> The pistons on the Liverpool and Manchester Railway are generally brass. This is an advantage in horizontal or inclined cylinders, as the softness of the material, and the greater lightness of the piston, considerably reduce the wear of the cylinder. Brass pistons have been, on this account, much used for locomotive engines; one drawback, however, to their employment, is, the inferior elasticity of the metal, which renders the employment of artificial springs necessary.

Rocket's piston rods, which appear to be of wrought iron, are machined to 1⅜-in.-diameter, the machining marks remaining on its unworn portion. Where the rod has operated through the piston-gland, the wear along its length is up to 0.090 in.
The piston rods appear to have been lubricated from an oil pot fitted to a tapped hole in a brass bracket, cantilevered out from the rear slide-bar support brackets. The left-side oil-pot bracket remains *in situ*, suggesting that oil was wick-fed from the pot to

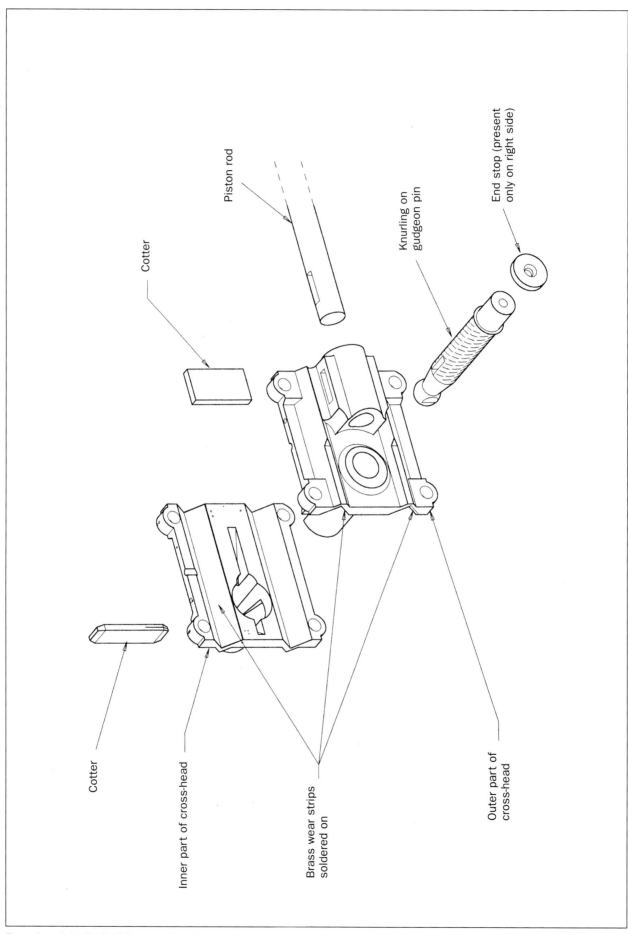

Cotter

Piston rod

Knurling on
gudgeon pin

End stop (present
only on right side)

Cotter

Inner part of cross-head

Brass wear strips
soldered on

Outer part of
cross-head

Drawing 4.39 Left side cross-head
Projection: isometric view, upper front left *Scale:* 1:5

the rod. This arrangement was probably added during the life of the locomotive, there being no similar fitting on *Invicta*.

The rods are slotted for fitting to the cross-head with cotters, a feature which appears to have been introduced in 1828. *Lancashire Witch* was sketched in that year with a threaded fitting to its cross-head, whilst *Pride of Newcastle* may have been the first locomotive to have had a slotted piston-rod end for fitting to its cross-head with a cotter. The evolution of the fittings may be traced in Fig. 4.59, p116.

4.9.5 Cross-heads and slide-bars

Rocket's cross-heads are well worn and probably date from the manufacture of the locomotive in 1829. They are each formed of two bronze castings enclosing the slide-bars, and a wrought-iron transverse gudgeon-pin (Drawing 4.39). The outer castings incorporate the piston-rod sockets, slotted to receive cotters (Fig. 4.59, p116), and a transverse spigot. The inner castings incorporate locating sockets, precisely machined to receive the outer-casting spigots. The casting pairs are secured to each other by four square shoulder bolts fitted with hexagonal shoulder nuts.

A gudgeon-pin is fitted through each spigot, the outer end being the 'little end' pin for the connecting rod, and the inner end having an eye for a water feed-pump drive-rod. Neither rod has survived. The pin-ends were tapped to receive 'little end' retaining collar bolts; the right-side collar and counter-sunk bolt remain *in situ* (Fig. 4.59, p116). The gudgeon-pins, which transmitted the driving forces between pistons and connecting rods, have been hand-knurled to ensure a tight fit within the spigots, to the ends of which they are secured with split wrought-iron cotters (Fig. 4.60, p117). The pins are now a slack fit, however, indicating significant use since they were knurled.

The cross-head castings enclose the upper and lower square-section slide-bars which are set on edge. The guidance forces were alternately distributed between the two upper and two lower faces of each guide-way, the upper faces thus wearing more than the lower faces in forward motion, and the lower faces wearing in reverse. A lubricating hole, flanked by two tapped holes, indicates the former presence of an oil reservoir, which would have wick-fed oil onto the upper slide-bars. The lower slide-bars apparently relied on surplus oil dripping from the upper bars. The lubrication was, however, insufficient to prevent considerable wear on the guide-ways. The loss of metal thus had to be restored, perhaps on more than one occasion, when the locomotive was in works for overhaul. Brass strips, 1/8-in. thick, were soldered onto the worn surfaces to build them back up to an acceptable clearance.

The guides all show considerable wear from prolonged use, on both the upper and lower faces. Five of the eight faces have lost their brass strips, and the other three, all on the lower faces, have worn through revealing the solder. This suggests that the locomotive had done more work in a forward direction than in reverse. The cross-heads were clearly not attended to in the locomotive's last days of operation, the increasingly slack fitting serving to accelerate the rate of wear. The guides are now particularly ill-fitting, with a slackness which probably contributed to *Rocket*'s withdrawal from service from the Naworth collieries line (Fig. 4.61, p117).

The wrought iron slide-bars are 1 1/16-in. square, set on edge. They are supported at both ends by wrought-iron 'spectacle' brackets, the flanged arms of which are bolted to the cylinder mounting plates (Drawing 4.36). The spectacle brackets were fitted in 1831 when the cylinders were lowered and mounted on the plates. Both ends of the slide-bars appear to have been turned to fit through eyes forged in each bracket, to which they were secured with hexagonal shoulder-nuts and washers. Two of the slide-bars show signs of repair, possibly arising from accident damage. The left-side upper slide-bar has a stud at its rear end, which appears to have been fitted by drilling and tapping, and secured by two 3/8-in. pins brazed into place and ground flush with the remainder of the bar. Both this and the right-side upper slide-bar have square section spacers. The cross-heads and slide-bars are the only components on the locomotive which have hexagonal shoulder-nuts, apparently fitted on the same occasion.
The implication of these precision-made nuts is that they were fitted by an engineering establishment, rather than a maintenance workshop.

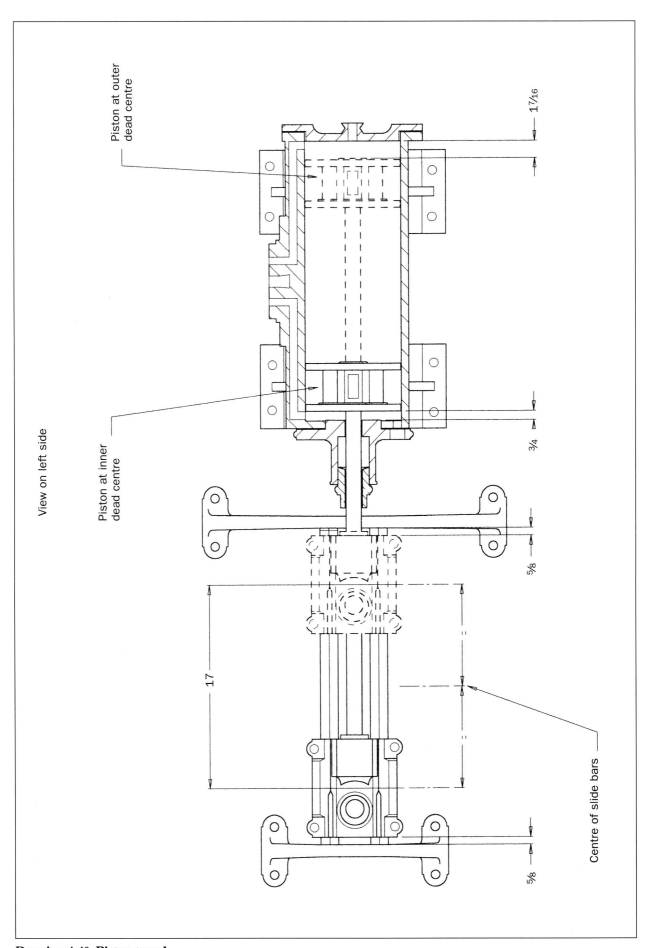

View on left side

Piston at outer dead centre

Piston at inner dead centre

Centre of slide bars

17

1⅟₁₆

¾

⅝

⅝

Drawing 4.40 Piston travel

Scale: 1:8 *Dimensions:* inches

4.9.6 Connecting rods

Neither of *Rocket*'s connecting rods has survived. The wooden replica rods, fitted during the restoration in 1862, were historically inaccurate and had been removed by the Science Museum by 1922.

The connecting rods would have been forged iron, approximately 42 in. long between the big and little end centres. Bearing brasses were fitted to both ends with straps, gibs and tapered keys. It would seem, however, that the connecting rods fitted to drive the crank-strap wheels at the end of *Rocket*'s service career on the Naworth collieries railway were not the same as those fitted to drive the wheels with ball-ended crank-pins, as depicted in the 'Crewe' drawing of 1836, and as now fitted to the locomotive (Section 4.3.2). Fig. 4.62 (p117) compares the two crank-pin fittings, together with the surviving fittings on *Invicta*.

The 'Crewe' drawing shows the big-end brasses apparently encompassing a ball-ended crank-pin, and the little-end with an end-collar on the gudgeon-pin. At each end, the bearing brasses are held to the connecting rod with a strap, single gib and taper key. Each inner brass has a flat back. The arrangement shown on the 'Crewe' drawing is comparable with that now seen on *Invicta*, albeit fitted with a cylindrical crank-pin.

The 'Thompson'/'Stephenson' drawings, however, appear to show a later arrangement, with both ends of the connecting rod apparently encompassing a cylindrical pin with an end-collar. At each end, the bearing brasses are held to the connecting rod with a strap, two gibs and a taper key. All the brasses have round backs.

It would thus seem that the connecting rods shown on the 'Thompson'/'Stephenson' drawings were replacements made necessary by the substitution of the crank-strap wheels and bearing brasses during the locomotive's operating period on the Naworth collieries railway. However, the return of the ball-ended crank-pin wheels to the locomotive when *Rocket* was selected for preservation, would have required the original bearing brasses and connecting rods, which may not have been retained. It is thus likely that none was refitted at Kirkhouse when the locomotive was being made ready for the move to Newcastle in 1851.

4.9.7 Water feed-pumps

Neither of *Rocket*'s water feed-pumps has survived and there are no illustrations of the original water feed-pump arrangements for the locomotive. However, the 'Crewe' drawing shows a cross-head water feed-pump fitted to the left-side of the locomotive in 1836. This would appear to be the same as that later depicted on the 'Thompson'/'Stephenson' drawings, the rear view of which confirms that cross-head water feed-pumps were fitted on both sides of the locomotive by the end of its service (Fig. 4.63):

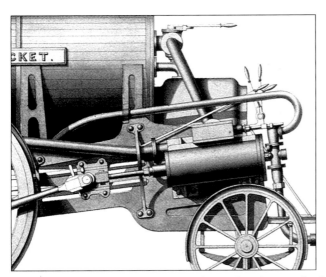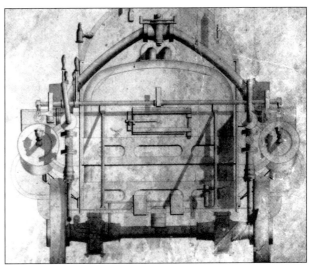

Fig. 4.63 Cross-head water feed-pumps
Source: "Crewe' drawing, Fig. 3.11 and 'Thompson' drawing, Fig. 3.15

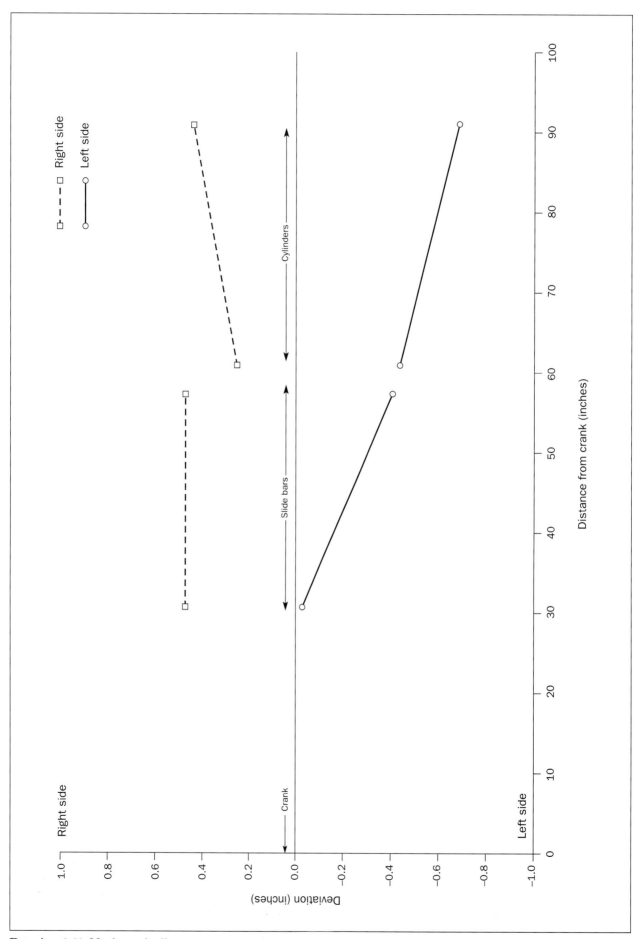

Drawing 4.41 Motion misalignment

The pumps were fitted towards the rear ends of the cylinder mounting plates, inboard and parallel to the cylinders. The pump-rods were fitted to the eyes on the ends of the cross-head gudgeon-pins (Section 4.9.5), which provided the pumping action when the locomotive was in operation. The water was drawn from the tender through leather pipes, which were attached to the pump's feed-pipes under the foot-plate.[74] The boiler feed-pipes were routed over the steam chests and down, between the vertical arms of the cylinder mounting plates, to the boiler clack-valves (Section 4.7.7). The left-side boiler feed-pipe deviated more than the right in order to avoid the valve-handles. Fitting holes on the rear mounting-plate arms provide evidence of securing brackets for these boiler feed-pipes.

4.9.8 Piston travel

The original piston stroke was 16½ in. and the end clearances were each ¾ in.[75] Assuming there were no discs in the cylinders to reduce their clearance volume, the original pistons would have been 5¼ in. long. It would seem that in February 1831, when the cylinders were lowered to 8°, the stroke was increased to 17 in., thus increasing the locomotive's power by 3 per cent. This was made possible because the vertical displacement of the driving axle would have less effect on the piston position. At the same time a replacement driving wheel-set, probably the surviving set, would have been provided, with crank centres correspondingly increased.

It is assumed that, at that time, the connecting-rod length had been set so that the clearance between the cross-heads and the spectacle brackets at the ends of the strokes were equal (at ⅝ in.), as depicted in Drawing 4.40. When the left-side connecting rod was fitted therefore, its length between centres was 42½ in. The right-side connecting rod would appear to have been ¼-in. longer. As a consequence of the fitting of the new shorter pistons in 1833, the overall clearance volume was excessive, and greater at the rear end. The inner dead-centre piston clearance became ¾ in., whilst the outer dead-centre clearance became 1⁷⁄₁₆ in. To reduce the latter to ¾ in., the disc bolted to the rear cover-plate (Section 4.9.3) would have been ¹¹⁄₁₆-in. thick.

4.9.9 Alignment of the driving motion

Rocket's major components are misaligned due to several factors:

• The main frame is out of parallel (Section 4.2.1)

• the driving axle is misaligned by half a degree

• the cylinder mounting plates are both leaning to the left by ½ in. and are not quite parallel to the centre-line

• the slide-bars are not parallel to the mounting plates by ³⁄₁₆ in. on the left side and by ¼ in. on the right side

• the cylinder mounting-blocks on each side vary in width by up to ¼ in.

These are manufacturing and fitting errors, in addition to which there has been general deterioration, for example the right-side cylinder mounting plate has come loose from its angle iron at the front. All of these discrepancies have led to a misalignment of the driving motion.

The cylinders, slide-bars and crank-pins are as much as ½ in. each side of the nominal 5 ft. 8 in. centre-line (Drawing 4.41). These discrepancies were previously addressed by a Science Museum curator (probably Mr E A Forward) in a technical file note.[76] Prior to the removal of the 1862 replica connecting rods , Forward wrote that they were 'very much out of line with the piston rods; that on the right side being jammed against the guide bar bracket and bent'. As he further noted, the distance between the cylinder centre lines is 5 ft 8⅞ in., whilst that between the ball-ended crank-pins on the wheels is an inch less at 5 ft 7⅞ in.

It seems likely that when the locomotive was erected in 1829, it was intended that the cylinder, motion and crank-pin centre-lines were to be 5 ft 8 in. apart. At these

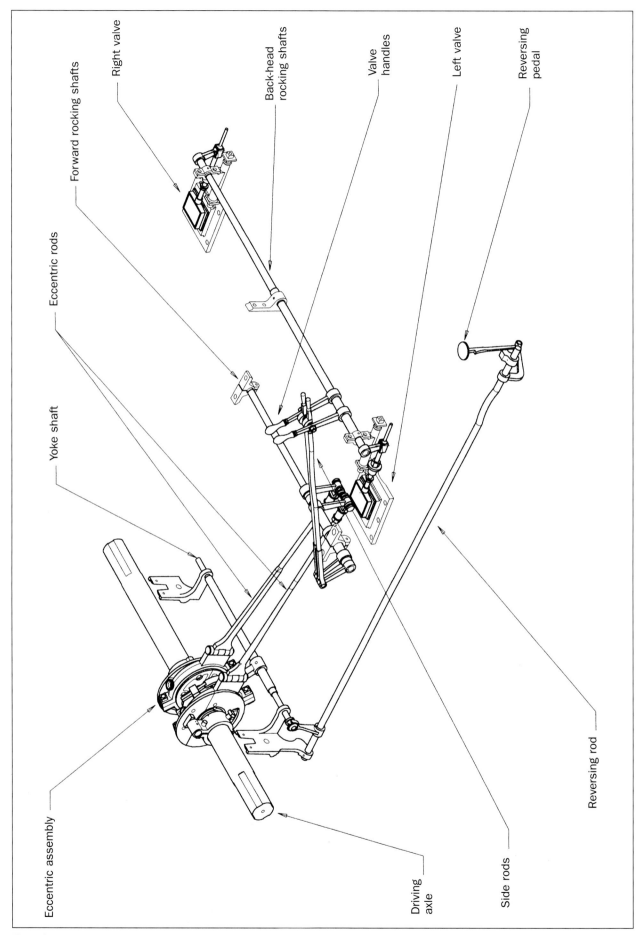

Right valve

Forward rocking shafts

Back-head rocking shafts

Valve handles

Left valve

Reversing pedal

Eccentric rods

Yoke shaft

Eccentric assembly

Reversing rod

Driving axle

Side rods

Drawing 4.42 Valve gear
Projection: isometric view, upper rear left *Scale:* 1:16

centres, the hollow, cast-iron spacer blocks, between the feet of the cylinder castings and the original cylinder mounting-frames would each have been 4½-in.-thick, but adjusted by the fitters to allow for discrepancies.

When the cylinders were lowered, the new mounting plates were fitted further away from the centre-line than the original mounting plates. The left-side plate was 1½ in. further out, whilst the right-side plate was 2½ in. further out to avoid fouling the misaligned firebox saddle (Section 4.6.2). The cylinder spacing blocks, which were probably reused, were, therefore, correspondingly cut back, but by 1 in. and 2 in. respectively. This led to the cylinder centres being one inch further apart than hitherto – namely 5 ft 9in. The corner of the leading left-side upper cylinder spacing block had to be cut back to accommodate the route of the valve-gear side-rods (Fig. 4.66, p118).

The Stephenson Company's 1831 description book retrospectively records 5 ft 9 in. for this centre-line measurement, which may either have been an error or it perhaps recorded the advice from the L&MR of a subsequent change.[77] This increase in the centre-distance suggests that the wheel-set then fitted to *Rocket* correspondingly had a crank-pin centre separation of 5 ft 9 in. However, the surviving wheel-set has 5 ft 8 in. crank-pin centres, which would, nevertheless, have run satisfactorily, this being one of the advantages of ball-ended crank-pins. Slackness in the little-end bearings would have allowed for the connecting rods to be out of alignment by 0.7° as they only moved through an arc of 23°. This might have contributed to the slackness of the gudgeon pins in the cross-heads.

It would seem, therefore, that after 1831, *Rocket* operated successfully for several years with both connecting rods misaligned in respect of their slide-bars, and with the overall cylinder and motion centre-line separation tapering from slightly over 5 ft 9 in. to 5 ft 7⅞ in. at the crank-bosses.

4.10 Valves and valve motion

4.10.1 Introduction

Rocket's original valve motion, to reciprocate the steam valves in the valve chests on the underside of the cylinders (Section 4.9.1), would have been driven by eccentrics fitted to the locomotive's driving axle. Robert Stephenson inferred that the arrangement was a significant advancement over that employed on *Lancashire Witch*, when he reported to Henry Booth that 'I expect the mode for changing the [valve] gear will please you it is now as simple as I can make it and I believe effectual.'(Section 3.3). Stephenson was also reported to have stated that 'this Hand Gear on one of the Locomotives at Liverpool answers as well as any thing possibly can do, and the men like it very much'.[78]

It would seem that the requirement for rapid directional changes at the Rainhill Trials (Appendices 1–3) had induced Stephenson and his team to improve upon the 'limited travel' slip-eccentric valve gear, with which the earlier Stephenson locomotives had been fitted. The surviving arrangement drawings show the method adopted, notably on *Lancashire Witch* and on *Rocket* for the Stockton & Darlington Railway (Section 2.1). The drawing for the latter, which was completed just before *Rocket* was dispatched to Rainhill, shows the axle-stud and eccentric-slot which provided the limited travel slip-eccentric system (Fig. 4.64).

It is likely that *Rocket*'s surviving 'dog-clutch' slip-eccentric valve gear (Drawing 4.42), is largely the 'simple' and 'effectual' valve gear which was fitted to its original 3¼-in.-diameter driving axle. Forward and reverse 'drivers' were clamped to the driving axle, requiring the eccentric cluster to be 'slipped' between them using a pedal-operated reversing mechanism. An improved eccentric cluster was installed when its 4-in.-diameter axle was fitted (Section 4.3.1), but an indication of the form of the original cluster is provided by the surviving assembly fitted to *Invicta*. The new valve gear seems to have been so successful that *Lancashire Witch* was refitted with what was probably a dog-clutch valve gear in September 1829, after only 14 months operation.[79]

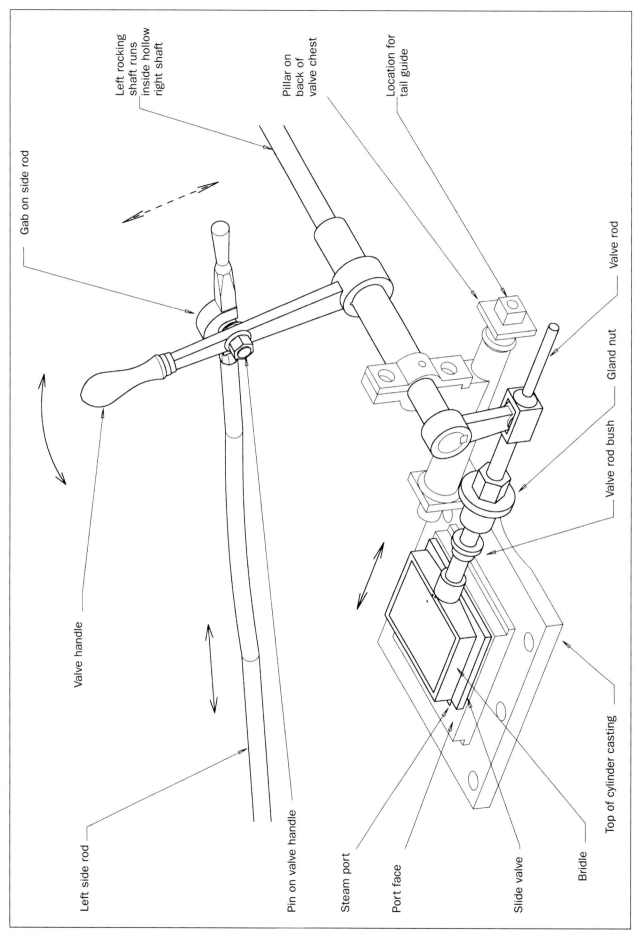

Drawing 4.43 Left valve

Projection: isometric view, upper rear left *Scale:* 1:4

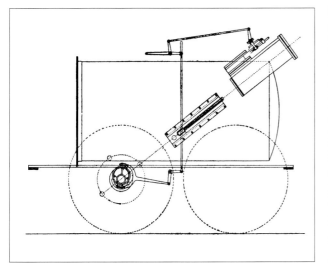

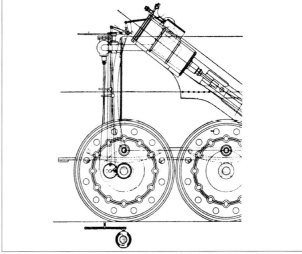

Travelling Engine No.11 *Lancashire Witch*, July 1828   Travelling Engine No.16 *Rocket*, September 1829

Fig. 4.64 Limited travel slip-eccentric valve gear in 1828 and 1829

It is possible that further alterations were made to the valve-gear during *Rocket*'s time on the Liverpool & Manchester and Naworth collieries railways. Repairs may have been necessary, for example, following the serious grooving of the surviving driving axle by the left-hand driver (Section 4.3.4). This could only have been caused by *Rocket* being moved by an external motive force with the valve motion engaged, whilst for some reason being jammed and immovable. Damage to the valve motion, which was possibly caused when *Rocket* was moved from Kirkhouse in 1851, may have been repaired in 1862.

The surviving wrought-iron valve motion was driven by eccentrics through eccentric-rods, forward rocking-shaft, side-rods, valve-levers and back-head rocking-shaft. The 'slip-eccentrics' had a $2\frac{1}{4}$-in. freedom-of-axial-movement between the forward and reverse drivers, which were clamped to the axle. Reversal of the valve motion was achieved by shifting the eccentric cluster between the drivers with a 'yoke' and slider, through a yoke-shaft and reversing-rod, from a foot pedal on the footplate. The valves were manually positioned by the valve levers following disengagement of the side-rod gabs and re-engagement whilst in motion. When the locomotive was moving slowly to a halt, it was possible to reverse the valve motion without the necessity for manual valve positioning, by shifting the slip-eccentrics to engage with the alternative driver.

4.10.2 Steam chests and valves

The 11 in. × 10 in. steam chests are each formed of four-sided, cast-iron bodies secured to a base, formed as part of the top of the cylinder casting (Section 4.9.3), with five bolts into tapped holes (only one bolt remains *in situ* on each side, however). They were closed with a cover-plate, similarly secured with seven square-headed shoulder-bolts (Fig. 4.65, p118).

The steam-chest bodies each incorporate a flange for the steam-inlet pipe from the regulator (Section 4.9.2) and a tapped boss for the valve-spindle gland. The bronze gland-nuts have hexagonal heads. The thread between the left-side gland-socket and the gland is filled, somewhat strangely, with hemp. The hemp would originally have been in the packing space but at some stage after the end of service it has been incorrectly refitted. Also on the rear face there is an $11\frac{1}{4}$-in.-long pillar, which supports a bronze bearing for the back-head rocking-shaft. It also supported the valve-rod tail-guide, which is now missing.

The $4\frac{1}{4}$ in. × $5\frac{3}{4}$ in. conventional 'D'-type bronze slide-valves are each fitted to a cast-iron bridle, on the rear of which is a tapped socket to receive the threaded end of the valve rod (Drawing 4.43). There are two tapped holes and a hollow square on the inside of the left valve chest cover. These were for a spring arrangement to hold the valve against its seat when the cylinders were in their original position (Section 4.9.1).

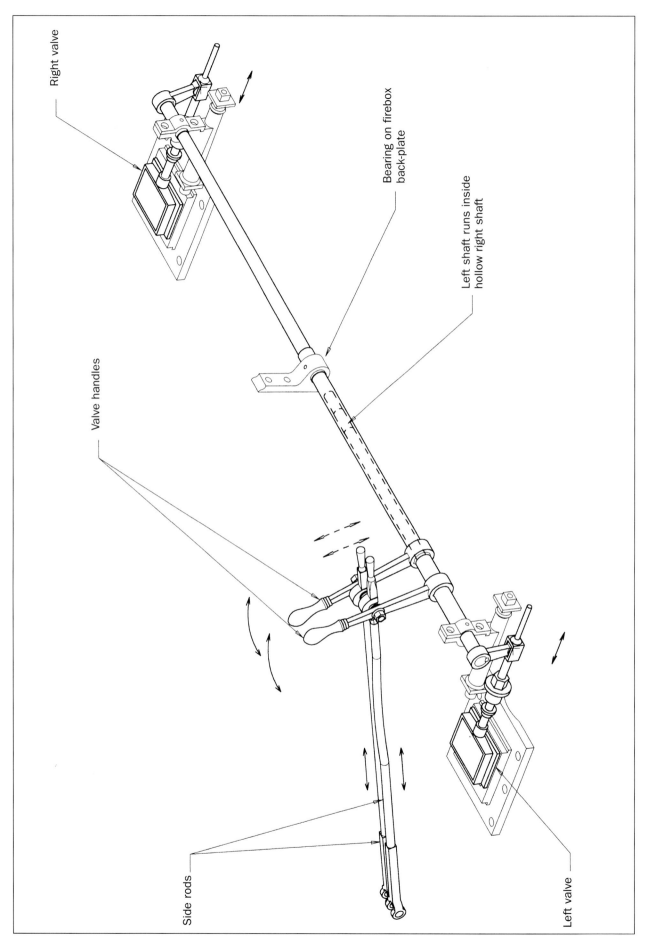

Right valve

Bearing on firebox
back-plate

Left shaft runs inside
hollow right shaft

Valve handles

Side rods

Left valve

Drawing 4.44 Valve gear back-head rocking shafts
Projection: isometric view, upper rear left *Scale:* 1:8.4

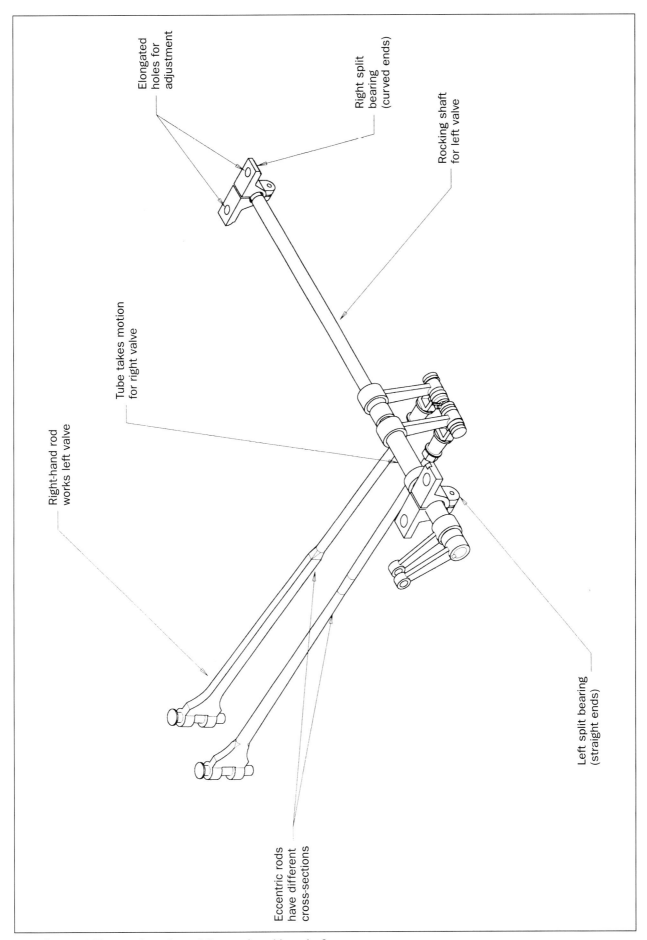

Drawing 4.45 Eccentric rods and forward rocking shafts
Projection: isometric view, upper rear left *Scale:* 1:8

Elongated holes for adjustment

Right split bearing (curved ends)

Rocking shaft for left valve

Tube takes motion for right valve

Right-hand rod works left valve

Left split bearing (straight ends)

Eccentric rods have different cross-sections

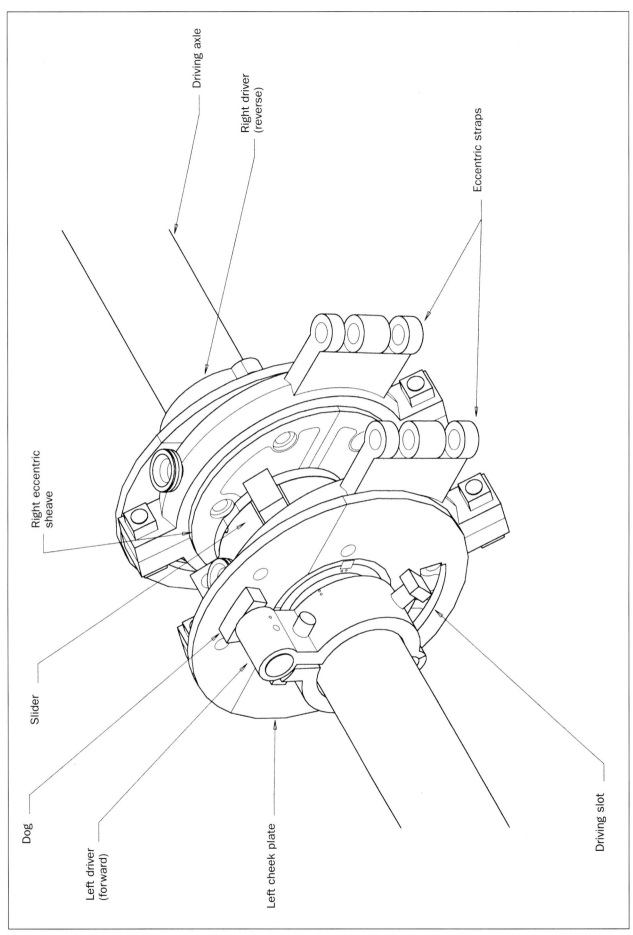

Driving axle

Right driver
(reverse)

Eccentric straps

Right eccentric
sheave

Slider

Dog

Left driver
(forward)

Left cheek plate

Driving slot

Drawing 4.46 Eccentric assembly

Projection: isometric view, upper rear left *Scale:* 1:4

There are no marks left by any such mechanism on the back of the valve, indicating that the valves are not original.

4.10.3 Valve rods and levers

The ³⁄₄-in.-diameter valve rods have buckles which were reciprocated by round-ended levers, keyed to the ends of the back-plate rocking-shafts. The inner end of the 1¹⁄₂-in.-diameter left-side rocking-shaft was machined down to ¹⁵⁄₁₆ in. and inserted within the 1³⁄₈-in.-diameter tube-ended rocking-shaft serving the right-side valve, to permit concentric oscillation of the two shafts (Drawing 4.44). The centre bearing is bolted to the firebox back-plate above the firehole. When the rocking-shaft was repositioned, probably in February 1831, the firebox door had to be reduced in height and the upper part of the firehole was blanked off (Section 4.6.3).

The rocking-shafts were oscillated by two wrought-iron valve levers, which were normally driven by the side-rods, through pins fitted at 6-in. centres to the shaft. The levers would have been disengaged by the locomotive's driver to allow manual positioning of the valves for reversal and starting from stall (Fig 4.66, p118).

The side-rods, on the left-side of the locomotive, transmitted reciprocating movement from the side-rod levers on the forward rocking-shaft to the valve-lever pins, a centre to centre distance of 44 in. Gabs and handles were forged into the rear ends of the rods to allow the driver to disengage them from the valve-lever pins. The forging of the handles differs slightly, suggesting the work of different smiths. The left-hand rod was joggled into a shallow crank to avoid the steam pipe.

The forward rocking-shafts were formed as two concentric components. That serving the left-side valve is an 1¹⁄₈-in.-diameter rod, from the right-side frame-mounted bearing to the outer side-rod lever on the left side of the locomotive, to which is keyed its lever-arm (Drawing 4.45). That serving the right-side valve is a 1³⁄₄-in.-diameter tube, through which the left-valve rocking-shaft passes, from the inner side-rod lever and frame-mounted bearing to its eccentric-rod lever. This arrangement thus sees a crossover of the motion, with the left-side eccentric-rod driving the right-side valve and vice-versa.

The two forward rocking-shaft bronze bearings may not be those originally fitted to the frames, as there is evidence of alterations on the frame and cut-outs in the rear of the cylinder mounting-plate angle irons (Section 4.2.8). The rocking-shaft was moved 1¹⁄₂ in. to the left when the cylinders were repositioned, so that the side-rods avoided the mounting plates. The right-side bearing was repositioned to the left to allow the same cross-shaft to be used. Each bearing is formed of two halves joined with a square shoulder-screw. The two bearings, bolted to the frame with elongated fixing holes to allow for adjustment, are of different formation and material, suggesting different sources.

The forward rocking-shaft levers are attached to the eccentric-rods with knuckle-joints, to which they were screwed for adjustment. There is a lock-nut on the left rod (Fig. 4.67, p118). The two eccentric-rods, which transmitted reciprocating movement from the eccentrics to the forward rocking-shaft, are of different form and length, suggesting one is a replacement. The left-hand rod is 44⁵⁄₈ in. long between the hinge and knuckle-joint centres, the right one being 43¹⁄₈ in. At their leading end, they were forged into a rectangular section with twin eyes, hinged to the eccentric-strap. They are identified with a painted 'LT' and 'RT' on their inner front faces.

4.10.4 Eccentric assembly

The eccentric assembly on the driving axle is offset 5 in. to the left of the locomotive centre-line (Drawing 4.46). The assembly, comprising straps, eccentrics, slider, cheek plates and sleeve, is an improvement upon that fitted on *Invicta*, which is not split and could not be fitted with the wheels in place (comparison Fig. 4.68, p119).

The eccentrics on *Rocket* are fitted to a sleeve which allows the assembly lateral movement along the axle between the drivers (Drawing 4.47). The 8-in.-long iron

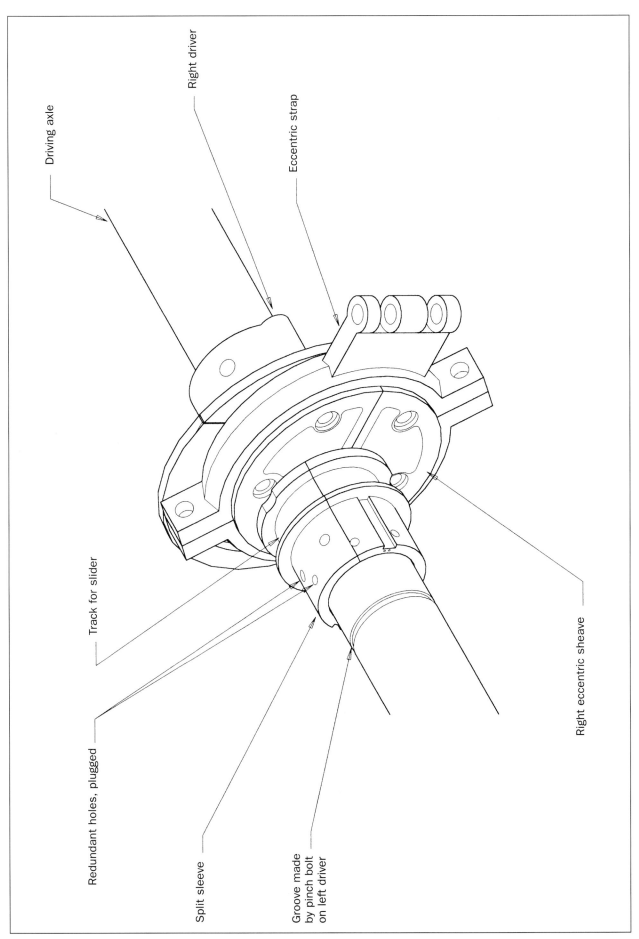

Driving axle

Right driver

Eccentric strap

Track for slider

Redundant holes, plugged

Split sleeve

Groove made
by pinch bolt
on left driver

Right eccentric sheave

Drawing 4.47 Eccentric assembly, left-side components removed
Projection: isometric view, upper rear left *Scale:* 1:4

sleeve, split along its length into halves, shows evidence of two sets of alterations, which were either refitments during the life of the locomotive or multiple attempts to achieve the surviving fitting. It is divided axially into three sections by two ribs, the outer sections being for the eccentrics and the centre for the slider. Both ribs were originally 0.485 in. wide, but the left-hand has been machined down to 0.238 in. to accommodate a wider slider (Fig. 4.69, p119).

The eccentrics are fitted to the sleeve by axial keys and radial, counter-sunk screws fitted into tapped holes. There is evidence in the sleeve of two previous attempts to tap these fixing holes. One of the holes has tapped through into the existing keyway, indicating the pre-existence of the latter. Also, at each end of the sleeve, there is a set of 1/2-in.-diameter radial holes which have been plugged. They were for fixing a different type of eccentric sheave.

The two eccentrics are each formed of two 2³⁄₈-in.-wide cast-iron sheaves, the split line being along the line of eccentricity, and not at right angles to it as became conventional on later locomotives. The casting was not of the highest quality with several 'blow-holes' being evident. The throw is 1½ in. The sheaves were located to each other with tongue-and-groove joints, and were held together with a stud and square nuts. Keyways were cut in both sheaves to coincide with the sleeve keyways. One of the left-hand eccentric sheaves has broken through a corner of the keyway, and the broken piece is held in place by the cheek-plate and eccentric-strap. The rim of the castings is a strap-bearing surface, through which counter-sunk holes were drilled to receive the sleeve-fitting screws. There is evidence of a change in the location of these fitting holes, the redundant holes having been plugged and ground smooth to the profile of both the strap-bearing and sleeve surfaces. The features of the eccentrics are shown in Fig. 4.70, p119.

The eccentric casting is extended to form a spigot on which to locate the cheek-plates. Each sheave also incorporates two holes through which bolts are inserted which are screwed into tapped holes in the cheek-plates. The cheek-plates, which are each formed of two asymmetric 0.475-in.-thick wrought-iron plates, whose external diameter is 13 in., are each bolted across both eccentric halves (Drawing 4.48).

The larger cheek-plates incorporate 2³⁄₄-in.-long concentric driving slots for the driver dogs, which are much longer than those cut into the cheek-plates on *Invicta*. The latter are only just larger than the dogs themselves and valve-gear reversal in motion was only possible at slow speeds. It is possible that *Rocket*'s slots were of a similar size to begin with, but have been significantly extended as a means of reversing at higher speeds. This may have been undertaken on the Naworth collieries system, where frequent changes of direction while shunting coal wagons may have been called for. There is a witness of a groove caused by the rubbing of the dogs prior to engagement in the slots. In addition, the driving surfaces have been worn by the surviving dogs, which are approximately ¼-in. narrower than the slots. The cheek-plates are shown in Fig. 4.71, p120.

The sleeve and driving axle show no evidence of the use of a 'limited travel' reversing stud, as has been suggested may have been used to make reversal of *Rocket*'s valves easier and achievable at a higher speed.[80] An axle-fitted stud within a circumferential slot in the sleeve would have allowed it to rotate around the axle, the limitations of which would be adjacent to the dogs themselves, allowing ready engagement. It is possible that such an arrangement was included with the early eccentric assembly fitted to the 3¼-in.-diameter axle, but there is no evidence of its use on *Invicta* and, had it been successful, it would have featured in the surviving assembly.

The eccentric-straps are two-piece bronze castings (with 11-in. outside diameters), the rear ones including a three-eye extension for the eccentric-rod hinge. The castings, which ran within the eccentric channels, have lugs at both ends that are joined by square-headed bolts. The upper castings are fitted with lubrication-oil cups which are screwed into tapped holes. Each casting is stamped with an identification number and fitters' marks (Fig. 4.72, p120). The numbers are 15, 16, 19 and 02, which suggests that they were drawn from a batch of at least 5 sets of straps, possibly indicating an early example of standardisation for locomotive components.

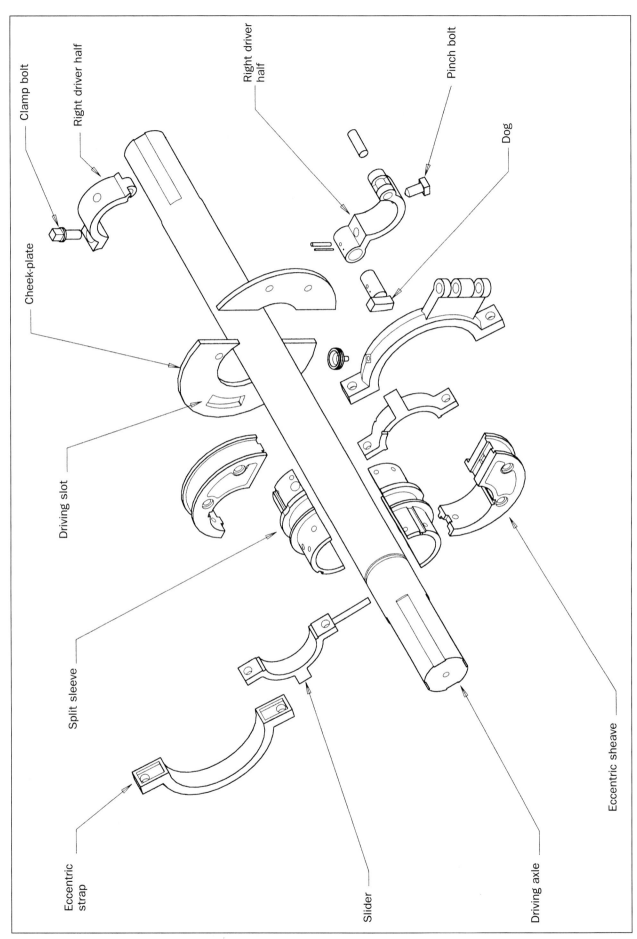

Drawing 4.48 Eccentric assembly, right-side components, exploded
Projection: isometric view, upper rear left *Scale:* 1:8

4.10.5 Drivers

The 2½-in.-wide drivers, fitted to the 4-in.-diameter driving axle, are each formed of two castings, hinged with a pin to enable them to be fitted around the axle and adjusted (Drawing 4.48). The halves are drawn together with square-headed clamp-bolts into tapped holes, tangential to the axle, and tightened to clamp the driver around the axle. The drivers on *Invicta* are similarly clamped in this way (Fig. 4.68, p119).

In addition, however, each driver is secured to the axle with a radial pinch-bolt tightened onto the axle. Provision appears to have been made for a second or alternative bolt, as there is an unused hole in the other half of the driver. It is likely that the pinch-bolts were the additional means of securing the drivers, which was undertaken on all the L&MR locomotives from April 1833 by order of the Directors and on the recommendation of John Melling (Section 3.8). However, it should be noted that the bolts are tightened onto the axle, rather than into the axle as recorded in the minutes. The dog of the left-hand driver was engaged in the cheek-plate on the occasion that *Rocket* was moved, seemingly with its valve-gear jammed, and which caused the tightened pinch-bolt to score a deep groove around the axle circumference (Section 4.10.1). There is an adjacent 1¼-in.-long scar which suggests that the driver had slipped on at least one occasion since 1833.

Each dog is a forged extension to a 1⁵⁄₁₆-in.-diameter pin inserted into an axial eye in the casting outside of the clamp-bolt. The dogs may have been changed during the working life of the locomotive, as experience was gained in the requirements for a robust fitting to avoid undue maintenance and refitting. It is possible that the original dogs, around the 3¼-in.-diameter axle, may have been similar to the surviving slender examples on *Invicta* (Fig. 4.68, p119), which were extensions to the drivers themselves. *Rocket*'s surviving dogs (0.808 in. high) are wedge-form and concentric to the axle (Fig. 4.73, p121).

It is possible that an earlier form may have been 1⅛ in. high as suggested by the size of the driving-slots in the eccentric cheek-plates. That the slots in the latter have been worn to the smaller dimension further suggests that the present dogs had been fitted for much of the latter part of the locomotive's life. The left-hand dog, which drove the valves in forward motion, is 2.33 in. long, whilst the right-hand dog for reverse motion, is only 2.03 in. long. Both drivers have an 18° freedom-of-movement within the driving-slots.

4.10.6 Reversing mechanism

The surviving reversing gear is possibly the original mechanism adapted to suit the later 4-in.-diameter axle (Drawing 4.49). The eccentric assembly is shifted between the drivers by a slider, between the ribs of the sleeve, which is moved by a 'yoke' attached to a cross-shaft. This compares with a much simpler 'yoke' worked directly off a cross-shaft on *Invicta*, as shown in Fig. 4.74, p121.

The slider is a two-part forged ring, bolted together through front and rear lugs. The lower rear lug has a peg screwed into it for insertion into the yoke. The top and bottom of the ring centres have forged radial lugs with 'D'-form holes, through which are inserted the yoke pegs. On each side of the upper leading face of the slider is a half-hole, through which lubricant would have been fed to the slider's bearing surface.

The forged yoke has 4½-in.-long upper and lower 'D'-form pegs, extending from its 'U'-form jaws, which were fitted into the slider's lugs. The yoke's square-section body is drilled with an 0.530-in.-diameter hole to receive the slider's peg (Fig. 4.75, p122).

There is evidence that the yoke was originally keyed to its cross-shaft, but the fixing has latterly been a ⁷⁄₁₆-in.-diameter pin. The yoke shaft has been machined to four different diameters along its length to suit its bearings, the yoke itself and the reversing-rod 'bobbin'.

The two yoke-shaft slide-bearings are simple eyes in the arms of brackets bolted to the rear of the driving-axle horns with the keep-bolts (Section 4.2.6). The brackets may be original fittings, which were adapted to the replacement horns, following the

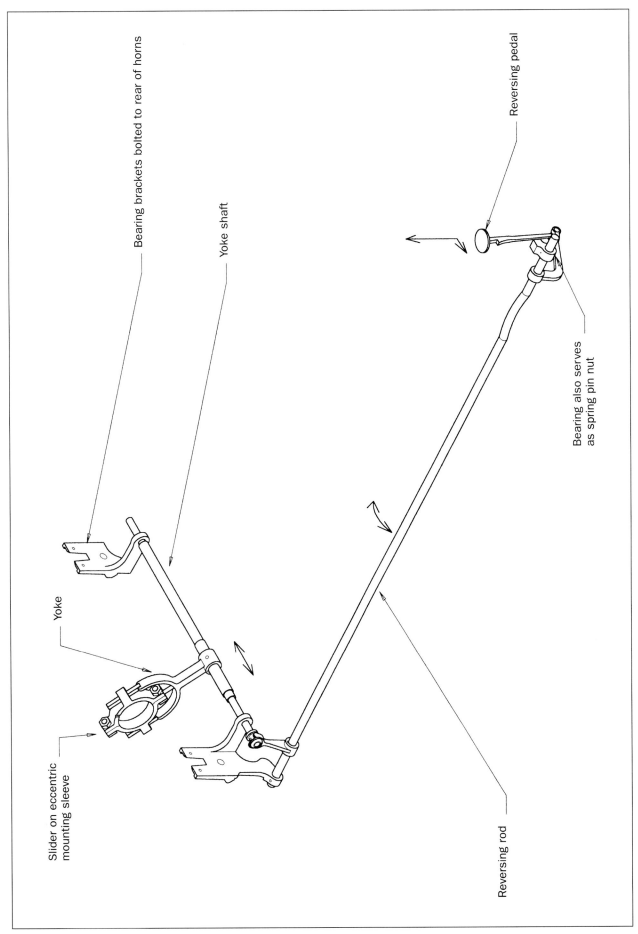

Drawing 4.49 Reversing gear
Projection: isometric view, upper rear left *Scale:* 1:12

introduction of the 4-in.-diameter driving axle. This indicates that the original horns were the same width as the surviving ones. Two holes on their upper edge were not reused. The left-side bracket is forged with an eye on an underside extension, being the bearing for the leading-end of the reversing rod (Fig. 4.76, p122).

The yoke shaft is slid sideways by a fork-ended lever, engaged in the 'bobbin' fitted to the left-hand end of the yoke shaft. The lever is keyed onto the 1-in.-diameter, 8 ft 2-in.-long reversing rod, which is routed along the left side of the locomotive from the bearing bracket to a rear-end bearing under the footplate. The rod has a shallow crank towards the rear to avoid a conflict with the rear axle. The rear bearing is a forged eye with a short arm, tapped to receive the trailing spring-hanger pin (for the carrying wheelset) to which it is secured.

The wrought-iron pedal shaft, which is keyed onto the reversing rod, was cranked in the erroneous belief that it would provide better leverage with the arm at a right-angle to the pedal. It passes between the rear spring-hangers and the horn of the carrying-axle, the springs for which had been fitted to its underside (Section 4.2.6). The pedal shaft is attached to the pedal with a knuckle joint. The 12-in.-long pedal, which passes through the footplate, has a 4-in. foot-travel. A leaf-spring, probably 'J'-shaped and bolted to the right side of the footplate (Section 4.2.5), would have held the pedal in the up position for forward travel. For operating the locomotive in reverse, the pedal would have been depressed and latched, with a notch, under the footplate (Fig. 4.77, p122).

4.10.7 Valve events

The angles between the dogs (drivers) and cranks were measured. The right-side (reverse) dog and axle adjacent to it are each marked with a single centre punch mark and scribe line. Calculations indicate that this driver might be in its original position. The left (forward) dog and the axle adjacent to it are marked with double dots but no scribe line (Fig. 4.19, p110). Similar calculations show that it is also in a position near to where it would have driven the locomotive in reverse. Its position would have allowed the eccentric assembly to engage with either driver without rotation, and the locomotive could not have operated in this condition. This infers that the valve gear was reassembled in these positions, and marked with punch marks, after the end of its working life, probably in 1862, by a fitter who did not understand its operation. The scoring caused by the left-hand dog slipping round the axle has obliterated any marks left by the pinch-bolt in its original position, which could not, therefore, be ascertained. The valve event calculations were performed using the reverse position for the left-hand cylinder. The angle of advance and steam lap were measured to be 20° and 0.081 in. respectively. The results of the calculations are shown in Appendix 9 and the valve ellipse is illustrated in Fig. 4.78.

The steam cut-off was estimated to be 95.5 per cent of the piston stroke at the head end and 94 per cent at the crank end. The pressure-volume graph (Fig. 4.79), consequently, is nearly rectangular. Such a long cut-off allowed very little expansion, but would have been ideal for use on the colliery railway. A long cut-off would give the maximum tractive effort and reduce the chances of one cylinder being cut off when the locomotive was starting from stationary. No account has been taken of the lost motion. There was considerable wear in the four joints and in the bearings of the two rocking-shafts. The effect would be to lengthen the cut-off.

In the absence of the original eccentric assembly and valves, it is not possible to estimate the original valve timing, but since one of the main limitations on locomotive performance was steam generation, it is likely that the Stephensons used a shorter cut-off. A longer valve would have been necessary to achieve this.

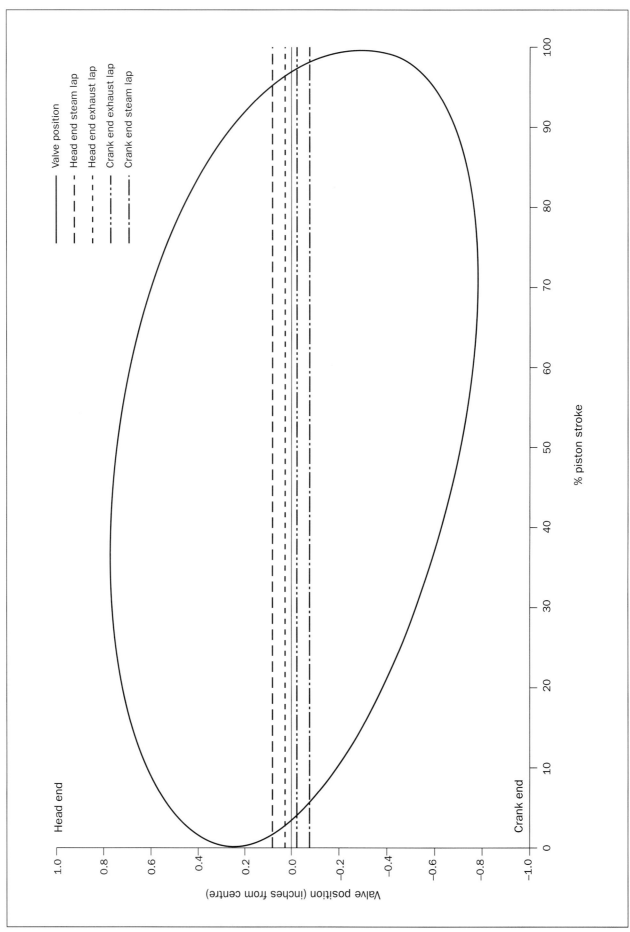

Fig. 4.78 Valve ellipse

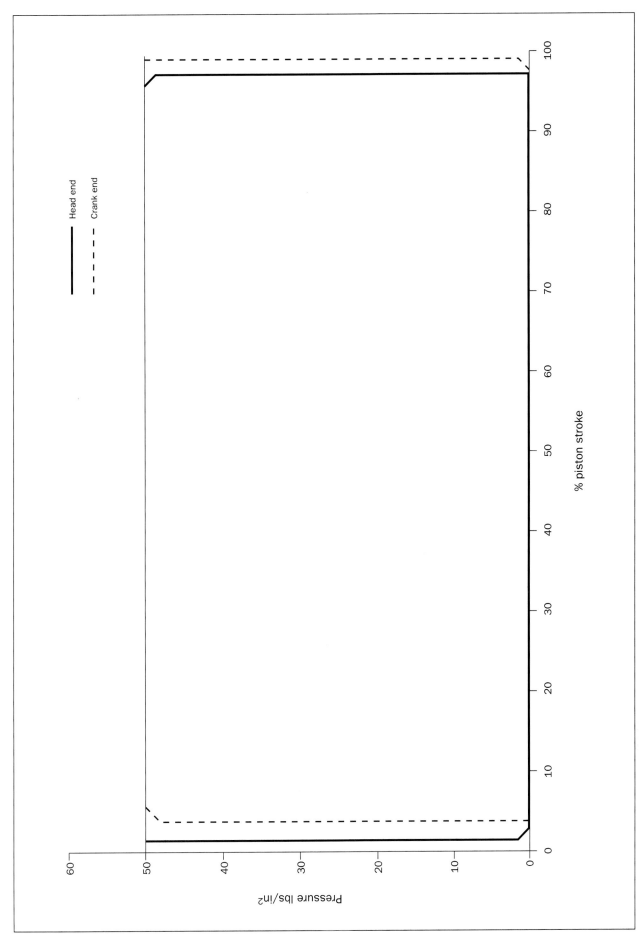

Fig. 4.79 P-V diagram

1 *Larger & Working Objects, A Guide to their Preservation and Care*, Museums and Galleries Commission, 1997, relevant pieces of 'statute law' are listed on p52, 'A Forest of Legislation'.

2 *Ibid.*, section 2, 'Care and Conservation', pp13–16.

3 W P Marshall (for R Stephenson & Co.), *Description of The Patent Locomotive Steam Engine* &c., first published in Thomas Tredgold, *The Steam Engine: Its Invention and Progressive Improvement* &c. (London, 1837) and separately published by John Weale (London, 1838) p60. However, in the work by Chev. F M G De Pambour, *A Practical Treatise on Locomotive Engines Upon Railways* (London, 1836) p29, he refers only to horsehair buffers being in use on the L&MR during the trials on the line in 1834.

4 Michael R Bailey, *Robert Stephenson & Co. 1823–1836*, unpublished MA thesis (University of Newcastle on Tyne, 1984) pp306–310.

5 Nicholas Wood, *A Practical Treatise on Railroads* &c, second edition (London, 1831) p72.

6 Three of the crank rings from *Pride of Newcastle* have been preserved in the Smithsonian Institution, Washington DC. Two wooden driving wheels, believed to have been fitted to 'John Bull', built by R Stephenson & Co. in 1831 for the Camden & Amboy Railroad in New Jersey, USA, have been preserved. One wheel was presented to the Smithsonian Institution in Washington DC by the Pennsylvania Railroad in 1894 (USNM 181194), whilst the other is now on display in the Railroad Museum of Pennsylvania. Corroborative provenance is, however, lacking, and it is possible that the wheels are of later, American manufacture. They are of different construction from the surviving wheels on *Rocket*.

7 R Stephenson & Co. Ledger 1823–1831, R Stephenson & Co. Collection, National Railway Museum, folio 214.

8 *Ibid.*, folio 288.

9 Notebook of John Rastrick, Science Museum, inv. no. 1945-108, p18, entry for 5 October 1829.

10 James Scott Walker, *An Accurate Description of the Liverpool and Manchester Rail-Way* (Liverpool, 1830) p29.

11 R Stephenson & Co. 'Description Book 1831', R Stephenson & Co. Collection, *op. cit.* (7), entry for the 'Liverpool Prize Engine'. Also, Rastrick's Notebook, *op. cit.* (9), p18, confirms the axle diameter as being 3¼ in.

12 R Stephenson & Co. works order and delivery books, R Stephenson & Co. Collection, *op. cit.* (7), *passim.*

13 Thomas Hunt, letter to *The Engineer*, 24 October 1884, p320.

14 Minute book of the Directors of the L&MR 1833–1836, PRO Rail 371/3, p41, entry for 3 June 1833, relating to failure of several locomotive wheels.

15 Marshall, *op. cit.* (3), p54.

16 Similar reinforcing bands have been noted by the authors, fitted to the naves of the *c.*1840 *Braddyll* locomotive in the Timothy Hackworth Museum, Shildon, County Durham.

17 Lieut. Peter Lecount, entry 'Railways' in the seventh edition of *Encyclopaedia Britannica*, reproduced as a separate publication, *A Practical Treatise on Railways* &c. (Edinburgh, 1839) p129.

18 Science Museum *Rocket* technical file, ScM 60, internal memoranda on Department of Science and Art stationery and confirmation of order from H & S Barker & Co.

19 R Stephenson & Co. Ledger, *op. cit.* (7), folio 210, entry for 11 August 1829, itemises all the company's boiler-plate intake for the previous quarter.

20 *Invicta* of 1830 is displayed at the Canterbury Heritage Museum, and 'John Bull' of 1831 at the Smithsonian Institution, Washington DC. See John H White Jr, 'John Bull: 150 years The Restoration', published in *American Heritage* (August–September 1981), *Railroad History*, Bulletin no. 144 (1981) of the Railway & Locomotive Historical Society, and *Railfan & Railroad* (January 1982) pp40 and 43.

21 Rastrick, Notebook, *op. cit.* (9), referred to the thickness as being '¼ In thick full'.

22 William Fairbairn, *Useful Information for Engineers*, fourth edition (London, 1864) pp41–43.

23 N P Burgh, *A Practical Treatise on Boilers and Boiler-making* (London, 1873) p366.

24 Rastrick, *op. cit.* (21).

25 R Stephenson & Co. Ledger 1823–1831, *op. cit.* (7).

26 Walker, *op. cit.* (10), p29. When writing, Walker states (p46) that *North Star* had been delivered and another (i.e., *Planet*) is expected (arrived September 1830).

27 *Memorandum on the Replica of the "Rocket" Constructed by Robert Stephenson & Co., Limited* (Darlington, 1929) for Henry Ford Esq., pp10 and 11.

28 R Armstrong, *A Practical Essay on Steam Engine Boilers* &c. (Manchester, 1838) pp34–5, Art. 52.

29 James Nasmyth sketch of September 1830, reproduced in *The Engineer*, 12 September 1884, p210.

30 Rastrick Notebook, *op. cit.* (9), p18.

31 During the manufacture of the 1979 replica, Mr Michael Satow OBE, agreed with Michael Bailey that the dome was historically erroneous, but that it would be operationally and aesthetically important for what was to be a 'high-profile' replica.

32 Frances Anne Kemble, *Record of a Girlhood*, 3 vols (London, 1878) vol.1, p160, letter written from Liverpool on 26 August 1830.

33 Nasmyth sketch, *op. cit.* (29).

34 Letter IWB [Isaac Boulton] to *The Engineer*, 26 September 1884, p244.

35 The importance of the water level was understood by the consultants (Messrs E A Forward, Science Museum curator, J G H Warren, former Chief Draughtsman at Robert Stephenson & Co. and C F Dendy Marshall, locomotive historian and later President of The Newcomen Society, in consultation with R Stephenson & Co.) who considered *Rocket*'s original design when preparing the drawings for the 'Ford' replica in 1929. The Memorandum of their findings, however, *op. cit.* (27) pp2–8 and 13–14, states that the mean water level was 1¾ in. above the boiler centre-line, indicating that they made two incorrect assumptions. Firstly, they believed that the original water gauge had been

centrally fitted in respect of the water level and, secondly, that the mean water level would have been in the centre of the water gauge.

36 Rastrick Notebook, *op. cit.* (9) pp64–71.

37 R Stephenson & Co. Ledger, 1823–1831, *op. cit.* (7) folio 228, debit entry for quarter ending 31 December 1829.

38 Bailey, *op. cit.* (4) pp298–301.

39 Correspondence between BICC Ltd and Michael Bailey, January 1980. The history of the company does not pursue this claim; see John Morton, *Thomas Bolton & Sons Ltd. 1783–1983* (Ashbourne, 1983) pp32–35.

40 Rastrick Notebook, *op. cit.* (9) p64.

41 Manuscript memorandum by J D Wardale to accompany his two drawings of *Rocket*, dated 25 January 1858. See chapter 3, note 41. Other authors have repeated the 2½ in. dimension, for example William Prime Marshall, 'Evolution of the Locomotive Engine', *Minutes of Proceedings of the Institution of Civil Engineers*, CXXXIII (1898) p256.

42 Rastrick Notebook, *op. cit.* (9) pp64–5.

43 There is extensive correspondence in the Science Museum files concerning the design of the firebox, between the replica consultants, Messrs E A Forward, J G H Warren, and C F Dendy Marshall and Mr C N Goodall, Managing Director of Robert Stephenson & Co. Ltd; Science Museum correspondence files ScM60, ScM1631 and R427.

44 Memorandum, *op. cit.* (27) pp2–8, 13–14.

45 Report in the *Manchester Guardian*, Saturday, 4 September 1830. An assembled crowd at Edge Hill tunnel mouth witnessed the glare and sparks as the trains passed under Wavertree Lane.

46 Minutes of the Sub-Committee of Management of the L&MR 1832–1833, PRO Rail 371/8, p233, entry for 24 January 1833.

47 Minutes of the Sub-Committee of Management of the L&MR 1833–1839, PRO Rail 371/10, p35, entry for 27 June 1833.

48 Patent no. 7410, enrolled 26 January 1838. For a general description, see also Luke Hebert, *The Engineer and Mechanics Encyclopaedia* &c., 2 vols (London, 1849) vol. II, p475.

49 Patent no. 6920, enrolled 2 May 1836. Gray's proposal was considered by the L&MR's Sub-Committee of Management, *op. cit.* (47) p138, entry for 26 November 1835.

50 Wardale Memorandum, *op. cit.* section 3.4, note no. 41.

51 *Newcastle Courant*, 1 August 1829.

52 R Stephenson & Co. Ledger, *op. cit.* (7) folio 214.

53 Sub-Committee minutes, *op. cit.* (46) p23, entry for 27 July 1831.

54 John Abbot made the copper tubes for the later Stephenson locomotives in 1830. R Stephenson & Co. Ledger, *op. cit.* (7) folio 277, entry for 30 September 1830.

55 Samuel Smiles, *Lives of the Engineers*, vol.III (London, 1862) p264. Also J C Jeaffreson, *The Life of Robert Stephenson FRS*, 2 vols (London, 1864) vol. I, pp139–140.

56 Letter from George Phipps to *The Engineer*, 24 September 1880, p230.

57 David Stevenson, 'Observations on the Liverpool & Manchester Railway', *Transactions of the Royal Scottish Society of Arts*, I (1841) p47, paper read before the Society on 25 February 1835.

58 Rastrick Notebook, *op. cit.* (9) p18.

59 Bailey, *op. cit.* (4) pp301–303.

60 Stevenson, *op. cit.* (57) p47.

61 Sub-Committee minutes, *op. cit.* (46) p212, entry for 15 November 1832.

62 Sub-Committee minutes, *op. cit.* (47) pp11–12, entries for 18 and 24 April 1833.

63 Rastrick Notebook, *op. cit.* (9) pp64–71.

64 Letter from Rob. Stannard to *The Engineer*, 17 October 1884, p303.

65 Bailey, *op. cit.* (4) pp33–35 and 275–6.

66 Rastrick Notebook, *op. cit.* (9) p18.

67 Incorrectly entered as 35° in the Stephenson Company's Description Book, *op. cit.* (11).

68 The left-side cylinder and piston from *Pride of Newcastle* is displayed in the Smithsonian Institution, US National Museum, Washington DC, collection no.180,922.

69 Elijah Galloway, *The History of the Steam Engine*, second edition (London, 1828) pp75–6.

70 John Scott Russell, 'On The Nature, Properties, and Applications of Steam and on Steam Navigation', *Encyclopaedia Britannica*, seventh edition (Edinburgh, 1841) p339.

71 Note from Smithsonian Institution to R Stephenson & Co., 28 May 1935, contained in R Stephenson & Co. Collection, *op. cit.* (7) folder 9.

72 Marshall, *op. cit.* (3) p29.

73 John Bourne, *A Treatise On The Steam Engine* (London, 1846) p195.

74 Walker, *op. cit.* (10) p29.

75 Rastrick Notebook, *op. cit.* (9) pp18 and 71. Also, Wood, *op. cit.* (5) p382.

76 Science Museum technical file note (1862–5), headed 'Lowering Cylinders Connecting rods', undated but from Edwardian period.

77 R Stephenson & Co. Description Book, *op. cit.* (11) p6, entry for 'Premium Engine'.

78 Robert Stephenson quoted by Harris Dickinson, Chief Clerk to R Stephenson & Co. in letter to the Stockton & Darlington Railway, Newcastle-upon-Tyne 29 October 1829, PRO, Rail 667/984.

79 R Stephenson & Co. Ledger, *op. cit.* (7) folio 214. The entries are for '2 Eccentric Sheeves & 4 Plates' weighing 2 qr. 7 lb. and charged out at 9/2d, and '4 Brass Eccentric Straps & Nuts', weighing 22 lb. and charged out at 25/8d.

80 Ian Davidson, 'Reversing Rocket', *The Newcomen Bulletin*, no.157 (December 1993) pp14–16. Also correspondence with Michael Bailey, July–October 1989.

5 Interpretation of *Rocket*

5.1 Introduction

Rocket is displayed in much the same condition as it was in 1862, apart from the removal of some original and erroneous replica components and the replacement of its trailing wheels and chimney. When the locomotive was being prepared for exhibition in that year, the Patent Office Museum, with the assistance of Robert Stephenson & Co., had pursued a strategy for its presentation, albeit one which was historically inaccurate. Although unwritten, it would seem that this had been to recreate a complete locomotive from the surviving remains to display the prime example of motive power from the dawn of the main-line railway era. Such strategy ignored one of the fundamental opportunities of the locomotive's interpretation, however, namely the extent and speed of the technological evolution in the four years or so between *Rocket*'s manufacture in 1829 and its last major modification in 1833. Hence, there was a blurred and confusing interpretation between the locomotive as built and in its end-of-service condition.

Between 1862 and 1914 there developed a growing interest in, and understanding of, *Rocket*'s history and its contribution to technological development. Some minor changes were made, including the substitution of the carrying wheels, which did not however lead to greater authenticity (Section 3.10).[1] In *c.*1914, the Science Museum curator, Mr E A Forward, proposed significant improvements to *Rocket*'s interpretation.[2] He determined that '…any restoration should tend to complete the engine as it was in its last working state…', to meet which requirement, he proposed replicating most of the missing components and replacing the erroneous 1862 replica components with improvements.

To fulfil this strategy, however, Forward proposed to return the locomotive to its 1836 condition, probably because of the existence of, and his reliance upon, the 'Crewe' drawing (Fig. 3.11) as providing the best evidence of *Rocket*'s latter-day appearance. At that time, the provenance of the 'Stephenson' drawing (Fig. 3.14, p107) would not have been understood and the 'Thompson' drawing (Fig. 3.15, p107) remained in the private possession of his heirs and was not known at the Science Museum. The strategy appears to have been delayed by the First World War, but was taken up again in a piecemeal way thereafter (Section 3.10). For the most part, erroneous replica components were removed but not replaced, leaving the remains increasingly difficult to interpret. Regrettably, Forward's adoption of the 'Crewe' drawing as the blueprint for *Rocket*'s interpretation led to the removal of the 'Kirkhouse' braces and supplementary buffers in 1923, and the fitting of the present replica chimney (but without a spark-arresting screen) in *c.*1935.

The remainder of Forward's proposals were never acted upon and it would appear that, since the mid 1930s, there has been no strategy for an improved interpretation of the artefact. Apart from the recent cleaning of the buffer beam, *Rocket*'s presentation has not been altered since *c.*1935.

With the survey being carried out in the main gallery at the National Railway Museum, it was apparent that *Rocket* was of considerable interest to visitors from both Britain and overseas. The survey was retarded by their many questions and expressions of interest, and it was clear that the level of explanation they received was warmly welcomed. It was equally clear from this dialogue, however, that the visitor found difficulty in interpreting *Rocket*'s surviving components and the dynamic and thermodynamic principles that lay behind them. As the proportion of visitors without memories of working steam locomotives grows, it would seem that this difficulty will increase.

The difficulty is partly one of preconception arising from the visitor's expectation to see the locomotive in its 'as-built' condition, with livery being only a small part of this expectation. The position of the cylinders, the addition of the smokebox, and the lack of a firebox, boiler tubes, dome, safety valves, water sight-gauge, water feed-pump and coupling rods all contribute to the interpretative problem. One of the basic messages which visitors find difficult to understand, and which apply to many artefacts in technical museums, is that machinery has undergone modification and improvements during its working life, arising from operating experience and advancement in technology and material knowledge.

From both the historical and interpretative standpoints therefore, mechanical artefacts should be displayed in their end-of-service condition, incorporating the evidence of the improvements made during their working life. They should be accompanied by interpretative material to enable the visitor to understand the technological progression and the reasons that brought about the improvements. This is particularly true of *Rocket*, whose modifications as discussed in this report form an important part of the artefact's history. In the absence of an interpretative strategy, however, the locomotive now has a derived rather than planned appearance, which neither relates to its end-of-service configuration nor fulfils visitor requirements.

This current survey of the locomotive, and the resulting increase in knowledge about it, therefore provides the opportunity for a much improved interpretation for the Museum visitor. The recent availability of the 'Stephenson' drawing (Section 3.8, Note 173), and 'Thompson' drawing (Section 3.9), has provided new evidence towards a more comprehensive understanding of *Rocket*'s form at the end of its service. Based on this evidence, it is now possible to consider a strategy for *Rocket*'s future interpretation, by offering the opportunity to recreate those components which would enhance the visitor's understanding of the locomotive.

5.2 *Options for interpretation*

The debate concerning an improved interpretation for *Rocket* would need to take account of both the importance of the surviving components as historic artefacts for the discerning visitor to see and understand, and the need to develop the locomotive's display for the benefit of the majority of visitors. There are four basic options for *Rocket*'s future display, with several variations according to circumstance:

i) continue to display the locomotive in its current form, without alteration

ii) as i), but with the replacement of the erroneous replica chimney and trailing wheels with correct versions based on the 'Thompson'/'Stephenson' drawings

iii) replicate some of the missing components to combine the advantages of showing both the remains and providing an improved interpretation

iv) replicate all of the missing components, based on the 'Thompson'/'Stephenson' drawings, and fit them to the locomotive to restore it fully to its end-of-service appearance.

In the light of the discussion in Section 5.1, option i) would not take advantage of the greater knowledge about the locomotive that is now available, whilst option ii) would at least correct the errors made during the locomotive's time in the Science Museum. The extent to which it would be desirable to replicate missing components is itself conditioned by interpretative opportunities and the need to meet the needs of the discerning visitor.

It is therefore recommended that option iii) be considered, with the replication of both a new chimney and trailing wheels, and some of the missing components, based on both the 'Thompson'/'Stephenson' drawings and the evidence that has been obtained from the survey. The important principles of this strategy are:[3]

• it should be fully reversible, thus ensuring that further changes could be made should additional evidence become available

• it should not in any way be damaging to the remains

• the replica components should be made, as far as possible, from the same materials as the original ones

• the components should be fitted to the remains using surviving holes and studs, with replicated bolts and nuts

- the components should be stamped with the Museum name and date to clarify their origin for future generations

- full records of the changes should be kept.

There are a number of variations to partial replication, but to stimulate the debate about its extent, it is proposed that, in addition to a replacement chimney and trailing wheel-set, one side of the locomotive should be fitted with replica components, leaving the other side in its present form. This would provide the visitor with the opportunity to view the locomotive from alternate sides, both in its end-of-service condition and in its present condition.

5.3 *Proposed presentation of* Rocket

It is proposed that one side of the locomotive should be 'clothed' with missing components, including:

- copper firebox saddle fitted to the rear tube-plate and front and back firebox plates

- manifold and water feed-pipe from the boiler to the saddle and firebox back-plate

- copper communicating-pipe between the saddle and tube-plate

- cast- and wrought-iron firegrate

- pine boiler-cladding and cladding bands

- water gauge-cocks and/or sight gauge

- bronze water feed-pump, wrought-iron drive-arm and associated copper pipework

- exhaust pipe between cylinder and smokebox side

- connecting rod, complete with bearing brasses, straps, gibs and keys.

In addition to the fitting of a correct chimney, other boiler-top components could include:

- brass dome and collar

- wrought-iron safety valve and lever, and brass spring-balance

- brass lock-up safety-valve cover

- brass 'cone and cup' whistle,

- wrought-iron chimney damper-arm and lever, and rear tube-plate support.

The fitting of a correct trailing wheel-set would also need to be accompanied by two steel spring-sets.

To assist with the interpretation for the visitor, both the firebox saddle and the dome could be sectioned along the top centre-line, the latter providing the opportunity for fitting a wrought-iron internal steam-pipe.

With the assistance of textual and diagrammatic displays, *Rocket*'s progression from its 1829 to its *c.*1840 configurations, based on the findings of the survey, could thus be fully explained to future generations of Museum visitors.

5.4 *Conservation and livery*

The locomotive's surviving iron components had suffered surface corrosion in the twenty-two years or so up to its restoration in 1862 (Section 3.10). There is evidence of oxidation and lamination and, although some of the surface appears to have been wire-brushed in preparation for its display at South Kensington, pockets of rust remain, particularly in less accessible places.

The surfaces appear to have been painted with a black lead-based paint, probably in 1862, to which has later been added oil-based protective substances such as linseed oil, which have formed sticky and congealed patches in some areas. The boiler-barrel paint layer has become quite thin, perhaps worn down by years of dusting and polishing, causing the surface to craze at the high spots. It is now showing a mottled effect (Fig.5.1, p122).

During the survey, the surface was probed in several places to reveal hidden features, such as redundant studs which have been ground down to the surrounding surface level. Evidence of original paintwork was sought but none was found, having been lost to the oxidation and subsequent brushing. A few bright green spots found on the left-side wheel-hub appear to have been residues from the brass cleaner used on the works plate. The driving wheels appear to have been revarnished, probably in 1945 when the locomotive was stripped down and prepared for display after the Second World War (Section 3.10).

The locomotive's buffer beam was the subject of cleaning and conservation by the Science Museum in 1997 which served to highlight the green base and yellow top colour of the legend 'No. 1'. It is possible that this green paint was the same shade as that which was probably applied to *Rocket* from *c.*1830, this apparently being the regular colour employed by the L&MR.[4]

In spite of the surface condition and the thinning of the original paintwork, there is no evidence of further deterioration of the ironwork. It would, however, be beneficial to *Rocket*'s long-term wellbeing if the congealed areas were cleaned and thinned and a more even protective coat applied.

The boiler cladding, as portrayed on the 'Thompson'/'Stephenson' drawings appears to have been deep-varnished timber without colour, similar to the buffer beam, and this same scheme could be adopted for the replicated cladding. The boiler bands appear to be iron rather than brass and were probably painted black.

1 Science Museum technical file (inv. no. 1862-5) for *Rocket* contains no note relating to an interpretative strategy for the artefact between 1862 and 1914.

2 Science Museum technical file, *ibid*, proposal by E A Forward, curator, undated, but endorsed 'Amended 1914'.

3 Museums and Galleries Commission, *Standards in the Care of Larger & Working Objects* (1994) sections 4 and 5, pp22–27.

4 T T Bury, *Coloured Views on the Liverpool and Manchester Railway* (London, 1831) *passim*.

Appendix 1 Stipulations and conditions of the Rainhill Trials

Rail-way Office, Liverpool, 25th April 1829

STIPULATIONS AND CONDITIONS

*On which the Directors of the Liverpool and Manchester Rail-way offer a Premium of £500
for the most improved Locomotive Engine.*

~ ~ ~ ~ ~ ~ ~ ~ ~ ~ ~ ~ ~ ~ ~ ~ ~ ~ ~

1st. – The said Engine must 'effectually consume its own smoke,' according to the provisions of the Rail-way Act, 7th Geo. IV.

2nd. – The engine, if it weighs Six Tons, must be capable of drawing after it, day by day, on a well-constructed Rail-way on a level plane, a Train of Carriages of the gross weight of Twenty Tons, including the Tender and Water Tank, at the rate of Ten Miles per Hour, with a pressure of steam in the boiler not exceeding 50 lb on the square inch.

3rd. – There must be two Safety Valves, one of which must be completely out of the reach or control of the Engine-man, and neither of which must be fastened down while the Engine is working.

4th. – The Engine and Boiler must be supported on Springs, and rest on Six Wheels; and the height, from the ground to the top of the Chimney, must not exceed Fifteen Feet.

5th. – The weight of the Machine, *with its complement of water* in the Boiler, must, at most, not exceed Six Tons; and a Machine of less weight will be preferred if it draw after it a *proportionate* weight; and if the weight of the Engine, &c. do not exceed *Five Tons*, then the gross weight to be drawn need not exceed Fifteen Tons; and in that proportion for Machines of still smaller weight – provided that the Engine, &c. shall still be on six wheels, unless the weight (as above) be reduced to Four Tons and a Half, or under, in which case the Boiler, &c. may be placed on four wheels. And the Company shall be at liberty to put the Boiler, Fire Tube, Cylinders, &c. to the test of a pressure of water not exceeding 150 lb per square inch, without being answerable for any damage the Machine may receive in consequence.

6th. – There must be a Mercurial Gauge affixed to the Machine, with Index Rod, shewing the Steam Pressure above 45 pounds per square inch; and constructed to blow out at a Pressure of 60 pounds per inch.

7th. - The Engine to be delivered complete for trial, at the Liverpool end of the Rail-way, not later than the 1st of October next.

8th. – The price of the Engine, which may be accepted, not to exceed £550, delivered on the Rail-way; and any Engine not approved to be taken back by the Owner.

N.B. – The Rail-way Company will provide the *Engine Tender* with a supply of Water and Fuel, for the experiment. The distance within the Rails is four feet eight inches and a half.

Appendix 2　First Rainhill Trial requirements

LIVERPOOL & MANCHESTER
RAIL WAY OFFICE

The Engines to be ready at ten o'clock on Tuesday morning [6 October].

The running-ground will be on the Manchester side of the Rainhill Bridge.

The load attached to each engine, will be three times the weight of the engine.

No person, except the Directors and Engineers, will be permitted to enter or cross the Rail-road.

Liverpool, Oct. 5. 1829.

Appendix 3   Second Rainhill Trial requirements

TRIAL OF THE LOCOMOTIVE ENGINES

LIVERPOOL & MANCHESTER
RAILWAY.

The following is the Ordeal which we have decided each Locomotive Engine shall undergo, in contending for the Premium of £500, at Rainhill.

The weight of the Locomotive Engine, with its full compliment of water in the boiler, shall be ascertained at the Weighing Machine, by eight o'clock in the morning, and the load assigned to it, shall be three times the weight thereof. The water in the boiler shall be cold, and there shall be no fuel in the fire-place. As much fuel shall be weighed, and as much water shall be measured and delivered into the Tender Carriage, as the owner of the Engine may consider sufficient for the supply of the Engine for a journey of thirty-five miles. The fire in the boiler shall then be lighted, and the quantity of fuel consumed for getting up the steam shall be determined, and the time noted.

The Tender Carriage, with the fuel and water, shall be considered to be, and taken as part of the load assigned to the engine.

Those Engines that carry their own fuel and water, shall be allowed a proportionate deduction from their load, according to the weight of the engine.

The Engine, with the Carriages attached to it, shall be run by hand up to the Starting Post, and as soon as the steam is got up to fifty pounds per square inch, the engine shall set out upon its journey.

The distance the Engine shall perform each trip, shall be one mile and three quarters each way, including one-eighth of a mile at each end for getting up the speed, and for stopping the train, by this means the engine with its load, will travel one and a half mile each way at full speed

The Engine shall make ten trips, which will be equal to a journey of thirty-five miles, thirty miles whereof shall be performed at full speed, and the average rate of travelling shall not be less than ten miles per hour.

As soon as the Engine has performed this task, (which will be equal to the travelling from Liverpool to Manchester,) there shall be a fresh supply of fuel and water delivered to her, and as soon as she can be got ready to set out again, she shall go up to the Starting Post, and make ten trips more, which will be equal to the journey from Manchester back again to Liverpool.

The time of performing every trip shall be accurately noted, as well as the time occupied in getting ready to set out on the second journey.

Should the Engine not be enabled to take along with it sufficient fuel and water for the journey of ten trips, the time occupied in taking in a fresh supply of fuel and water, and shall be considered and taken as part of the time in performing the journey.

J.U. RASTRICK, Esq. Stourbridge, C.E.}

NICHOLAS WOOD, Esq. Killingworth, C.E.} Judges

JOHN KENNEDY, Esq. Manchester}

Liverpool, Oct. 6, 1829.

Appendix 4   List of known sketches, drawings and photographs of *Rocket* 1829–1970

(Which provide primary evidence, or interpretation of its form, and excluding republished views)

S = Sketches D = Drawing P = Photographs

Year		Draughtsman/Artist/ Photographer	Present owner	Comments	Fig. no.
1829	S	John U Rastrick	Science Museum	Four views in his Rainhill Notebook (inv. no. 1945-108): Side elevation of firebox, boiler and chimney End elevation of firebox and boiler Safety valve, and isometric view of firebox	4.37
1829	S	*Mechanics' Magazine*	Published	First published illustration (24 October 1829)	3.2
1829	S	*Mechanics' Magazine*	Published	Minor revisions (28 November 1829)	3.4
1830	S	Henry Booth	Published	*An Account of the Liverpool & Manchester Railway* p74	3.5
1830	S	William Smoult	Published	Printed from stone by Geo. Smith of Liverpool	–
*c.*1830	S	A B Clayton	Published	View of Olive Mount cutting First published by J F Cannell Later published by Engelmann, Graf and Coindet	3.3
1831	S	Nicholas Wood	Published	*Treatise on Rail Roads*, second edition, p383. Also: revision in third edition (1838) p325	3.6
1831	S	T T Bury	Published	R Ackermann prints of Olive Mount excavation and Edge Hill cutting	3.7 & 3.8
1836	D	Liverpool & Manchester Railway	Science Museum	'Crewe' drawing (inv. no. 1923-569)	3.11
*c.*1840	D	Unknown	National Railway Museum	'Stephenson' drawing – formerly in possession of R Stephenson & Co.	3.14
*c.*1840	D	Unknown	Privately owned	'Thompson' drawing – formerly in possession of James Thompson	3.15
1858–9	D	J D Wardale	Science Museum	Tracings of three speculative views of *Rocket*, namely: cross-sectional side-end and plan views (R119), side view of loco. only (R121), and side view of loco. and tender (not listed)	3.16 & 3.17
1876	P	Col. Stuart Wortley	Science Museum	Side view (copy negative no. 454/56)	3.18
1876	P	Col. Stuart Wortley	Science Museum	¾ front view (copy transparency RLO/C000170)	3.19
1877	S	South Kensington Museum	Published	*Catalogue of Special Loan Collection of Scientific Apparatus at South Kensington Museum*, third edition, facing p457.	–
1876	S	*The Engineer*	Published	Issue for 30 June, p481	–
1880	S	*The Graphic*	Published	Issue for 3 January, front page	–
1892	D	Thomas Coates	Science Museum	2 ink and colourwash drawings (inv. no.1892-187)	Draw. 3.1
Pre-1909	P	Science Museum	Science Museum	Side view taken between 1892 and 1909 (old neg. no.23556 – new copy neg. in preparation)	–
1922	P	Science Museum	Science Museum	Right-side rear ¾ view – neg. no. 1648	–
1923	P	Science Museum	Science Museum	Left-side view – neg. no. 1838	–
1923	P	Science Museum	Science Museum	Left-side rear ¾ view – neg. no. 1839	–
1923	P	Science Museum	Science Museum	Left-side front ¾ view – neg. no. 1840	–
1924	P	Science Museum	Science Museum	Right-side view – neg. no. 2125	–
1931	P	Science Museum	Science Museum	Left-side rear ¾ view – neg. no. 547/96	–
1936	P	Science Museum	Science Museum	Right-side view – neg. no. 8441	–
1945	P	Science Museum	Science Museum	Set of six views of dismantled locomotive neg. nos 114/45, 152/45–155/45, 157/45.	4.21
1970	P	Science Museum	Science Museum	Left-side rear ¾ view – neg. no. 96/70.	–

Appendix 5   Summary of *Rocket*'s ownership

From	To	Owner
September 1829	October 1829	George Stephenson, Henry Booth
October 1829	November 1829	George Stephenson, Henry Booth, Robert Stephenson
November 1829	October 1836	Liverpool & Manchester Railway Company
October 1836	May 1838	Earl of Carlisle
May 1838	July 1851	James Thompson
July 1851	September 1852	Estate of James Thompson (Deceased)
September 1852	July 1862	Maria Thompson & Sons
July 1862	March 1876	Commissioners of Patents (Exhibited in Patent Office Museum)
March 1876	July 1878	Commissioners of Patents (On loan to the South Kensington Museum)
July 1878	December 1883	Commissioners of Patents (Exhibited in Patent Office Museum)
January 1884	1886	Department of Science and Art (Exhibited in Patent Office Museum)
1886	1899	Department of Science and Art (South Kensington Museum)
1899	1909	Board of Education (Science Division of the Victoria & Albert Museum)
1909	1983	Science Museum (Government administered)
1983	1989	Science Museum (Museum Trust)
1989	Date	Science Museum (National Railway Museum – Rail Transport Collection)

Appendix 6   List of all known full-size replicas of *Rocket*

Year	Manufacturer	Type	For whom made	Present location	Comments
1881	Crewe Locomotive Works	Non-working	London & North Western Railway	Scrapped *c.*1975, metal components used for 1979 replica	Probably rebuilt in Crewe Works as 'new replica' in 1911
1892	Crewe Locomotive Works	Wooden	Columbian World's Exposition	B & O Railroad Museum, Baltimore	Initiative of Col. J G Pangborn Some parts transferred from 1881 replica
1923	Buster Keaton/ Joseph M Schenk Productions California	Non-steam operable	Film prop for the film *Our Hospitality*	Smithsonian Institution, Washington DC	Film starring Buster Keaton
1929	R Stephenson & Co. Ltd, Darlington (order no. E137, works no. 3992)	Operable	Henry Ford	Henry Ford Museum, Dearborn, Michigan	On display
1930	Derby Locomotive Works	Non-working	London Midland & Scottish Railway	Probably scrapped in 1930s	Made by 'T Robinson' for Centenary Pageant, Liverpool
1930	R Stephenson & Co. Ltd, Darlington (order no. E149, works no. 4071)	Sectioned	Museum of Peaceful Arts, New York	Shawnee Mission, Kansas	Now privately owned
1931	R Stephenson & Co. Ltd, Darlington (order no. E150, works no. 4072)	Operable	Museum of Science & Industry, Chicago, Illinois	Museum of Science & Industry, Chicago, Illinois	On display
1935	R Stephenson & Co. Ltd, Darlington (order no. E155, works no. 4089)	Sectioned	Science Museum, London	National Railway Museum, York	On display
1979	Locomotion Enterprises, Springwell Workshops, Co. Durham	Working	Science Museum (National Railway Museum)	National Railway Museum, York	Operated at York and other sites

Appendix 7 *Rocket* models

The possibility that further information may be obtained from a contemporary model, or a model otherwise made by persons who had close knowledge of *Rocket*, has been pursued. No reference to a contemporary model has, however, been found.

One *Rocket* model appears to have become a Stephenson family heirloom. The evidence strongly suggests, however, that this model was not completed until 1862. It was made by 'a working man', George Lucas of Eccles Street, Prescot in Lancashire, and was sent for display at the International Exhibition in London that year. Lucas hoped that it would be bought by 'some wealthy gentleman' and that he would receive £30 for it. Two views of the model were photographed by R E Bleasdale (catalogue reference no. 1268).

It is likely that the model was purchased by George Robert Stephenson (1819–1904), George Stephenson's nephew, and retained by him until his death. The model was loaned to the editor of *The Engineer*, who reproduced a drawing of it.[1] A request from Sir John Coode to Stephenson that he might donate the model to the Science Museum in 1890 was rejected: 'I cannot see my way to part with the last & only machine that brings the past before me.'[2] In 1904, the model was bequeathed to his son, Thomas St Lawrence Stephenson (1859–1934), whose will, in turn, left the model to his nephew, George Stephenson (born 1877). Apparently, in 1954 the model was donated to Babcock & Wilcox Ltd, to join the collection of models in its private exhibition hall in Salisbury Square House, London.[3] Enquiries have been made to the successor company, Babcock International of Amersham, Buckinghamshire, but the present whereabouts of the model are now unknown.[4]

It was claimed in 1954 that this model had been made by an employee of Robert Stephenson & Co. soon after 1848, but the appearance of the model owes much to the erroneous characteristics of J D Wardale's 1858 drawings (Figs 3.16 and 3.17) and is most likely to have been made after that date.

The 1954 article in *The Engineer* also claimed that another model, perhaps that referred to as having been made soon after 1848, had been presented to Robert Stephenson (1803–1859). The whereabouts of this model are not known.

A model of *Rocket* was also owned by Henry Booth (1789–1869). His daughter, Mary Anne (1822–1908), later wrote: 'I remember, too, how for many years subsequently the model of the 'Rocket' was kept in a room in our house in Abercromby square...'[5]

1 *The Engineer*, 17 September 1880, p210.
2 Letter from George Robert Stephenson, Glen Caladh Castle, Kyles of Bute, to Sir John Coode, South Kensington Museum, 29 August 1890, Science Museum nominal file ScM60.
3 *Engineering*, 15 August 1954.
4 Correspondence with Mr Robert Martin, Assistant to the Group Company Secretary.
5 Undated letter reproduced in *Alfred Booth, Some Memories Letters and Other Family Records* (Printed for private circulation, Liverpool, 1917) p25.

Appendix 8 The Alston election returns, 8 August 1837

Following the parliamentary election of 7–8 August 1837, the voting returns were conveyed from Alston to the Returning Officer of the East Cumberland Constituency in Carlisle in a record short time, probably on the late afternoon of 8 August. It would seem that this followed detailed planning and arrangement, with the intention of breaking the journey record, as well as ensuring an early declaration of the election result. The *Carlisle Journal* reported:[1]

> By six o'clock the whole of the returns had been received [in Carlisle] – that from Alston having been brought a distance of 30 miles in an hour and two minutes! – 9 miles on horseback, and the remainder of the way by railroad…

The same newspaper made the claim eleven years later that *Rocket* had been used:[2]

> …for conveying the Alston express with the state of the poll from Midge-holme to Kirkhouse. Upon that occasion the *Rocket* was driven by Mr. Mark Thompson, and accomplished its share of the work – a distance of upwards of four miles, in 4½ minutes – thus reaching a speed nearly equal to 60 miles an hour!

This newspaper claim has greatly exaggerated *Rocket*'s capabilities, but the claim has been accepted and repeated in several publications.[3] In the absence of any known contemporary account of the event in a public archive, the following assessment seeks to form a better understanding of how the 'Alston express' may have achieved its 62-minute record.

The following assumptions have been made:

• A Deputy Returning Officer accompanied the returns throughout the journey

• The Deputy travelled by horse from Alston town centre (NY717465), along the turnpike road to Carlisle (present-day A689)

• The Deputy transferred to *Rocket* at the point where the turnpike road crossed the route of the Naworth colliery railway at Halton-Lea-Gate near Midgeholme (NY653585)

• *Rocket* conveyed the Deputy from Halton-Lea-Gate to Kirkhouse (NY566600)

• A locomotive of the Newcastle & Carlisle Railway conveyed the Deputy from Kirkhouse to London Road station, Carlisle

• The Deputy completed the journey on horseback from London Road station to the Returning Officer in Carlisle Town Hall or other central location.

The following distances and gradients have been estimated:

• Turnpike road from Alston to Halton-Lea-Gate, 10.0 mile route over undulating terrain with heights ranging from 985 feet to 692 feet above sea-level

• Naworth colliery railway line from Halton-Lea-Gate to Hallbankgate (NY578598), 5.0 miles, the track being laid on a gentle downhill gradient of just over 1 per cent

• Kirkhouse incline from Hallbankgate to Kirkhouse, 1432 yards long, the (normally rope-worked) line descending at gradients of 1:28 and 1:18

• Naworth colliery railway line from Kirkhouse to Brampton Junction (NY552601), 1500 yards long, the track being almost on the level

• Brampton Junction to London Road station, Carlisle, 12.875 miles, on falling gradients, including just under 4 miles at 1:106, with the last 1.75 miles into London Road station being level track

• London Road station to the Market Place, Carlisle, half a mile on level roads.

The total distance was thus almost exactly 30 miles, confirming the *Carlisle Journal*'s statement. However, the distance the returns would have been conveyed by horse was greater than its estimate, being 10.5 miles in total.

The following assumptions have been made to determine how the 62-minute journey might have been achieved:

• The 10-mile journey on horseback was probably achieved with three separate horses, the relief horses waiting by the roadside. It is estimated that an average speed of 22 miles per hour could have been achieved, and the journey completed in 27 minutes.

• *Rocket* is estimated to have taken a quarter of a mile to reach a top speed of 35 miles per hour, and within an eighth of a mile to slow down to 15 miles per hour, at which speed to descend the Kirkhouse incline. It is likely that *Rocket* normally faced eastwards, and would therefore have run backwards thus ensuring that the firebox crown was not uncovered during the descent.[4] The 5-mile run to the bank top would therefore have taken about 10.5 minutes. The run down the incline at 15 miles per hour and stopping at the bottom would have taken about 3.5 minutes.

• The journey from Kirkhouse to Carlisle would have been made using one of the Newcastle & Carlisle Railway's locomotives that regularly worked through to Kirkhouse. The identity of the locomotive was not recorded but it would have been one the railway's 2-4-0 or 0-4-2 types with 14-inch cylinders, of which nine were in service by that date. It is assumed that, with the acceleration from Kirkhouse and deceleration for Brampton Junction, and a top speed of 20 miles per hour, this first part of the journey was completed in 3.5 minutes.

From Brampton Junction to Carlisle, it is likely that a continuous speed of 48 miles per hour was achieved by the 'light engine'.[5] The journey would thus have been completed in 16 minutes, allowing for acceleration away from Brampton Junction and deceleration to a stand in London Road station.

• The horseride into the centre of Carlisle would have taken about 1.5 minutes.

Whilst the absence of detail from the contemporary newspaper report makes it impossible to confirm the events of the 8 August 1837, the above assumptions show that it would have been feasible to have achieved the 62-minute journey with *Rocket* travelling at a maximum speed of 35 miles per hour rather than the 60-mph speed erroneously reported in 1848.

1 *Carlisle Journal*, 12 August 1837, p2.
2 *Carlisle Journal*, 15 September 1848, p2, Obituary, 'The Late George Stephenson, Esq.'.
3 For example, *The Athenaeum*, 2 December 1848 and Samuel Smiles, *The Life of George Stephenson, Railway Engineer* (London, 1857) p289, and subsequent editions.
4 Article, 'The Brampton Railway and Its Engines', no author, but probably W B Thompson, *The Locomotive*, 15 November 1907, p202, states that 'It has always been the custom to have all the engines on the Kirkhouse Colliery line facing eastwards, so that if an engine should require to go up or down the inclined plane there should be plenty of water over the firebox'.
5 Francis Wishaw, *The Railways of Great Britain and Ireland* (London, 1840) table M, p.x, provides details of recorded runs with the Newcastle & Carlisle Railway's locomotives in 1839, showing that they achieved over 40 mph with service trains over the line to Carlisle.

Appendix 9   Valve events

Valve ellipse and P-V diagram
Engine: Rocket

CYLINDERS		Head end			Crank end		
Number/Acting		2			2		
Bore	in	8					
Stroke	in	17					
Clearance volume	in³	158			158		
Piston rod dia.	in				1.375		
Con. rod length	in				43.2		
VALVE GEAR							
Steam lap	in	0.081			0.081		
Exhaust lap	in	0.023			0.023		
Eccentric throw	in	1.5					
Angle of advance	deg	20					
Eccent. rod length	in	52					
Lever ratio	1:	0.5156					

STEPHENSON LINK			
Arrangement		none	
Link length	in	0	
% of full gear	%	100	
App. eccentric throw	in	1.5	
App. angle of advance	deg	20	

Steam pressure	lbf/in²	50	
Back pressure	lbf/in²	0.3	
Gamma	1:	1.3	
Speed	RPM	72	
Wheel diameter	in	56	
Philipson factor		0.85	

CALCULATIONS							
Ground speed	mph	12.0					
Piston speed	ft/min	204					
Valve events							
Lead	in	0.174			0.193		
St opens	%/°/°	-1.8	346	-14	-1.4	345	-15
St closes	%/°/°	95.6	153	153	94.0	154	154
Ex opens	%/°/°	-3.2	157	-23	-4.0	159	-21
Ex closes	%/°/°	97.1	342	342	97.6	340	340

1) by Philipson's Formula

Tractive effort	lbf	826
Torque	lbf ft	1927
Approx HP	hp	26

2) from P-V diagram

Tractive effort	lbf	904
Torque	lbf ft	2110
Indicated HP	hp	29

Appendix 10   Design process and performance

10.1 Design process

Rocket was designed specifically to exceed the Stipulations and Conditions for the Rainhill Trials by a small margin (Section 3.2 and Appendix 1). The competitors had the option of building a six-wheeled locomotive weighing up to 6 tons and drawing 20 tons, or a four-wheeled locomotive weighing up to 4½ tons and drawing 13½ tons. All the entrants chose the four-wheel option.

The Stephensons' design process and calculations have not survived but the following calculations have been made using data and knowledge available at that time. The most comprehensive works on the theory of locomotives written before 1829 were by Thomas Tredgold and by Nicholas Wood.[1] Wood was Viewer of Killingworth Colliery where a number of Stephenson locomotives were in use, and he was also a judge at the Rainhill trials. Data on the density, pressure, temperature and latent heat of steam were available to reasonable accuracy, and were published in such books as Farey's *Treatise on the Steam Engine*.[2] However, the figures available often covered a wide spread, and it is impossible to know which values the Stephensons would have used. They also had their own information which was more up-to-date and more relevant than that published.

10.1.1 Speed

The trial stipulations called for a speed of 10 miles per hour. The Stephensons designed *Rocket* for 12 miles per hour. This was stated in a later report.[3]

10.1.2 Tractive effort

The rolling resistance of wagons had been estimated by Wood and others at between 10 lbf./ton and 17 lbf./ton. The tractive effort required to haul a load of 13½ tons at 12 lbf./ton on the level would have been 162 lbf.

The force needed to accelerate the locomotive and its train to the design speed could also be calculated. Assuming that this speed was achieved in 220 yards, the force required was 294 lbf. (Newton's third law of motion).

The tractive effort required was therefore 456 lbf. and the power required was 14.6 hp.

10.1.3 Wheel diameter

The driving-wheel diameter was chosen at 4 ft 8½ in. and this very conveniently meant that the number of revolutions in 10 seconds equalled the speed in miles per hour.

10.1.4 Mechanical efficiency

Wood estimated the mechanical efficiency of various locomotives under differing conditions and produced figures of between 30 per cent and 70 per cent. It is not known what efficiency was used in the design calculations, but 50 per cent might be a reasonable assumption. The indicated power required was therefore about 30 hp.

10.1.5 Cylinder volume

The maximum boiler pressure was stipulated to be 50 lbf./sq. in. The swept volume per cylinder end was therefore about 0.48 cu. ft. [Horsepower = (pressure × swept volume × number of power strokes per second)/550].

10.1.6 Squareness ratio

Lancashire Witch and *Pride of Newcastle* (Travelling Engine Nos 11 and 12 – Section 2.1) both had a cylinder bore of 9 in. and a stroke of 24 in. giving a bore-to-stroke ratio of 0.375:1. The *Rocket* for the Stockton and Darlington Railway (Travelling Engine No. 15) and Travelling Engine No. 17 both had a cylinder bore of 11 in. and a stroke of 20 in. giving a bore-to-stroke ratio of 0.55:1. A squareness ratio of 0.5:1 and a volume of 0.48 cu. ft. gave a bore of 8 in. and a stroke of 16½ in.

10.1.7 Adhesion

Wood had conducted various experiments to ascertain the coefficient of friction. He estimated that in good conditions the coefficient was greater than 0.11 and in the worst conditions was about 0.047. He recommended that a figure of 0.04 be used. (These figures seem to be on the low side.) It seems that the Stephensons used a figure of 0.08, which indicated that the weight carried by the driving wheels should be 2½ tons.

10.1.8 Steam requirements

From the data given by Farey, the specific volume of steam at 50 lbf./sq. in. could be calculated as 6.98 cu. ft/lb. (A figure of 6.66 cu. ft./lb. is given in more recent tables).[4] From this the evaporation rate could be calculated as 1190 lb/h.

10.1.9 Heating surface

Wood had measured the quantity of water evaporated in the earlier engines and found that 1 square foot of heating surface would evaporate about 20 lb of water per hour. (This estimate may have been high due to priming.) For *Rocket,* therefore, about 60 sq. ft. of heating surface would be needed. The actual heating surface of the boiler as built was more than twice this. It was not known how effective the tubular boiler would be, and so the designers erred on the high side.

10.1.10 General arrangement

As discussed in Section 3.2, *Rocket's* arrangement was largely based on *Lancashire Witch*. That had hauled loads of 33 tons, had travelled light at about 12 miles per hour, and had developed nearly 22 hp. However, it weighed 7 tons and so the design had to be scaled down to meet the Rainhill stipulations. The same basic layout of four wheels, a light bar frame and sloping cylinders was used. Only the leading wheels, however, were used for driving. This avoided the extra friction of coupling rods and the possibility of binding due to inaccuracies in quartering or uneven wear of the tyres. *Rocket* was therefore freer-running than its competitors. The adhesion was achieved by positioning the axles so that the load on the driving wheels was 2½ tons, i.e., greater than that on the trailing wheels. The bar frame was cranked down to accommodate the firebox.

The expansion gear as on *Lancashire Witch* was not used on *Rocket*, and the 'limited-travel' slip-eccentric reversing gear was replaced by the 'dog-clutch' gear.

The cylinders, cross-heads and valve gear were similar to those used on *Lancashire Witch*. It is probable that the same patterns were used, with minor modifications, for such castings as the rear boiler supports.

10.1.11 Boiler

The radiant heating surface of the boiler was 20 sq. ft. and the convective area was 118 sq. ft. The fire grate was 6 sq. ft.

The ultimate tensile strength of wrought-iron boilerplate at that time was about 20 ton/sq. in. The factor of safety used for calculating the hoop stress in a boiler at that time was 12. The design hoop stress might therefore have been 1.67 ton/sq. in. The thickness of the plate could then be calculated at 0.268 in.

The cross-sectional area of the flue tubes was 177 sq. in. To maintain the same area in the chimney its diameter would have been 15 in. Robert Stephenson allowed for the flue gases being cooler and had it made 14 in. (Section 3.3). Rastrick, however, noted that it had a 15 in. diameter.[5]

10.2 Performance

10.2.1 Killingworth

Rocket was first tried out under load at Killingworth in September 1829 and hauled a load of 25 tons up a gradient of 1:480 at 8 miles per hour (Section 3.4). This represented about 9½ hp assuming friction at 12 lbf./ton. It achieved 12 miles per hour on the level.

10.2.2 Rainhill Trials

At the Rainhill Trials, speed, water and coke consumption were closely monitored (Section 3.5). During the first few trips on 8 October the speed was kept to about the design speed of 12 miles per hour (Figure 10.1). The Stephensons would have been aware that running too fast would use steam at a greater rate than it could have been generated. As confidence increased, on the eastbound legs (with the locomotive travelling forwards) the speed was gradually increased to 15 and then to 16 miles per hour. On the last eastbound leg of the morning session the speed of 21.4 miles per hour was achieved and on the last eastbound leg in the afternoon sessions, after travelling over 65 miles, the Stephensons went as fast as they dared, at 24.1 miles per hour, twice the design speed.

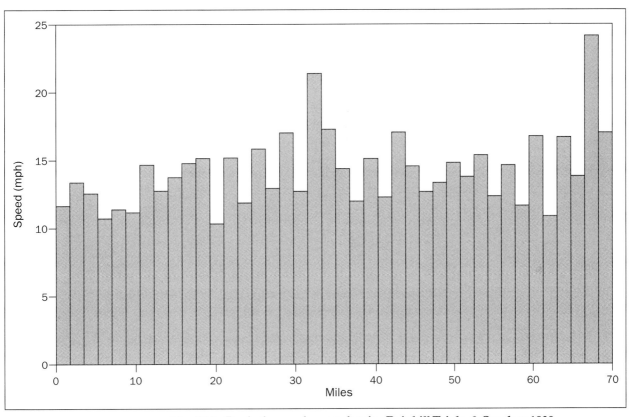

Fig. 10.1 *Rocket*'s **speed on each trip, Rainhill Trials, 8 October 1829**

Assuming 100 per cent cut-off, perfect cushioning, 50 lbf./sq. in. boiler pressure and no back pressure, the consumption per mile would have been 103 lb/mile. Rastrick, in calculating the theoretical steam consumption, added an allowance of 12.5 per cent to the swept volume as the clearance volume and arrived at the figure of 932.765 cu. in. of steam per cylinder end. Worked out in terms of consumption, this would have been 115 lb/mile. No allowance has been added for priming or condensation due to heat loss.

The actual quantity of water used in the trial was 579 gallons and, assuming that no steam was used in the braking area, the consumption was 89.7 lb/mile, i.e., less than calculated. This implies that either the boiler was not able to deliver more steam, that the cut-off was significantly less than 100 per cent, or that the regulator had not been fully open for most of the trial. Because of the speed of the last eastbound leg, the implication is that the performance was limited by the caution of the drivers and not the steam generation of the boiler.

Rastrick calculated the theoretical power of *Rocket* at 10 miles per hour as 12.45 hp, using, effectively, a mechanical efficiency of 50 per cent. He gave the steam temperature as 298 °F. Dendy Marshall made a note that the temperature would have been 249 °F.[6] Modern steam tables give the temperature as 298 °F.

10.2.3 Subsequent to the formal Trial

In demonstration runs after its formal Trial, *Rocket* ascended the Whiston incline (1:96) with 20 to 30 passengers at between 15 and 18 miles per hour (Section 3.5). It also made two runs light on the level at 35 miles per hour, three times the design speed. Adjustments were made to the blast pipes and on 19 October it hauled a load of 42 tons at 13¾ miles per hour, equivalent to 18½ hp.

10.2.4 Discrepancy with the original design calculations

The two main factors in *Rocket's* improved performance were that the effectiveness of the boiler had been underestimated and that the mechanical efficiency was nearer to 85 per cent than the 50 per cent assumed. The mechanical arrangement and construction were also sound.

10.2.5 Replica of Rocket

A brief observation was made of the performance of the replica of *Rocket* belonging to the National Railway Museum, on the Kent and East Sussex Railway on 15 July 1999. The tractive effort was estimated to be about 670 lbf. It would be interesting to carry out performance trials on the replica, as have been done on the replica of *Planet* from the Museum of Science and Industry in Manchester.[7]

1 Thomas Tredgold, *A Practical Treatise on Rail-Roads and Carriages...* (London, 1825); Nicholas Wood, *A Practical Treatise on Rail-Roads* (London 1825).
2 John Farey, *A Treatise on the Steam Engine* (London 1827).
3 R Stephenson and J Locke, *Observations on the Comparative Merits of Locomotive and Fixed Engines as Applied to Railways...* (Liverpool, 1830).
4 R W Haywood, *Thermodynamic Tables and other Data*, 2nd ed. (Cambridge, 1960).
5 John Rastrick's 'Rainhill' Note-book, Science Museum, inv. 1945-108, p71.
6 C F Dendy Marshall, noted in *Centenary History of the Liverpool and Manchester Railway* (London, 1930), p181, that the temperature would have been 249 °F. Modern steam tables give the temperature as 298 °F.
7 Michael R Bailey, 'Learning through Replication: The *Planet* Locomotive Project', *Transactions of the Newcomen Society*, vol. 68 1996–7, pp109-136.

Appendix 11 Screw threads

The pitch and diameter were measured on several of the screw threads on *Rocket*. On a very limited number of threads the form was examined by making a silicon rubber mould. The mould was sliced along a radius and then scanned into a computer. A steel rule laid adjacent to it gave a scale. The form could then be compared on a screen with standard thread forms. It was found that an excellent formulation of silicon rubber was dental putty. This has good definition and elastic memory, and is available in various viscosities. Internal and external threads in any position could be moulded with the product chosen (Provil® Soft Fast Set Dental Putty).

Many threads were similar in pitch and diameter to the standard proposed by Joseph Whitworth in 1841. He did not create new thread dimensions, but standardised on the most commonly used pitch and diameter combinations and a uniform thread angle of 55°. Some threads on *Rocket* did not conform to his series. The ¾ in. bolts on the valve gear drivers have 16 tpi threads, much finer than Whitworth's standard of 10 tpi. In spite of this, the left-side driver still slipped (Section 4.10.5). Another thread is noteworthy. The clamp bolt on the right bearing of the forward valve-gear rocking-shaft has a pitch of 15 tpi, a pitch not on the usual thread gauge. The thread angle was generally found to be wider than 55°.

Figure 11.1 shows the printout of a typical mould. In this case the root of the thread has a large radius but the peak is quite sharp. On some bolts, three burrs could be seen at the end of the threads, signifying that they had been cut with a die (right-hand forward slide-bar support, top left bolt). In other cases, the run-out suggests that the thread had been struck out with a single-point tool.

Bolt heads and nuts were generally square. There are also some bolts with square shoulder heads, and some of these have hexagonal shoulder nuts. There are also a number of plain hexagonal nuts and it is thought that these are not original.

In many situations a bolt and tapped hole were used on *Rocket* where, in later times, a nut and bolt would be used. For example, the original stays on the front of the boiler were secured at their lower ends with bolts in tapped holes in the cross member of the frame. The reason for this might have been that it was no more expensive to tap a hole in the frame than in a nut. The lower ends of the chimney stays were fastened with studs in tapped holes into the boiler. In this case there was an access problem.

Bolt   Air   .05"

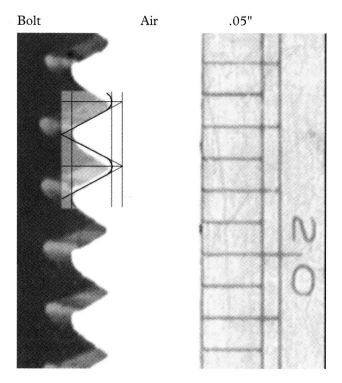

Fig. 11.1 Bolt section
Left eccentric strap, lower bolt, 5 February 1999, magnification: ×6.66

	Bolt 1	**Nearest Whitworth: 3/4"**
Diameter:	.740"	.750"
Pitch:	10 tpi	10 tpi
Thread angle:	28° + 35° = 63°	27.5°+27.5° = 55°
Depth of thread	.059"	.064"
h/H	.77	.667